Quality Handbook
for the Architectural, Engineering, and Construction Community

Also available from ASQC Quality Press

TQM: A Step-by-Step Guide to Implementation
Charles N. Weaver

Total Engineering Quality Management
Ronald J. Cottman

Deming's 14 Points Applied to Services
A. C. Rosander

Quality Management for the Constructed Project
ASQC Construction Technical Committee

Construction Quality Program Handbook
Eliot S. Mickelson

To request a complimentary catalog of publications, call 800-248-1946.

Quality Handbook
for the Architectural, Engineering, and Construction Community

Roger D. Hart

ASQC Quality Press
Milwaukee, Wisconsin

Quality Handbook for the Architectural, Engineering, and Construction Community

Roger D. Hart

Library of Congress Cataloging-in-Publication Data

Hart, Roger D.
    Quality handbook for the architectural, engineering, and
construction community/Roger D. Hart.
        p.   cm.
    Includes bibliographical references and index.
    ISBN 0-87389-245-3
    1. Construction industry—Quality control.   2. Structural
engineering—Quality control.   3. Architectural design—Quality
control.   I. Title.
    TH437.H29   1994
    690' .068' —dc205   93-49745
                                                              CIP

10 9 8 7 6 5 4 3 2 1

ISBN 0-87389-245-3

Acquisitions Editor: Susan Westergard
Project Editor: Kelley Cardinal
Production Editor: Annette Wall
Marketing Administrator: Mark Olson
Set in Garamond and Optima by Montgomery Media, Inc.
Cover design by Montgomery Media, Inc.
Printed and bound by BookCrafters, Inc.

ASQC Mission: To facilitate continuous improvement and increase customer satisfaction by identifying, communicating, and promoting the use of quality principles, concepts, and technologies; and thereby be recognized throughout the world as the leading authority on and champion for, quality.

For a free copy of the ASQC Quality Press Publications Catalog, including ASQC membership information, call 800-248-1946.

Printed in the United States of America

  Printed on acid-free recycled paper

 ASQC
Quality Press
611 East Wisconsin Avenue
Milwaukee, Wisconsin 53202

To my wife, Anna;
our children, Sherri, Melissa,
Elizabeth, and Jennifer;
and my parents.

Contents

Foreword

At last, here's a book that provides the reader with a practical road map to achieving significant increases in construction quality. Not much has been written about this elusive, but much desired, result in the construction industry. This industry is faced daily with the effects of deficient construction. Now is the time for industry to focus strong management effort on obtaining down-to-earth results in eliminating deficiencies in construction.

Roger Hart brings many years of experience in the quality field, where he has

- Emphasized the quality message to many project management teams at design and construction sites.
- Directed the Institute for Construction Quality at the University of Massachusetts–Lowell.
- Served the oldest and most world-renowned society of quality professionals, ASQC, by chairing the Construction Technical Committee in 1991. His leadership contributed to the committee's upgrade to the Architectural/Engineering and Construction (A/E&C) Division within a year.

And now Mr. Hart continues his quality teaching by presenting a much-needed, practical book. It's a how-to quality handbook that explains the world of quality assurance including such items as the ISO 9000 series of standards (world construction quality systems), MIL-Q-9858A (military and aerospace construction), ASME NQA-1 (nuclear construction), the new draft ANSI/ASQC E-4 (environmental) and DOE-5700.6C (Department of Energy quality assurance) standards, total quality management (TQM), and the Malcolm Baldrige National Quality Award (MBNQA), just to name a few.

He focuses on the basic role of the owner who must understand the quality trade-offs, initiate the concepts and criteria, and ultimately pay for quality up-front to assure a project's ultimate success. He then describes the key roles of the architect, the engineer, those involved in procurement, and the contractors. This book explores in detail those formalized quality programs, their advantages, and their shortcomings. You visualize the project management processes that contribute to quality program successes and failures. You learn what organizational approaches and project training and indoctrination in quality concepts spell the difference between cost-effective quality programs and those which have given quality a bad name in some construction circles.

So have at it, readers! Absorb these concepts. Put them into practice with your project team. Let's start building our homes, office buildings, and infrastructures in the twenty-first century with greater focus on customer satisfaction. As Roger Hart tells it, "that's what quality is all about." And yes, that is what this book is all about!

John Jackson

Author's note: John Jackson is a registered professional engineer, a long-term practitioner of quality assurance in the construction industry, a founder and co-chairman of Management Analysis Company, a long-term member and fellow of ASQC, and a senior member of ASCE. He has presented over 20 papers on construction quality assurance domestically and internationally. He is chair-elect of the Architectural/Engineering and Construction (A/E&C) Division of ASQC.

Preface

Almost five decades have passed since the institution of modern concepts of quality in the United States and around the globe after World War II. The concept of quality means different things to different people. Quality can become quite elusive in the massive architectural/engineering and construction (A/E&C) community of industries. I say it specifically this way, community of industries, because, although it is common to think of this community as only one industry, in fact it is several: power, transportation, environmental, midrise construction, and many more. This text is for the all-encompassing A/E&C community.

Additionally, the A/E&C community has rather unique industrial processes that are dramatically different from the manufacturing industrial community. To fully understand these differences, one should compare the major characteristics of each industrial community. These characteristics are as follows:

For the Manufacturing Community

- A complex industrial process with complex interactions.
- The product of the process is numerous, different, and simple compared to the process.
- The process is continuous and on-going.

For the A/E&C Community

- A complex industrial process with complex interactions.
- The product of the process is the process.
- The process has a beginning and a very abrupt end after only one product (the completed facility).

The reader should compare the similarities of and differences between these two business communities. In reviewing the above comparisons, one can note that both are complex industrial processes with complex interactions; however, the product for the A/E&C community is the process itself. In addition, the process begins with early concepts; a design is produced; a facility (building, system, or roadway) is built which itself is the product. The completed A/E&C process (the facility) is the product. These differences and similarities are addressed in this text to translate quality management techniques for a business community with a unique product. When one understands the nature of quality management and the A/E&C industrial process, quality improvements can be significant and dramatic.

The A/E&C community is worldwide. Its U.S. capital assets alone exceed those of all the companies listed on the New York Stock Exchange (over one trillion dollars). The application of the quality improvement techniques and systems described in this text can aid the reader in achieving significant cost and schedule savings on design and construction projects. Current estimates on improving rework and repair indicate the potential to exceed $15 billion a year,[1] but I believe that this may be closer to $50 billion. Within the A/E&C community, organizations can spend money on quality in one of two ways: investing in good quality or paying for poor quality.

This is a general statement in which good ideas of quality are preached. Is this the real world of our industry? What about the case of a hard-money, fixed-price contract? Can anyone really afford this early cost on a project? The thesis of this text is that you simply cannot afford not to invest in sound prevention measures to enhance quality in the design and construction process.

In the present phase of the A/E&C community's development, improving quality as described in this text can easily reduce the costs of a project on the order of 25 percent.[2] This is a phenomenal statement when one realizes that A/E&C community expenditures are a very significant percentage of the gross national product in most developed countries of the world.

This text is a guide, a road map, to a fully functioning quality system for any A/E&C organization. Further, this text is designed to provide a very comprehensive and in-depth treatment of the subject.

The text is not designed with a lot of glitz and glamour. Instead, it is based in the real world, while looking toward this industry's future in the next century.

With the 1993 change in leadership in the United States, there may be a chance for dramatic changes in this industry. It is hoped that this text may provide the framework for a significant positive impact into this change. Finally, the theme of this text is to be innovative and to continuously improve.

Acknowledgments

It is impossible to thank everyone who encouraged and advised me in the preparation of this text. All of the members of the executive leadership of the ASQC Architectural/Engineering and Construction Division, having asked many good questions, have steered me toward the topics that needed emphasis. Other members of the A/E&C community offered suggestions, and a special word of thanks goes to them. Among those I should like to mention are Eugene F. Trainor, Bert Mazo, John P. Jackson, Bruce Brummel, Eugene Danylyshyn, Sheryl Cooley, and the entire staff at Fluor Daniel, Quality Press, and ASQC.

Notes

1. ASQC Construction Technical Committee. *Quality Management in the Constructed Project.* Milwaukee, Wis.: ASQC Quality Press, 1987. Also Hart, Roger D. "The Quality of Construction." *Transactions of the 41st ASQC Annual Quality Congress.* Milwaukee, Wis.: ASQC, 1987.

2. Construction Industry Institute. Publication 10-2, *Measuring the Cost of Quality in Design and Construction.* 1989. Also Hart, Roger D. "Construction Quality Institute." *Transactions of the 43rd ASQC Annual Quality Congress.* Milwaukee, Wis.: ASQC, 1989.

1 How to Use This Text

Background and Subject Matter

- The Technical Discipline of Quality in This Industry
- The Purpose, Application, and Scope of This Text

Organization of the Text

- Flow Patterns of A/E&C and Quality Engineering
- Knowledge Base, Chapters 2–5
- The A/E&C Quality System, Chapters 6–11
- A/E&C Quality for Different Business Lines, Chapters 12–17
- A/E&C Quality for Different Contractual Arrangements, Chapters 18–19

Background and Subject Matter

As a technical discipline, the quality field has been growing, particularly in the architectural/engineering and construction (A/E&C) community. This technical science and its application to this industrial community have been evolving over the last 15 years to respond to ever-increasing complex construction projects, particularly when applied to state-of-the-art technology. In addition, technological advances—especially in the computer sciences area—have made this community much more adaptable to traditional quality engineering techniques. Finally, significant recent advances in the quality discipline have necessitated a significant reassessment of quality engineering's applicability to this community in the following areas:

- Urgent need to excel on construction projects for economic reasons
- Popularity of total quality management (TQM) methods
- Increased importance of the international quality standards, ISO 9000, to this industrial community
- Need to provide distinct and consistent approaches to quality irrespective of the size and complexity of the project
- Emphasis placed on technical excellence and customer satisfaction, particularly through the Malcolm Baldrige National Quality Award (MBNQA), on U.S. industry

This text uses these areas as the basis for an applicable set of quality programs for the A/E&C community, from the simplest construction projects to the most complex. This text is designed to be comprehensive in its treatment of the subject. However, one must understand that any particular project or company may be required to use only a small portion of material in this text. This is due to the text representing a diverse industrial community that serves several other industrial sectors. In any case, a comprehensive reading of the text is necessary to fully understand the effective application of quality programs in one segment of the A/E&C community.

This text distinguishes between two important quality activities: quality-affecting and quality-assuring activities (the doers and the checkers). Too often on a construction project, this difference is not distinguished. The result is an inefficient quality operation, which causes the cost of quality (COQ) to increase.

This text also distinctly identifies and clarifies the role that quality assurance (QA) plays relative to other entities such as the *soft quality* (defined in chapter 10) aspects of TQM and the traditional project management functions.[1]

Considerable thought and research have gone into this text. This can best be illustrated by the significant counsel the writer has received from several members of the A/E&C Division of ASQC. These individuals provided policy assistance and comments.

The fundamental purpose of this text is to provide a leadership model or guideline that the various segments of the A/E&C community may implement as appropriate. This text is intended to be user friendly and its purpose is to have readers capitalize on new and latest technology.

This text is intended to have worldwide application in the A/E&C community.[2] The text provides distinctive guidelines for the A/E&C community and should instill a commitment to quality excellence into the next century.

This text should bring a significant and positive added value to businesses that fully implement the book's ideas.

Organization of the Text

This text is organized to show the interaction of two logic flow patterns: that of a traditional A/E&C project and that of the current quality engineering discipline in any general industrial process. These two patterns are illustrated here.

Flow Pattern of A/E&C Projects	Flow Pattern of Quality Engineering in Any Industrial Process
• Owner's conceptual work	• Quality leadership
• Design criteria	• Customer quality focus
• Conceptual design	• Strategic quality planning
• Detailed design	• Quality of design
• Field engineering support	• Quality of procurement
• Site mobilization	• Manage quality process
• Procurement/purchasing	• Inspection and test
• Earthwork/geotechnical	• Surveillance and audit
• Civil work/structural	• Nonconformances
• Enclosure/rough work	

- Heating, ventilating, and air conditioning (HVAC)/ mechanical work
- Electrical/specialty
- Start-up/operational
- Maintenance
- Decommissioning/demolition

- Corrective action
- Quality records
- Motivation and statistics
- Quality results and feedback

Further, this text is organized to effectively blend these two logic flow patterns together on a chapter-by-chapter basis, building on the knowledge base of previous chapters.

- Fundamental quality ideas in this industrial process (chapter 2)
- Quality policies and innovation in the A/E&C community (chapter 3)
- Quality criteria for cost and scheduling (chapter 4)
- Quality in relation to industry codes and standards (chapter 5)
- The quality system
  - Leadership, organization, and responsibility (chapter 6)
  - Programs, procedures, and strategic plans (chapter 7)
  - Assuring external requirements, customer focus, and satisfaction (chapter 8)
  - Managing process quality (chapter 9)
    Design quality
    Document and record quality
    Purchased items and service quality
    Quality identification of items
    Quality of the A/E&C and operations and maintenance (O&M) process
    Inspection, testing, and its status and equipment
    Nonconforming and corrective action to assure quality
    Quality in handling, storing, and shipping
    Quality audits and assessments
- Motivational and human resource management (chapter 10)
- Quality results and statistical methods (chapter 11)

After chapter 11, readers should concentrate on the segment of the particular A/E&C community in which he or she belongs. It should be noted that this is not an all-or-nothing issue. There may be considerable overlap among industries described in chapters 12–17. These parallel chapters, which represent business lines of the A/E&C industrial community, include:[3]

- Strongly regulated industries (chapter 12)
- Petroleum and petrochemical industry (chapter 13)
- Other industrial and process business (chapter 14)
- Transportation industry (chapter 15)
- Medium construction (chapter 16)
- Light and residential construction (chapter 17)

The remaining two chapters deal with the application of quality engineering to contractual arrangements that require special treatment. These contractual arrangements can be categorized into two types:

- Quality systems on hard-money or fixed-price contracts (chapter 18)
- Quality systems on cost-plus contracts (chapter 19)

When the material in this text is fully implemented on a project, significant improvements to the bottom line can be achieved. As mentioned in the preface, studies have shown that a 25 percent improvement is not unusual for an A/E&C company in today's business environment. Acknowledgment of this fact will make any company competitive during the bidding process. Enjoy your reading, studying, and future rewards.

Notes

1. 1993 Malcolm Baldrige National Quality Award Criteria.

2. Although the text often uses references from the United States as examples (particularly in regard to codes and standards in chapter 5), this is primarily because the author is most familiar with these sources. International codes and standards have direct correlation.

3. Please note that these chapters and the appendices contain considerable detail. However, specific technical specifications shall always supersede this text. These chapters and appendices are guidelines that

have to be tailored to projects. Further, this text has been developed under the published procedures of ASQC to ensure a balanced representation. While these procedures ensure the highest degree of care, neither the author nor ASQC and those participating in its activities accepts any liability resulting from compliance or noncompliance with provisions given herein, for any restrictions imposed on materials or processes, or for the completeness of the text. Users of this text should consult applicable federal, state, and local laws and regulations. The author, ASQC, or those participating in its activities do not by the publication of this text intend to urge action not in compliance with applicable laws, and this document may not be construed as doing so.

2 Fundamental Quality Ideas in This Industrial Process

The A/E&C Process

- The A/E&C Community As an Industrial Process

Education and Training in This Industrial Process

- Introduction to Quality in the A/E&C Community
- Introduction to A/E&C Quality As an Industrial Process
- Quality Engineering Analysis Methods in This Process

The fundamental quality ideas addressed in this chapter are the result of the accomplishments and activities of the American Society for Quality Control (ASQC) Architectural/Engineering and Construction (A/E&C) Division, formerly the Construction Technical Committee (CTC). ASQC is a worldwide leader in the development, promotion, and application of quality and quality-related technologies for quality professionals in the private sector, government, and academia. ASQC serves more than 130,000 individual members and 1000 corporate members in the United States and abroad through numerous publications, courses, national and international conferences and seminars, and professional certification programs, 20 divisions, and four technical committees. Among numerous other activities, ASQC administers the Malcolm Baldrige National Quality Award (MBNQA) for the U.S. Department of Commerce. In 1992, the CTC progressed to become a formal division of ASQC, the A/E&C Division, by unanimous vote of the ASQC board of directors.

CTC was originally established in 1984 to provide guidance to the construction community on quality-related matters. In its initial effort, CTC developed a widely read guidance document published by Quality Press.[1] This guidance document is currently in high demand. In addition, CTC sponsored numerous speaking programs on the subject of A/E&C quality. And, in May 1992, the ASQC Annual Quality Congress—with attendance in excess of 4000—featured a significant program on construction quality.

Let's take a moment to look at current activities of ASQC in the A/E&C community. Some of the results of a key strategic planning meeting that was held in 1992 follow:

- The decision was made to fully align CTC in a relationship with the Design and Construction Quality Institute (DCQI) located in Washington, D.C., to further the efforts in bringing sound, sensible quality initiatives to our industry. Other alignments are being made with professional organizations such as the American Society of Civil Engineers, Project Management Institute (PMI), Association for Project Managers (PMA), and the Construction Industry Institute (CII).
- CTC would achieve division status within ASQC, to become the A/E&C Division.

- An overall strategy was developed focusing on providing consistency with future standards or guidance documents developed in the industry. The strategy includes the assessment of existing quality standards that affect the A/E&C community both domestically and internationally.
- This new ASQC division would sponsor an international conference in 1993 on A/E&C quality and would focus on ISO 9000 and related international issues. The conference would have a program dedicated to the quality of all types of constructed projects in the A/E&C community worldwide, with special emphasis on small to medium-sized projects and on certain complex A/E&C projects.
- The new division would turn its efforts toward the world community and make contributions to long-term goals for technological innovation in A/E&C quality.

As this list makes clear, ASQC has a full commitment to bring a much-needed influence to the A/E&C industry. To accomplish this successfully, broad participation from the entire A/E&C industrial community is needed. ASQC welcomes support, suggestions, and ideas for the betterment of quality in the A/E&C industry. A fundamental quality idea that has come from ASQC in the A/E&C community is the application of traditional quality engineering concepts to an industrial process that is distinctly different from other types of traditional industrial processes such as manufacturing.[2]

The A/E&C Community As an Industrial Process
Both manufacturing and A/E&C are complex processes; their greatest difference is in their end products. In A/E&C construction projects, the process ceases to exist after the project has been completed. At this point, the product of the A/E&C construction project is the actual finished facility, building, or other physical work product. Any improvement in that A/E&C process by measuring the quality of the product is theoretically not possible.[3] However, the data gathered may be used to improve future A/E&C processes. In other words, in A/E&C the building is the end product; in manufacturing a widget is the end product. This is the essence of the difference.

What is this A/E&C process? It follows the natural issue of the work from beginning to end and contains the following basic work-flow pattern.

- The owner conceives a fundamental concept.
- The owner might want a pure research and development (R&D) project, and studies may be performed before a design has been started.
- Feasibility or other special studies (for example, environmental) can also be conducted.
- Design criteria and a preliminary design are established.
- Detailed design is then produced with output documents (for example, specifications and drawings).
- Engineering support of construction and procurement occurs.
- Procurement is executed for long- and then short-lead items.
- The site is mobilized and earthwork, including utilities, is initiated.
- Civil and structural activities occur, including frame erection.
- The roof and vertical enclosures are installed.
- Mechanical, heating/ventilating, and air conditioning (HVAC) systems, structures, and equipment are installed.
- Electrical equipment (as well as electronic systems) and material are installed.
- Finishwork is completed along with any specialty items.
- After operating the completed facility, modifications and maintenance activities may occur.
- Eventually, after long life and operation, the facility can be decommissioned and/or demolished.

The A/E&C process is systematic. Both the Construction Specification Institute (CSI) and the American Institute of Architects (AIA) use this logical order in their standard industry specifications.[4,5] Any good contractor can cite chapter and verse from these references simply from the specification number of CSI or AIA.

The items in the preceding list represent the logical progression of any A/E&C project. Many of these logic work-flow items (sometimes referred to as work-breakdown elements) occur in parallel or in series. A/E&C projects are diverse and occur in a wide range of industries. A particular A/E&C project may emphasize only one work-flow item from the list, but the fundamental logic flow pattern usually is maintained.

If one visualizes each work-flow element or subelement as a probability density function (pdf), one recognizes that there are complex interactions between pdfs with many probable combinations and permutations.[6] In

Figure 2.1. A constructed facility or building can be complex or relatively simple. In either case, the logic flow pattern during the A/E&C process does not change. The difference lies in the complexity and sophistication of the control mechanisms in the project's quality program.

other words, the entire PDF of the A/E&C project is a complex set of functional pdf interrelationships that can be represented as follows:

$$PDF = pdf_a \cdots pdf_b \cdots pdf_c \cdots pdf_d \cdots pdf_n$$

where PDF is the composite pdf for the entire A/E&C project.

To understand these functional relationships, one has to understand certain principles of quality that apply to the A/E&C community. Some fundamental A/E&C quality truths are

- Quality is most greatly affected in the early stages of the project. Work-flow items, from conceptual through detail design, have significantly more effect on quality than, say, construction and operation.
- Most quality problems in a particular work-flow element are usually caused by a previous element.
- Even within a particular work-flow element, its early internal stages have a significant influence on its later stages.

The early conceptual activities on an A/E&C project influence greatly the installation. For example, the installation of the structural steel in the facility is greatly affected by the accuracy of the foundation forms.

If one watches a set of dominos in which the particular pieces are aligned so as to cause a chain reaction in a pyramidal pattern, the first piece has great influence on the final piece. One domino near the end of the chain (project closeout) slightly out of position will not make a significant difference in the final outcome (project closeout). On the other hand, one small adjustment in the first piece (project conception) greatly affects any final outcome.

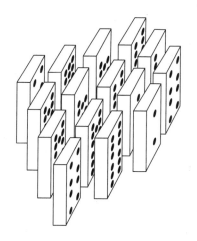

The A/E&C process *before* the work is done.

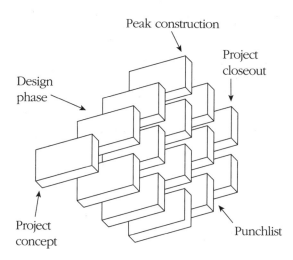

The A/E&C process *after* the work is performed correctly.

Figure 2.2. Example of interaction between pdfs.

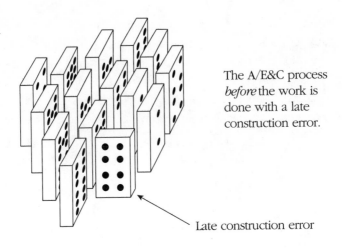

The A/E&C process *before* the work is done with a late construction error.

Late construction error

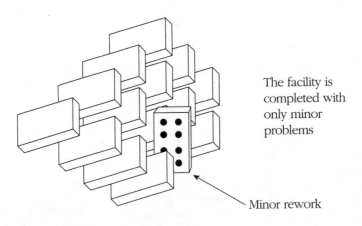

The facility is completed with only minor problems

Minor rework

Figure 2.2.   *continued*

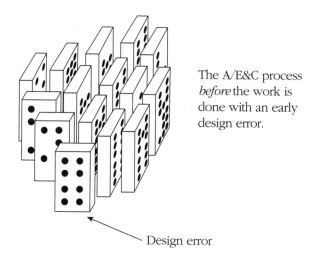

The A/E&C process *before* the work is done with an early design error.

Design error

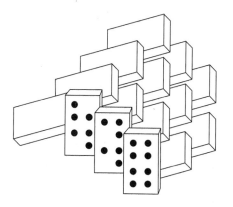

The facility is completed with major problems

Figure 2.2.   *continued*

This is an abstract illustration of an A/E&C project. One small adjustment in the early stages of the project greatly affects the final operating facility. In classical mathematics this is called a cascading effect, or something arranged in a succession of stages so that each stage derives from the acts upon the product of the preceding. Of all the tools in the quality profession, this functional relationship is similar to the mathematical tools of reliability engineering. Reliability engineering is not appropriate to describe the A/E&C process, because it describes an operating process, which occurs after the facility has been built.[7] However, the functional relationship of A/E&C project work-flow elements is similar to the science of reliability engineering; however, this relationship generates more complex interactions.[8]

This is because, in reliability, the operating facility is reasonably rigid and nonchanging. In the case of an A/E&C project, the process is ever changing and fluid. Corrections may have to be made in the later project stages to help correct an error from an early stage. However, it becomes increasingly difficult to correct errors as the physical structure and its systems are set in place. A quality program for a project in the A/E&C community has to be implemented in a manner that accounts for the characteristics of the A/E&C industrial process.

Education and Training in the A/E&C Industrial Process

Skill is required to understand the subtle differences between the A/E&C process and a typical manufacturing process. There are a growing number of educators in universities throughout the United States and abroad that are trying to come to grips with educating students in the A/E&C industrial process. For those educators, trying to come to grips with this new view of the A/E&C community, this chapter provides the basics for a standard introductory course in "Fundamental Quality Ideas and A/E&C Industrial Process." The course outlines in Tables 2.1, 2.2, and 2.3 are introductions that integrate standard quality engineering concepts with an understanding of the A/E&C process.[9]

Table 2.1.   Introduction to Quality in the A/E&C Community

Module Number	Percent of Course	Module Title
1	5	Introduction and Overview
2	14	Section 1: Quality in Industry. W. Edwards Deming, J. M. Juran, and Other Philosophy and Practices Section 2: Project Quality Programs Impact of Quality on a Project
3	8	A. The Construction Industry As an Industrial Process (and Its Work Elements)
4	5	B. The A/E&C Process and Quality
5	5	C. The Quality Profession in the A/E&C Community
6	10	D. Quality Tools and Related Mathematics Section 3: The Project Manager's Perspective
7	8	Perspective 1: Japanese and European Quality
8	10	Perspective 2: Management Analysis Techniques
9	10	Perspective 3: Nondestructive Examination (NDE) and Other Testing Methods*
10	5	Section 4: Quality Workshop and Interactive Feedback Lessons Learned
11	10	Site Visit
12	10	Examination and Certification

* Nondestructive examination (NDE) includes testing methods such as radiography (RT), ultrasonic examination (UT), magnetic particle (MT), and liquid penetrant (PT). See American Society of Nondestructive Testing (ASNT) standard SNT-TC-1A for details.

Table 2.2. Introduction to A/E&C Quality As an Industrial Process

Module Number	Percent of Course	Module Title
1	5	Introduction
2	8	Section 1: The Construction Industry As an Industrial Process
		Section 2: Project Quality Control and Systems
3	11	A. Use of Mathematics in A/E&C Quality Systems
4	6	B. Organization of Codes in the United States and Throughout the World
5	6	C. Organization of Quality-Related Local and State Codes and Regulation
6	11	D. Administration, Enforcement, Definition, Classifications, Limitations, and Special Use
		Section 3: Technical Portion: Light, Ventilation, and Sound Transmission
7	8	Means of Egress, Structural and Foundations
8	11	Materials and Tests. Steel, Masonry, Gypsum, and Lumber Construction
9	11	Building Enclosures, Walls and Wall Thickness, One- and Two-Family Dwellings
10	6	Application 1: Site Visit
11	6	Fire Resistance, Chimneys, Flues, and Vent Pipes; Mechanical Fire Protection; Signage; Electrical; and Plumbing
12	11	Practice Refresher
		Examination and Certification

Table 2.3. Course Outline for Quality Engineering and Analysis Methods in the A/E&C Process

Module Number	Percent of Course	Module Title
1	7	Introduction
2	7	Background
3	7	Mathematics and Quality Statistics of the Industrial Process
4	10	Root Cause, Quality Functional Deployment (QFD), and Other Analyses and Diagrams
5	10	Use of Pareto and Statistical Analyses
6	10	Use of Quality Cost Analysis and Return on Quality (ROQ)
7	14	Use of Decision and Other Management Analysis Techniques
8	7	Project Type A: Regulated Type Construction
9	7	Project Type B: Heavy Construction
10	7	Project Type C: Medium and Light Construction
11	7	Measurement of Quality Results
12	7	Future Use of Innovative Quality Engineering Technologies

When the student has established a firm foundation from the body of knowledge delineated in the three courses outlined in Tables 2.1, 2.2, and 2.3, he or she may apply traditional quality tools to the A/E&C process.

At this point, it is necessary to digress for a moment and discuss the issue proving the value of quality tools. How can we know if quality tools have been effective? Applying quality measurement tools requires an investment in time and money. In manufacturing, this investment can be justified through determining root causes and measuring effect on scrap, repair, or rework at the output of the assembly line. In the A/E&C process, this is usually not possible since the product does not occur until the process is complete. Traditional quality measurement tools in A/E&C projects have to be handled in a more strategic manner.

The strategic use of traditional quality measuring tools is an effective means to improve performance in A/E&C projects. Their early use requires careful thought and consideration. There are many factors that influence early decisions, such as contractual relationships, labor and craft relationships, site-specific characteristics, regulations, required facility reliability, and so on. These factors are normally a function of the complexity of the project.

This text will clearly demonstrate the tasks for improving performance in A/E&C projects. These tasks include

- Identifying practical opportunities
- Conducting quality cost analyses of improvement opportunities
- Defining responsibility
- Remeasuring the process to set new goals
- Performing problem and decision analyses
- Continuously improving the process

A significant subtask will be the proper use of root-cause analysis. As previously stated, A/E&C projects require a unique application because of the type of industrial process. This process includes conception, defining of criteria, design input, design output, procurement, site mobilization, installation, start-up, and operation, including maintenance. A viable quality improvement task must be able to address this type of industrial process.

In subsequent chapters, important conclusions about pilot programs that are currently using these mechanisms support significant quality and cost improvements with relatively modest investments early in the process. Also, the future of quality mechanisms that use such new and innovative technologies as artificial intelligence (AI) and robotics is discussed.

Notes

1. Construction Technical Committee. *Quality Management in the Constructed Project.* Milwaukee, Wis.: ASQC Quality Press, 1987.

2. Please note that there are many other organizations providing quality leadership in their respective areas. These organizations include International Conference of Building Officials (ICBO); American Society for Testing Materials (ASTM); British Standards Institute (BSI); Deutsche Institute Fur Nurmung (DIN); American Society of Civil Engineers (ASCE); American Society of Mechanical Engineering (ASME); Southern Building Code Congress International (SBCCI); National Fire Protection Association (NFPA); American Welding Society (AWS); Building Officials and Code Administrators (BOCA); and Canadian Standard Association (CSA). For the most part, these organizations have standards pertaining primarily to checking and inspecting. The direction of this text is toward prevention, management techniques, and quality engineering as a technical discipline.

3. Any exception is very limited. See chapter 4, "Tracking of a Design and Construction Process."

4. The CSI has a MASTERFORMAT that a lot of the A/E&C uses in describing this body of work. (For example, Sweet's Catalog follows this description of the A/E&C process.)

5. The AIA (in New York) has cooperated with the CSI on this description of the A/E&C work-flow process (see note 4).

6. Ireson, W. G. *Reliability Handbook.* New York: McGraw-Hill, 1966. Also Raymond H. Walpole and Ronald E. Myers. *Probability and Statistics for Engineers and Scientists,* 5th ed. New York: Macmillan Publishing, 1993, 50–52.

7. Reliability engineering is appropriate during operations and maintenance (O&M) tasks that may be evaluated during the design phase of the project.

8. Hart, R. D. "Quality Measurement Engineering and Construction." 46th ASQC Annual Quality Congress Transactions, 1992.

9. Chapter 10 pertaining to motivational and human resource management contains additional details on training programs.

3 Quality Policies and Innovation in the A/E&C Community

Introduction to Quality Policy and Innovation

- Developing a Quality Statement
- Writing the Quality Policy
- Drafting Quality Principles and Quality Operating Policy

Applying a Quality System and Developing Guidelines

Quality Policy and a Quality Organization(s)

Innovation in Quality

Innovation with Technology That Will Enhance Quality in the A/E&C Community

- Researching and Developing a Method for Fully Utilizing AI in the A/E&C Community
- AI Technical Description
- What is AI as Applied to A/E&C Projects?

Quality Measurement in A/E&C Organizations

Quality Cost Analysis and Its Use

Quality Cost Application on an A/E&C Project

Current Industry Advances in Measuring Quality

- CII
- ASQC A/E&C Division
- ASCE
- DCQI
- Industry Leaders

TQM

Introduction to Quality Policy and Innovation

What does the concept of a quality policy mean in the A/E&C community? It means getting the job done on time. It also means getting the job done within budget, and having extra monies left to install the luxury finishwork at the end of the job. A quality project includes all of these advantages.

An A/E&C organization striving to establish an effective quality program has to start from the top and work downward. Without the complete support of the chairperson and chief executive officer (CEO) or equivalent using a genuine open-door policy, an effective quality program cannot be implemented. A quality program cannot be effective without the consistent delegation of authority to lower levels of management and employees.

The CEO has to get involved directly. Any quality organization should report directly to the CEO.[1] The CEO has to be sufficiently educated in quality engineering tools to be able to directly manage this effort. His or her main tool must be the use of quality policy. A quality policy must be the method of translating the CEO's direction into practical application through the organization that will carry out any and all A/E&C activities. This quality policy has to be clear, be directly applicable to the organization, and encompass a program of innovation with the quality program. Old paradigms must be dispelled and a clear vision must be made part of the policy.

In creating this vision, one must not get preoccupied with the procedural aspects of determining overall missions, corporate policy, operating policy, policy versus procedure, and the like. It is important to set good overall quality policy, which cascades in a logical fashion throughout the company through consistent and increasingly more detailed corporate policies and procedures. The quality policy must be sufficiently clear and pervasive that employees can directly affect the quality of the A/E&C work-breakdown elements in a novel or innovative manner.

A company's policies should include guidelines for a quality system that provides clear quality operational consistency for all services. These guidelines should be designed to meet most current mandatory, external quality requirements and to be in accordance with such standards as the ANSI/ASQC Q90 series (or ISO 9000 internationally) quality system requirements. These guidelines should follow the Q90 elements and have a unique and innovative approach to adapting statistical applications to

A/E&C maintenance, and operational-type projects. What about statistical applications? Most A/E&C people believe that statistical applications do not apply to construction, but one of the main themes of this text is that they do in fact apply. A major problem in previous attempts to apply statistical techniques was that the wrong ones were used (see chapter 11).

Authority and responsibility for improving quality should be defined in precise terms. A company's quality operating policy should incorporate the latest industrywide innovations in quality management. (A sample policy can be found at the end of this section.) Standard quality references and definitions should provide a consistent approach to implementing a quality program. (These are provided in Appendix I of this text.) Finally, a perfect quality system should

- Describe a fully integrated, practical, and functioning quality organization at all levels.
- Provide practical guidance on implementing a plan for improving quality on every A/E&C project as well as for support groups and service organizations.
- Guide internal business entities through external mandatory quality requirements throughout their operations.
- Designate specific quality elements in A/E&C processes so that, if special attention is given to them, significant gains can be achieved.
- Provide consistent and distinct levels of assurance to accurately respond to client and project needs.
- Facilitate the implementation of companywide quality measures with emphasis on problem prevention in lieu of problem detection.
- Provide innovative quality technology in the areas of TQM, measurement of quality improvements, reliability concepts, and computerized methods in focusing quality information.

An organization's guidelines and quality policy should provide clear and definitive direction to implementing quality programs within the various business entities and should meet the basic principles of doing a good job. It should be an organization's policy to provide A/E&C and even maintenance and operational services that comply with regulations, codes, and contractual requirements. The project director or manager is responsible for implementing a project quality system that is consistent with the company quality policy and that will achieve the quality objectives of the project.

Developing a Quality Statement

To create an organization's quality statement, clearly state realistic quality expectations with special emphasis on directing the company's energies toward customer focus and satisfaction. Refrain from "motherhood and apple pie" statements and provide detail. Employees are smarter than they are sometimes given credit for. One must not be afraid to give away what may be considered trade secrets.

Writing the Quality Policy

Using its quality statement, the company should delineate a quality policy to ensure that projects are executed with clearly defined and communicated requirements. In addition, the policy should further ensure that A/E&C work activities are done right the first time, concentrating on the significant few work-breakdown items. When innovative quality tools are applied to these activities, significant quality gains can be achieved.

Drafting Quality Principles and Quality Operating Policy

The top management of the company must be firmly committed to its quality statement and quality policy by continuously improving quality, productivity, and competitive position, as well as establishing a new standard of quality for A/E&C projects. It requires an attitude of being the best or world class in the A/E&C community. In other words, a CEO must personally establish a new standard for the A/E&C community, remembering that significant gains can be achieved by investing in preventive quality measures rather than paying for mistakes. An organization's guidelines should describe these measures. They should also endorse the following quality principles:

- Ensure a leadership role in all quality facets of the business.
- Maintain a leadership role in TQM.
- Maintain a leadership role in new and innovative quality technology.
- Establish a strong preventive quality engineering role early in the life of A/E&C projects.

- Value and reward long-term relationships with all employees and suppliers.
- Enhance motivational team education and improvement in individual skills.
- Identify potential problems and solve them before they happen.

An organization should adopt guidelines that provide consistency to well-established and widely recognized quality methods. The implementation of a quality system on projects should be consistent.

On an individual project basis, a quality plan should be prepared which is tailored to the complexity, safety, type, phase, and mandatory requirements that mitigate adverse consequences. This quality plan can be as simple as a paragraph in the overall contract or as complex as an entirely separate manual. Quality plans may vary significantly from project to project. However, each should address appropriate elements of the quality system described in chapters 6–11. It is important to establish a quality plan at the start of every project.

Applying a Quality System and Developing Guidelines

The goals of any A/E&C organization's quality policy should include

- Maximizing return on investment (ROI) through the use of preventive quality measures
- Maximizing the use of specific and tailored quality techniques that delight the customer
- Maximizing the applicability of most current quality requirements, standards, and guides while focusing on customer needs
- Providing consistency of quality methods
- Minimizing the redundancy of quality activities

Quality guidelines should not define particular methodologies to be used in determining what constitutes an acceptable quality program; they should describe a framework for operations in which acceptable quality programs are derived for particular project use.

Finally, the extent to which any element of the quality system is ensured for any project is directly dependent upon how essential the element is to the project as a whole (focusing on true customer satisfaction). One must make every effort to understand the meaning of *true customer satisfaction*. Furthermore, the application of specific controls of quality to structures, systems, components, and their related activities is dependent on their importance in terms of public safety, need for reliability, criticality of function, and cost of replacement or impact of deficient operation. These quality guidelines should be everyone's responsibility.

Quality Policy and a Quality Organization(s)

The next steps in establishing a quality system and guidelines lie in determining who will be responsible for carrying them out, focusing on the guidelines as an active document, and periodically assessing their implementation. Does the company need an internal quality organization? Does it need assistance from an outside quality consultant? To whom should an internal quality organization report? To what extent should a quality organization be implemented as a function of the overall size of the company? All of these questions need to be clearly answered before implementing an effective quality program.

The quality organization should be chartered to provide QA and expert consulting to line management. This organization should be given the authority to carry out the company's quality principles beyond the customers' expectations. The methods employed by the quality organization should

- Focus on various project management and support departments throughout the organization to improve the quality system, thus creating additional consistency.
- Develop and use new and innovative quality technology beyond current industry standards.
- Apply quality engineering expertise throughout all project activities.
- Implement quality engineering expertise in all procurement contracts.
- Systematically train all personnel in the quality system.
- Efficiently and effectively standardize quality guidelines.
- Enhance business relationships, particularly through partnering, to improve quality.
- Strive for a leadership role in TQM.
- Focus on retaining and distributing quality information throughout the organization and to customers for effective quality system application.
- Meaningfully and realistically approach quality cost analyses.

Whether a company employs an external quality consultant or an internal quality department, quality professionals should have the freedom and authority to cross potential organizational barriers to ensure quality methods are used.

Instructions on how these methods should be practiced throughout the organization—and how they should be implemented—should be contained in a QA manual. The overall quality system described in this manual of the company should follow ANSI/ASQC Q91 (equivalent to ISO 9001) "Quality Systems—Model for Quality Assurance in Design/Development, Production, Installation, and Servicing" for commercial work (ISO 9002 may be used if the work is only construction).

Innovation in Quality

An organization's strategic quality plan should provide a vision of the latest technological innovations. It should be a vision that will remain effective well into the twenty-first century. Relying on traditional paper record-keeping procedures when design activities are handled through electronic media is not sufficient. Using automated field material handling techniques that electronically inspect incoming supplies will give you a distinct competitive quality advantage.

Recently, a seminar was held at a major East Coast university in which a panel of distinguished representatives included a district director for a member of the U.S. Congress, president of a major real estate and development firm, division engineer for the U.S. Army Corps of Engineers, and director of an institute on quality at another major university.[2]

Subjects of the seminar included

- The role of the architect, engineer, and construction manager
- The role of the planner, owner, and developer
- The role and intervention of various government entities
- The impact of international competition on the U.S. A/E&C community
- The impact of new technologies on the A/E&C community

The discussion format included the introduction of panelists, an opportunity for each panelist to address the individual subjects, questions by the moderator, and questions from the audience. In addition, discussion about the results of a study (conducted in the early 1980s by The Business Roundtable) indicated that construction's slow acceptance and use of modern management methods to execute projects resulted in delays and cost overruns. The study also concluded that owners, who are the prime beneficiaries of improvements, do not seem aware of the economic payoff of improving quality. There is a strong need in the A/E&C industry to quantify the cost benefits in improving quality of a project and to provide more effective quality programs.

The panel discussion developed the following questions, which need to be directly addressed by the A/E&C community:

- How can the A/E&C community support its customer industries in the years to come?
- Where can the A/E&C community do a better job to solve problems?
- How much control should government have in solving quality problems and helping the A/E&C community in major projects?
- How can a project truly be done right the first time?
- Is quality education and training adequate for the A/E&C community?
- How should the three components of A/E&C projects—cost, schedule, and quality—be balanced with due regard to safety?
- Everyone knows the U.S. real estate market has slumped. Is there anything the A/E&C community can do better to increase profitability?
- Sometimes construction workers build something different from what designers design. Why does this happen? Should something be done differently?
- There are tremendous and sometimes devastating happenings in the world today. Can the A/E&C community make a significant contribution to solving these problems?
- Is R&D in the A/E&C community adequate? Are there areas that should be expanded?
- Are A/E&C organizations investing in good quality rather than paying for poor quality?
- Should the standards for U.S. A/E&C organizations be improved to meet international competition?
- Does improving quality in the A/E&C community cost money, or will a small investment up front save tenfold in the long run?

- Can such advancing technologies as AI help the A/E&C community understand the "building before it is built" concept, which is a major foundation of a sound quality program?
- Should there be a national task force to find solutions to improving quality in the A/E&C community?

Innovation in quality is now being addressed in the A/E&C community through ASQC. These questions are indeed being addressed and solved by ASQC in the A/E&C Division established in 1992. The division's purpose is to

- Provide grass-roots support within the A/E&C community.
- Ensure industry needs and desires are addressed, especially as related to the previously cited concerns and questions.
- Provide industrywide guidelines and accepted practices.
- Disseminate quality information as a central source.
- Facilitate A/E&C quality education and training that will focus existing industry quality education and training. Unique quality training would be provided where weaknesses exist.
- Ensure R&D of quality technologies by reviewing new technologies and developing feasibility action plans.

Innovation with Technology That Will Enhance Quality in the A/E&C Community

Innovation and change in the A/E&C community is becoming increasingly more important as we approach the next century. The concept of innovative quality ideas has been mentioned in this text several times. This section describes the means to adapt these innovative ideas to the A/E&C community. Here reference is made specifically to improving the A/E&C community through the R&D of new quality technology.

Technology throughout industry is dramatically evolving and changing at an ever-increasing rate. The A/E&C community has to keep pace and excel in this effort. (A text could easily be authored on this subject alone.) Examples of this increasing technology that relate to quality include

- Using composite data bases such as GRASS[3]
- Applying distributed interactive engineering

- Applying interactive computer simulation
- Using neural networking and virtual reality
- Creating interactive domain models
- Applying AI and expert systems

One example of technology transfer, AI and expert systems, if fully implemented in the future, can make a tremendous impact and drastically reduce the A/E&C community's reliance on inspection.

Researching and Developing a Method for Fully Utilizing AI in the A/E&C Community

It is becoming increasingly apparent that using AI in the A/E&C community can make a significant contribution to productivity and quality. What is AI? Almost everyone is familiar with the present state of computer technology. The speed and capacity of computers are increasing by quantum leaps. New technologies, such as AI and expert systems, differ from conventional computer technology by letting computer systems learn from their own mistakes, and to think on the fly. The difference is that software is designed not by a step-by-step process, but by sets of algorithmic rules and goals.[4] This AI contribution to the A/E&C community can include the development of a construction job site that is automated to the degree in which

- Significant reductions can be obtained in the time required to control job-site material and equipment.
- Significant reductions can be obtained in the time required to control job-site project erection and installation; schedules can be enhanced.
- Significant increases can be obtained in the precision and accuracy of workmanship required to perform job-site project erection and installation.
- Significant increases can be obtained in the precision and accuracy of the design architectural and engineering aspects of the project.
- Significant increases can be obtained in the control of project cost and in estimating techniques, including the reduction of repair, rework, and scrap at a construction job site.

Figure 3.1. Innovation and change will be important components of a quality system in the twenty-first century. Novel and innovative projects will require novel and innovative quality programs.

The basic concept of this effort would be to provide a partially AI-controlled job site that includes erection and material-control equipment to assist site personnel by predicting activities. This system would take the A/E&C process from conceptual design through detailed design output documents, to material and equipment coordination through robotic excavation, and to controlled erection, finishing the process by confirming site completeness.

AI Technical Description

The term *construction* as it relates to AI here is intended to cover the field generally referred to as *construction engineering and management*. This is a broad area that includes planning and engineering of the temporary facilities for construction sites, management of the construction process, and rehabilitation, repair, and maintenance of facilities where the traditionally distinct design and construction roles have merged.

The scope, combined with the empirical nature of many facets of construction engineering and management practice, can lead to a significant amount of activity in this domain.

The following material is designed to paint a reasonably complete picture of the state of the art of expert systems in construction as of mid-1993. Library and on-line searches of engineering, computer, and business publications have been performed; U.S. and foreign universities known to be working in this area have been surveyed; and attempts have been made to contact private firms and government agencies engaged in the development of expert systems applications in the area of construction. Undoubtedly, however, expert systems applications have been missed, especially those in early stages of development and those outside the United States. This, therefore, should be considered a representative, but not exhaustive, catalog and discussion of ongoing expert system work in construction.

This subsection begins with a detailed definition of A/E&C to illustrate the types of decisions that might be used as rules and goals in expert systems. Next, the rationale for profitably using expert systems is examined, including some reasons that provide strong motivations for doing so. The balance of this subsection is devoted to descriptions of a series of applications, ranging from operational systems (in routine use by persons other than their developers) to projects still in conceptual stages. The purpose of these descriptions is to give a sense of both where the state of the art is currently, and where it might be headed over the next few years. At the end, there is a summary of the work described and speculation about the direction of future research and development efforts using the advance of quality technology.

Detailed Definition of A/E&C Projects As Related to AI

The A/E&C community, as previously stated, are divided into three areas: design and engineering of facilities; management of the construction process; and rehabilitation, erection, and maintenance of facilities.

Rationale for Profitably Using Expert Systems on A/E&C Projects

"Construction is a ripe, virtually untouched, and inevitable arena for robotics applications," says William Whittaker, director of the Construction Robotics Laboratory at Carnegie Mellon University.[5] This broad assessment has been echoed in recent years by many in both Japan and the United States who are feeling the effects of a steady drop in productivity, a shrinking skilled labor force, and, as construction projects become more complex, an increasingly dangerous work environment.

Construction is the single largest industry in the United States comprising about 5.5 million workers.[6] It contributes approximately 8 percent of the GNP. In Japan, this figure accounts for a staggering 20 percent of the GNP. Considering the Japanese thrust into robotics research and development in manufacturing, it is not surprising that Japan is well ahead of its counterparts in construction robotics research.

Although robot technology has staged significant advances, it has had minimal effects on the construction site. This is due to the unstructured and nonrepetitive nature of the work, the endlessly varying terrain, the customized requirements of each job, and the labor intensiveness of the work. The work site is also subject to daily and seasonal swings in the weather, making robotic applications difficult. These factors have led to stagnation in construction robotics research.

Evidence from current research shows that great strides are being made by those examining both cognitive and noncognitive robots. Many suggest that cognition attributes will ultimately dominate construction robots. Although the evolution of construction automation may initially require crude solutions, the complexities of the work site call out for cognitive solutions.

It is in this perspective that AI is based—AI as it applies to a smart work site. A partially AI-controlled work site would break interesting historical grounds in its application and combination of technologies. With up to 50 percent of the workweek wasted by either waiting for materials or waiting for a job assignment, the time is ripe.

Descriptions of AI Applications

Design and Engineering: This area of A/E&C business covers all the planning and design decisions related to the equipment and facilities involved in the construction process. These decisions are typically carried out by individuals who design the permanent facility. Decision-making tasks associated with this area are candidates for formalization via expert systems techniques.[7]

Design of Construction AI Methods: In practice, construction methods are largely left to the discretion of the contractor. There are few formal techniques for selecting construction methods; experience plays a large role in performing this task.

Experience-based decisions to be made in this area include configuration of crews; selection of equipment types, sizes, and combinations; design of transportation facilities (roads, railways, conveyors, cranes, hoists) for moving personnel, materials, and equipment around on the job site; and approaches to prefabrication or modularization of components for the permanent facility, including locating construction joints in slabs or walls.

Concrete As a Manufactured Material Using AI: The details of manufacturing and placing concrete in a permanent facility are almost always left to the contractor. Decisions to be made here include mix design, both to meet performance specifications and to accommodate the selected method of placement; design of crushers, batch plant, and transportation systems; and structural and functional design of formwork.

Proposed Application to Enhance the Quality of A/E&C Projects

The basic concept of this program is to provide an AI-controlled job site that has stationary erection and material-control equipment that assists onsite personnel. This system would take the construction process from conceptual design through detailed output specifications to material and equipment coordination and mobilization, through robotized excavation to controlled erection, completing the process by confirming site completeness. The tasks to implement this system are as follows:

—Feasibility study. Determined where in the A/E&C process AI should be applied.
—Software and hardware development. Clearly determine the domains, rules, and goals to be achieved, particularly in the area of software development. This step also includes the application of robotics, if necessary.

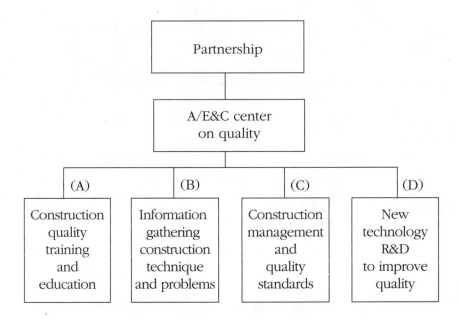

Figure 3.2. Partnership with a higher education institution.

—Full-scale nonlaboratory model project. A prototype may be necessary.
—Commercial project. This is a full-scale application with the use of quality cost analysis to determine its value on future projects.

Research and Development to Achieve Proposed Application

In order to achieve this proposed application to enhance the quality of A/E&C projects, a research and development program could be instituted in partnership with a higher education institution. The following is a suggested partnership arrangement with a higher education institution to develop this application.

The use of AI in quality technology deals specifically with the last objective, (D), researching and developing new technologies in related industries to improve the quality of A/E&C organizations. Objectives (A) through (C) have been implemented to one degree or another. The training function sponsored by several organizations—PMI, CII, ASCE, and ASQC—has also received some success. Because of its importance, the next objective to be fully implemented should be the research and development function. Therefore, the organizational structure shown in Figure 3.3 may be established.

Center (D)

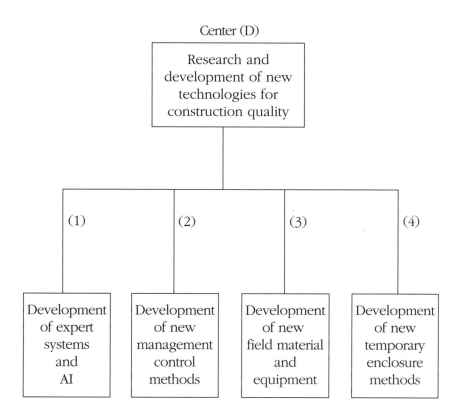

Figure 3.3. An organizational structure that emphasizes the research and devleopment function.

Based on (1) in Figure 3.3, a detailed literature search was undertaken to determine the needs of the construction industry as well as the existing construction systems now in place. Through this research process, it became clear that components of robotics and other systems do exist in the construction industry as components. However, they do not get sufficient interactive use to provide quality control of a complete project. Thus, it is suggested that development of AI and expert systems become the first task, organized in the manner illustrated in Figure 3.4.

Since the A/E&C community is diverse and members are commonly classified as light, medium, or heavy, it was determined that at least two of the three categories should be represented in a working field model. The following proposed field program is suggested.

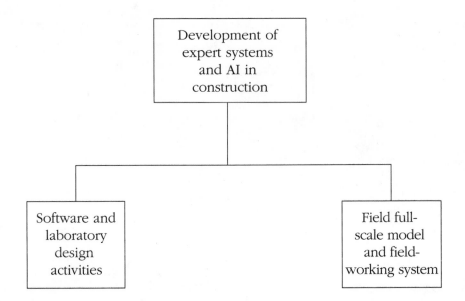

Figure 3.4.   An organizational structure that emphasizes the development of AI and expert systems.

- Use a relatively small prototype job site with a relatively short project duration.
- After implementing AI and expert systems at the prototype job site, provide full implementation at a larger site as an expansion of the prototype.

Quality Measurement in A/E&C Companies

To make significant progress in quality, the A/E&C community has to have a distinct method of measuring the results of current quality techniques. Traditional quality measuring tools provide effective means of improving performance in many A/E&C projects. Their use and application require careful thought and consideration. There are many factors that affect the way these tools are used and applied. These factors include contractual relationships, labor and craft relationships, site-specific characteristics, regulations, and facility operating reliability.

The A/E&C community currently uses an assorted array of tools to measure the performance of quality: drawing discrepancies uncovered during the checking process, too much slump concrete identified as it is discharged from the truck, partition walls found to be out of alignment, undersized air handlers put in place, lack of fusion welds in structural steel discovered, and so on.

Certainly, there are various ways of preventing or minimizing quality concerns and problems. The A/E&C community has attempted to provide numerous methodologies to provide solutions. These solutions are based primarily on a wealth of practical experience. For example, experience shows that it is more effective to perform supplier inspection at the supplier's facility than to wait until the supplier's material or component arrives at the construction site. In addition, generally speaking, it is more effective to inspect in-process welds than to wait until the weld has been formed and to rely on final inspection and test.

There are cases, however, where one may question the extent to which quality improvement techniques should be applied. That question may often be difficult to answer. At present, the answer comes from experience, trial and error, and intuition based on education, experience, and collective intelligence. Quality measurement tools can help A/E&C workers more efficiently solve problems by helping them understand the relationships among A/E&C work-flow activities.

In the hopes of finding any functional interrelationships among the vast assortment of potential concerns and solutions on even the simplest project, one has to compare the existing situation with a common base or common unit of measure. The most straightforward and easiest to use in the A/E&C industry is dollars (plain, old, and simple money). This focus and unit of base is the most appropriate one, given the present state of quality measurements in design and construction. With this in mind, quality cost analysis may be the method that most effectively addresses these functional relationships.

Quality Cost Analysis and Its Use

Quality cost analysis, which will be more directly addressed in chapter 4, is a method whereby one can systematically analyze a quality attribute to find the most effective application of prevention and appraisal techniques. There are many excellent, detailed texts on both quality cost analysis and COQ.[8] Therefore, the theory of quality cost analysis will not be discussed; its application to A/E&C projects will be.

A quality cost analysis measures the improvement of a particular quality attribute in one isolated case. Unfortunately, the design and construction process contains work-flow items that operate dependently and influence greatly the effect of other work-flow items on the same A/E&C project. The objective of this text is to present a method whereby this may be accomplished. Again, one has to get to the fundamentals.

As explained in chapter 2, there is a complex interactive set of pdfs and a method to measure their interaction in one isolated set in isolation (quality cost analysis or COQ). Again, it is unfortunate that this is still not practical in this industry. Even simple design and construction projects are complex tasks. Architects, engineers, and construction workers cannot afford to wait until one project is complete to understand its effect and to make any corrections before working on the next project. The A/E&C industry needs both a way of studying multiple interactions and the ability to make corrections quickly and effectively.

The technique known as *design of experiments* is a tool used to study multiple interactions.[9] A two-by-two or three-by-three experiment is easy to perform. As the experiment events increase, the experiment becomes more difficult to execute. This difficulty increases exponentially. However, the design and construction industry has generally agreed that a project usually has the significant few quality concerns and the trivial many. In other words, perhaps 20 percent of the items important to quality (the significant few) have 80 percent of the effect on it.[10] If it is assumed that attention to a handful of important items early in a project is what is really important to quality, one can then indeed design an experiment using, for example, no more than a five-by-five matrix.

Quality Cost Application on an A/E&C Project

Table 3.1 illustrates an application of the suggested quality cost analysis method. This example assumes a proposed warehouse project. A customer wanting to move into the building soon is driving the overall construction schedule. There is a standard set of prints. Trees and brush must be removed. Excavation will require some blasting. There are plenty of highly trained subcontractors in most disciplines. HVAC will be controlled in the building. The structure will be basically a concrete foundation,

Table 3.1. Relationships Between Work-Flow Items and Cost Items.

Cost Item / Work-Flow Item	Independent Estimate	Total Final Costs	Prevention Quality Costs	Appraisal Quality Costs	Failure Quality Costs
Permits/fees					
Architect fees					
Engineer fees			(a)		
Surveying			(b) & (c)		
Mobilization					
Miscellaneous billings					
Grubbing and clearing					
Earthwork/blasting					(a)
Underground utilities					
Foundations				(d)	(d)
Floor slabs			(d)	(d)	
Structural steel				(b)	(b)
Miscellaneous metals			(e)		
Roof labor and material					
Mechanical/HVAC			(a)		(a)
Electrical/security					
Siding enclosure					
Doors/windows					
Drywall/lathing				(e)	(e)
Painting/coatings					
Finishwork					
Tilework/carpeting					
Parking lot paving				(c)	(c)
Landscaping					

Notes to Table 3.1

a. Since a standard set of prints was provided, the design of the warehouse was complete and engineering changes were not necessary. However, the contractor decided to perform a design review by a qualified engineer to check for errors or potential concerns. The costs of this activity are quality costs associated with prevention. After review, the engineer concluded that two concerns existed in the design. First, a significant growth, or outcrop of bedrock may cause problems with blasting. Relocating the building south by 10 feet should eliminate the potential problem. Second, there is a possibility that the HVAC system may be undersized. By slightly increasing the size of the air handlers, this potential problem can be corrected.

b. Surveying is always required on construction sites in one form or another. The contractor on this project decided to bring in additional survey crews to ensure that the foundations, including locations of the embedded anchor bolts, are absolutely correct. The cost associated with this additional activity is a prevention cost to enhance quality. In erecting structural steel, some field welding and correction are normally expected. In this case, field welding does not become necessary, primarily because of the additional surveying performed on the foundation's concrete forms. This represents a significant savings in failure costs.

c. As stated in note b, surveying is normally required on construction sites. However, a contract has been written for the paving subcontractor explaining that he or she will be monitored carefully for conformance to specification and that any deviation from construction drawings will result in rejection. Again, any costs associated with additional work of the survey crews and with contract negotiations are appraisal and prevention costs, respectively. The savings resulting from lack of rework and conformance to drawings are measures of the positive effect of the steps taken to improve quality.

d. A concrete batch plant is relatively close to the construction site. A concrete inspector was hired, to be located at the batch plant rather than at the construction site. The costs associated with the inspector are considered appraisal costs, although often there is an inspector performing similar work on site before concrete placement. Having inspection at the batch plant should improve the quality of the concrete arriving at the site because problems will be corrected before the material leaves the plant. This situation should improve quality and reduce labor hours for installing both the foundations and the floor slabs.

e. Similar contracts were written for both the subcontractor installing the steel frame and the drywall installer, making their performance interdependent. The framing subcontractor's contract reads that full payment for services will not be made until the drywall contractor has signed off that the framing is correct. The costs associated with negotiating and writing this contract are prevention costs. The potential savings are obvious. There is now little or no need to perform inspection on the trueness of the frame; there is a reduction in labor hours for drywall installation; there is reduction of potential for drywall rework. Jurisdiction among trades is always a concern, but this simple quality device eliminated it on this project.

structural steel frame, and metal vertical enclosure with a bituminous membrane roof. The work-flow items are listed in Table 3.1.

Anyone familiar with the design and construction work-flow process will comment at this point that much depends on the scope of the project, the experience of the personnel, and many other factors, all of which is true. Use of quality cost analysis along with a five-degrees-of-freedom (maximum) experimental design, can help the A/E&C company identify significant interactions among variables, thereby maximizing the positive effect on quality.

Current Industry Advances in Measuring Quality

Several organizations are working on improving quality measurement techniques for the A/E&C industry. The scope of this book does not permit going into detail on these various methods. Instead, readers are encouraged to contact these organizations directly. They offer a variety of publications and periodicals on quality measurement techniques. A brief description of industry organizations that perform work to advance measurement in quality follow.

Construction Industry Institute

This institute was founded by a number of executives from the construction industry in the early 1980s and represents a solid group of top executives from several major owners, architects/engineers, constructors, and suppliers in the design and construction industry. CII has formed three committees on or related to quality, including one dedicated to finding reliable methods in measuring quality. CII can provide the results of studies that directly relate to the subject of this text.

Construction Industry Institute
3208 Red River, Suite 300
Austin, TX 78705-2650

ASQC A/E&C Division

The Construction Technical Committee (CTC) of ASQC was formed in the early 1980s to respond to Business Roundtable Study E4-1982, which began to address certain needs of the design and construction industry. In 1992, the committee advanced to divisional status as the A/E&C Division. It has recently formed centers around the United States to better respond to the construction industry. Representatives from several centers have expressed an interest in and are working on methods for measuring cost of quality.

ASQC A/E&C Division
17595 Harvard, Suite C215
Irvine, CA 92714

American Society of Civil Engineers

Like ASQC, ASCE is a long-established society sponsoring a particular discipline, in this case, civil engineering. It plays an important role in the A/E&C community. ASCE quality efforts also responded to Business Roundtable Study E4-1982. One of ASCE's successful quality tools is a comprehensive text that describes the proper execution of a project from beginning to end and covers aspects beyond quality that affect doing a good job. The cost of quality and methods to measure quality are addressed in this ASCE text in a general approach.[11]

American Society of Civil Engineers
345 East 47th Street
New York, NY 10017-2398

Design and Construction Quality Institute

This institute, formed in Washington, D.C., in the late 1980s by ACEC, also responds to the needs of the construction industry. The organization has been working closely with the A/E&C Division of ASQC. One effort in particular revolves around fostering the development of methods in measuring quality and understanding the application of the COQ.

Design and Construction Quality Institute
1015 15th Street NW, Suite 802
Washington, D.C. 20005

Industry Leaders

There are several other organizations, such as the Association of General Contractors (AGC), as well as union organizations, that have expressed an interest in and desire to address honestly the subject of quality and in particular COQ. In addition, industry leaders, such as major A/E&C firms, are supporting several professional initiatives.

Together, all of these groups will drive the enhancement of quality in the coming decades.

TQM

TQM is a term referred to in many current industry management practices. This expression is defined as those quality program elements that holistically affect product quality.[12] There are a number of appropriate elements or methods of TQM applicable to the A/E&C community, many of which are mentioned here. These methods are general in nature, and particular cases may not warrant their use. In addition, this list is not intended to be all encompassing, but to highlight some of the more effective methods, such as

- Providing conceptual alignment meetings with an owner prior to the start of conceptual design activities
- Relying more heavily on regular communication meetings among personnel responsible for work-flow items
- Performing extensive conceptual design reviews well beyond what is normally considered necessary
- Encouraging extensive training of project personnel or persons affecting quality in the performance of their assignments
- Providing steering committees and work process-improvement teams with genuine employee empowerment
- Encouraging state-of-the-art or technological advances to generate cost, schedule, and quality improvements
- Providing inspection in suppliers' shops rather than waiting until the structure, system, component, or material arrives at the construction site
- Providing contract incentive clauses for quality with subcontractors
- Providing contract clauses in which successful completion of one subcontractor's work is controlled by the succeeding subcontractor
- Providing more in-process checking or inspection rather than relying on final inspection
- Formally prequalifying and partnering with both suppliers and subcontractors based primarily on quality (not cost) even in the case of public-sector projects

Figure 3.5. In today's world, constructed facilities containing sophisticated electronic equipment are being built in the most remote areas of the world under the most extreme climatic conditions. A viable quality system for the A/E&C industry has to respond to the difficulties of such projects and drive improvement in the coming decades. For example, the principles of just-in-time (JIT) delivery become an important part of this system.

- Providing extensive housekeeping at the job site as a symbol of work quality, with the goal of improving the attitude and performance of all personnel
- Performing quality audits or quality evaluations and assessments using effective techniques to positively affect project management

In summary, there are numerous novel and innovative ideas in quality yet to be fully used. Readers should try a few simple ones. After success with an idea, readers should try another, then another, and so on. Use of these methods may cost the project some money up front, but the monetary rewards at the end will amaze almost anyone. Better yet, use of these techniques will enhance an organization's competitive edge.

Notes

1. In some cases, the chief operating officer (COO) is acceptable.

2. "Construction in the 21st Century." Institute for Construction Quality. University of Massachusetts-Lowell in affiliation with its Center for Productivity Enhancement. October 23, 1989.

3. A data base used by the U.S. Army Corps of Engineers that is gaining popularity; refer to Construction Engineering Research Laboratories (CERL), Champaign, Illinois 61826.

4. AI and expert systems are being developed by CERL for the A/E&C community. These include intelligent project development, quality assurance (QA) via condition monitoring devices, and robotic applications.

5. Whittaker, W. L. "Construction Robotics: A Perspective." Proceedings of the Joint International Conference on CAD and Robotics in Architecture and Construction, Marseilles, France, June 1986, pp. 105–112.

6. Sherman, P. J. "Japanese Contsruction R&D: Entree Into U.S. Market." *Journal of Construction Engineering and Management,* ASCE, Vol. 114, No. 1, March 1988, pp. 133–143.

7. Related research in AI and expert systems is being conducted at Carnegie Mellon University, Kajima Corporation, Komatsu, Massachusetts Institute of Technology, Ohbayashi Corporation, Shimizu Corporation, Taisei Corporation, Takenaka, Technion I.I.T., and Waseda University. For further information, see matrix "Robotics and Artificial Intelligence for the Construction Industry" by Dr. P. Krolak, University of Massachusetts-Lowell, Center for Productivity Enhancement, Lowell, Mass. Researched by T. A. Weiss, April 24, 1989.

8. Juran, J. M. *Jurans's Quality Control Handbook,* 4th ed. New York: McGraw-Hill, 1988.

9. Hicks, C. R. *Fundamental Concepts in the Design of Experiments*, 3rd ed. Orlando: Holt, Rinehart & Winston, 1982.

10. See note 8.

11. ASCE, *Quality for the Constructed Project*, New York: McGraw-Hill, 1990.

12. The elements of TQM and its criteria may be studied in the *1994 Malcolm Baldrige National Quality Award Criteria*.

4   Quality Criteria in Relation to Cost and Schedule

Quality Cost Analysis

- Quality Improvement Techniques to Be Used in Quality Cost Analysis
- The Significance of Investing in Good Quality
- Quality Concerns
- Tracking a Design or Construction Process

Scheduling a Project and Its Effect on the Quality of a Project

- Investing in Good Quality Rather Than Paying for Poor Quality
- Earlier Project Completion and Reduced Costs Accrue from Improved Construction Productivity
- Fast-Track Design-and-Build Project
- Cost-Plus-Fixed-Fee (CPFF) Project
- Hard-Money, Lump-Sum, or Fixed-Price Project

Maintaining a balance between cost, schedule, and quality is a challenge on most A/E&C projects. In this chapter, this balance will be addressed in relation to the eternal triangle: *cost, schedule,* and *quality.*

Quality Cost Analysis

Chapter 3 contains a discussion of quality cost analysis. This chapter will investigate its use in the A/E&C community more fully.

To perform a quality cost analysis, readers should develop and implement methods to identify and quantify quality-related costs. What are quality-related costs? Do they include inspection, checking drawings and calculations, quality planning of the project, accounting for the quality costs, and the like? The answer to all of these questions is clearly *yes.*

There are many direct and indirect quality costs. To fully understand the effect of any quality action, all actions must be considered. Since the quality function has traditionally required that performance be communicated in rejection and nonconformance reports, and since this information is often difficult to interpret in terms of cost, opportunities for savings or real quality improvement are often overlooked. Successful project quality management requires the use of sound financial quality planning and control. When quality failures are presented in financial terms, management attention and interest increases. Unfortunately, by the time management becomes aware, it is normally too late for the completed project.

Instead, two important quality principles should be considered initially.

- Failure costs, however caused, reduce profits, and quality control (QC) activities—as well as the appraisal of quality standards—cost money.
- Quality-related costs can be classified as prevention costs, appraisal costs, internal failure costs, and external failure costs. Investment in prevention and appraisal will substantially reduce internal and external failure costs and assist in maintaining client satisfaction.

These two important principles are particularly true of the A/E&C community in its present state. When expenditures are increased on prevention costs, the costs of failure fall. However, there is a point where the total costs are at their lowest (optimum). Conditions such as satisfaction, prestige, and safety often can make it more desirable to carry increased prevention costs.

Quality costs that are appropriate to the project should be identified and monitored. The classification of quality cost data should be relevant and consistent with the other accounting practices of the project so that direct comparisons can be made. Quality costs (direct and indirect) should be separately recorded within the accounting system such that they can be easily classified into

- Prevention quality costs (quality planning, quality engineering, training, education, and so on)
- Appraisal quality costs (checking, inspection, assessment, and so on)
- Internal failure costs (scrap, repair, rework, and so on)
- External failure costs (customer dissatisfaction, loss of market opportunity, operational repair, rework, and so on)

By knowing where certain types of quality costs have been incurred, action can be taken to control and reduce them. This should be accomplished by focusing on preventing problems (preventive quality costs), applying effective appraisal techniques, and implementing programs to preclude the repetition of both internal and external failures. Financial reports that contain accurate, separate statements of the costs of failure and the costs of operating quality measures should be presented to management. For control purposes, quality costs should be allocated to the accountable area and the appropriate codes within the cost centers. This allocation of all quality costs is important to the analysis and for the prevention of failures. Allocation should cover both direct and indirect quality costs.

To have sufficient impact, the report can be presented in a style similar to other management financial reports and can be supported by financial ratios and trend analyses related to the company's business in the A/E&C community. This report format should enable management to better understand the relevance of a quality system and to allocate effective financial resources to it.

Quality costs may be collated and reported according to the quality data collected. If one is approaching quality cost analysis for the first time, the first step to consider is a pilot study. A/E&C projects vary a great deal in scope, magnitude, and complexity. Choosing the right project or projects for this pilot study can become perplexing. Generally speaking, when making this decision, the following criteria should be employed.

• Most importantly, the project for the pilot study should be one that is scheduled to begin soon and will be completed in a short time. This permits measurement of the results quickly after project completion. Focusing on pieces of the project or project phases is not sufficient. To look at the whole quality picture, one must have a holistic approach to quality cost analysis.

• The project or projects should contain particular work-breakdown items that are important in a relevant way to making an impact on one's organization. This should be a strategic decision based on what is indeed important to one's A/E&C business.

• The project or projects should contain particular work-breakdown items that are easily quantified and measured. Some quality factors in an A/E&C project are complex and sometimes hard to quantify. In the pilot study, try to avoid this obstacle. Remember that finding the right items can sometimes be difficult; however, *all* quality factors can be quantified. (Be honest, pragmatic, and realistic.)

Before quality cost data collection for the pilot study begins, the scope of work to be carried out should be determined. Initially, the scope will be dictated by the work-breakdown structure. Preliminary figures should be established from a small area or single project to gain management approval and commitment to the total quality costing system. A list of categories and elements for operating quality costs should be included as the basis for developing the steps needed to meet the requirements of the customer.

During the pilot study, it is important that all possible quality costs be covered by an explicit and definitive element or work-breakdown item. In many cases, it does not always make sense to track all work-breakdown item quality costs. Any good project manager can review the list of work-breakdown items and know that many of them will have little, if any, impact on the quality of the project. Therefore, the work-breakdown items should be arranged in terms of importance to quality, and the few judged to have significant impact on quality should be selected. Pareto analysis (sorting out the significant few versus the trivial many) may be used to make this decision. (See "The Significance of Investing in Good Quality" in this chapter and chapter 11 for an explanation of Pareto analysis.) When experience is gained with this quality cost system, it will be apparent where these definitive elements can be combined or eliminated.

When the list of quality cost elements has been identified, the collection of cost data can begin. The costs directly and indirectly attributable to the quality function should then be accumulated. These initial quality costs should be concerned primarily with prevention and appraisal. Next, the internal costs of budgeted failures should be identified and recorded, and then the internal quality cost of unplanned failures should be completed. In many cases, one may have to wait until the pilot study project is complete to understand the magnitude of the quality costs. In this manner, an efficient collection system can be established before a full-scale quality cost program is established.

After all costs have been collected, they should be tabulated to present a breakdown of quality costs by element. The report format and frequency will depend upon the nature of the project or projects and the level of management to which the information is presented.

Figure 4.1 represents the relationship between COQ and quality on any project. The project objective is to minimize COQ while exceeding valid customer expectations.

The ounce-of-prevention-is-worth-a-pound-of-cure philosophy is particularly applicable to the A/E&C community. In manufacturing, a complex process produces repetitive products. A/E&C projects, except for certain isolated cases, are singular complex facilities, each of which is itself a unique product. In constructing a facility, one does not get a second chance; therefore, it is imperative to do it right the first time. This is a bit of an oversimplification; however, in principle it is very accurate.

Before discussing early prevention techniques, it is important first to review the entire A/E&C process. As discussed briefly in chapter 2

- A concept or idea of the facility to be constructed is developed (design criteria).
- Contractual arrangements are made with a firm to provide detailed specifications, plans, and drawings (design).
- Certain early equipment and materials are ordered (procurement).
- Earthwork and civil activities commence at the construction site.
- After foundation activities, structural, and certain mechanical work begins.

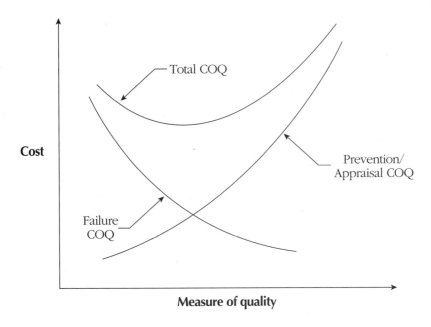

Figure 4.1.   The relationship between COQ and quality on any project.

- As the site work progresses, numerous discipline activities such as electrical; instrumentation and controls (I&C) and heating, ventilating, and air conditioning are completed.
- Specialty work is installed.
- The facility is checked for completeness.
- Preoperational testing of the facility occurs along with formal turnover of the facility to the client.
- Finally, some projects may include such activities as maintenance, decommissioning, and demolition or restoration.

This list can be greatly expanded for a complex construction process; however, the fundamentals remain the same.

A typical construction project can be graphed as a function of intensity of the A/E&C effort (see Figure 4.2).

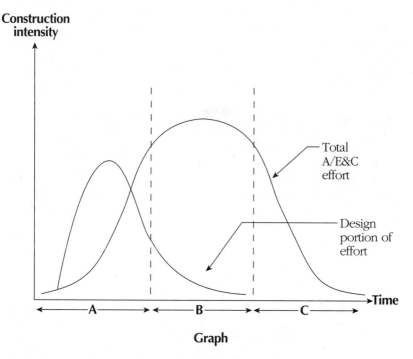

Figure 4.2. A typical construction project.

One can easily see that this is the shape of a pdf that may be skewed to the left or right, depending on the circumstances of the project (see chapter 2).

Can this intuitively be shown mathematically? The best description of the functional relationship of a project noted here is the Chi-square function. This function can be represented by

$$X^2 = \Sigma \frac{(y - Y)^2}{Y^2}$$

where y is a particular A/E&C level of activity at a point in time, and Y is the average level of A/E&C activity for the full project. When the sum of the y's (Σy) equals the sum of the Y's (ΣY), which is the case for the type of situation addressed here, the labor of computation can be reduced by the use of the following function formula.

$$X^2 = \Sigma \frac{y^2}{Y} - n$$

where n is the number of degrees of freedom for this function.

Figure 4.3 shows the Chi-square function for various degrees of freedom.

If it is assumed that the level of construction on a project follows this graph and formula as a function of time, then it becomes obvious that a project can be completed sooner with fewer degrees of freedom. In other words, with the reduction of free variables or independent choices (degrees of freedom), quality can be improved. Certain common project management principles follow this idea. Such design or construction management principles include the following examples for reducing free variables.

- Standardization
- Designing significantly ahead of construction
- Planning the project effort with great attention to detail

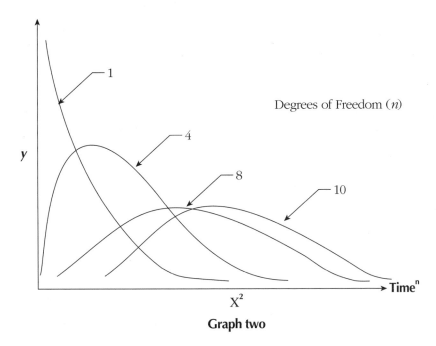

Graph two

Figure 4.3. This graph illustrates the Chi-square function.

These are project management principles that aim at reducing the number of degrees of freedom, thus doing it right the first time. In general, the more attention that is paid to early quality problem prevention in section "A" of Figure 4.2, the more significant will be the impact that quality improvement techniques will have on the finished project.

Quality Improvement Techniques
to Be Used in Quality Cost Analysis
What are quality improvement techniques? The three design and construction management principles listed in the preceding section are basic quality improvement techniques. It is well known that, if problems are permanently corrected, then the quality of the constructed facility improves. Money is saved through the reduction of operational downtime or by providing a more efficient design and construction process.

However, do the means justify the end? Does the cost of an analysis technique justify the benefit received in the end result? The quality improvement program on a project involves implementation of a quality cost analysis procedure plus correction of potential failures that may damage the project overall. This quality cost analysis procedure includes the following:

- Prevention. The act of developing the analysis program, including maintenance and training.
- Appraisal. The detection techniques used to collect the data necessary for detection of problems, including the actual analysis.
- Failure. Those items that encompass most of the factors affecting failure, including redesign, rework, repair, scrap, loss of operation or use, and customer dissatisfaction.

Readers who are familiar with the standard activities of quality will note that these factors are only a few of many more. However, the positive effect quality improvement techniques have on reducing failure is widespread, encompassing almost all of the factors of failure. As previously noted, a simple accounting procedure can track prevention, appraisal, and failure costs separately. In other words, quality improvement techniques are truly a micro-ounce of prevention worth a ton of cure.

Figure 4.1 shows the relationship among prevention, appraisal, and failure factors. This relationship may vary through the life of a project. Therefore, implementing a quality improvement system on a design and construction project early in its life is extremely important to success, and its cost is small in comparison to the potential savings that can be gained from preventing recurrence of or correcting significant failures.

Two fundamental questions that pervade the application of quality improvement techniques have to do with when and to what extent they should be used. These are probably difficult questions to answer in the planning of a design and construction project. They require careful thought and consideration because many factors (previously detailed) influence the attendant decisions. They affect the following types of projects.

- Heavy construction
- Nonresidential buildings
- Multiunit and single family residential buildings

Generally speaking, this list is in decreasing order of complexity of the A/E&C process. Some factors may skew this generalization, but the quality improvement techniques comprehensively discussed in chapters 12–17 are an excellent starting point.

The Significance of Investing in Good Quality

If you are implementing an analytical and computer-aided quality improvement system or an informal system on a small project, you should apply a quality improvement technique based on the importance of quality to the overall project. The first universal quality tool to be used is Pareto analysis. Pareto analysis is a relatively simple way to sort out the significant few from the trivial many. This analysis method is relatively straightforward.

- Uncover all potential quality concerns.[1]
- Measure them in relation to their effect on project failure, and then rank them by their importance, with the most important concern to the left on the horizontal axis.
- Draw a bar graph (which probably will look similar to Figure 4.4) of the concerns. Again, rank the most important concern first.

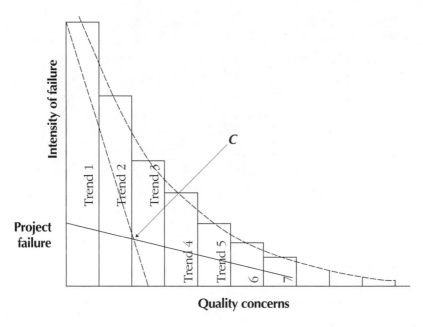

Figure 4.4.   This bar graph ranks the most important quality concerns first.

Quality Concerns
- Transform the bar graph into a best-fit line graph with central points, and then draw the best-fit curve.[2]
- Draw two tangent lines to the horizontal and vertical portions of the curve; these lines will always intersect at some point, called *C.*
- Without a great deal of statistical analysis, any points to the left of *C* (that is, quality concerns) along the horizontal axis are considered to be the statistically significant few, and any to the right of *C* are the trivial many.

With experience at using Pareto analysis on design and construction projects, one will realize that the trivial many of quality concerns are usu-ally associated with human errors that cannot be systematically improved or prevented—unless a unique or concept paradigm is introduced, such as using AI, which was discussed in chapter 2. Thus, it is important to expend one's energies only on the potential quality concerns that are among the significant few.

Tracking a Design or Construction Process

There are mathematical methods available for design and construction that can flag potential quality concerns as they occur. These mathematical or statistical methods are commonly referred to as statistical process control (SPC). A great deal of time can be expended in explaining such process capability study techniques. It is beyond the scope of this text to explain such methods as $\bar{X}$ and R charts, p and u charts, and others, except to say that they may be used when the design or construction process is being measured routinely and is occurring repetitively. Many excellent texts are available.[3]

It is important to understand the characteristics of the design or construction process being measured. Many statistical analyses of process characteristics assume a normal (Gaussian) distribution. However, a process characteristic relative to A/E&C projects may very well not be normal.

There are many design and construction process characteristics that cannot be tracked through SPC, and, therefore, cannot be used with SPC measurement. However, some can and some should. Examples of design and construction process characteristics that may be tracked in such a manner include

- Concrete test results, such as percent air or slump tests (see ASTM C-9 Standard for details)[4]
- Welding essential and nonessential variables on a recurring structure process (see ASME B/PV Code or AWS D1.1 Code for details)[5, 6]
- Receiving inspection defects on lots of similar material (see MIL-STD-105E for details)[7]

With the advent of 486 Intel computer technology and beyond, statistical analysis has become much more practical in terms of time and effort.[8] Whether one is using computer-aided analysis, or holding a project meeting to identify concerns, it is important to take timely and effective corrective actions (CAs). Any path forward or CA should be developed to address the entire quality concern rather than a portion of it. Responsible project management should consider previous action taken for recurring concerns to determine the general effectiveness of paths forward.

Scheduling a Project and Its Effect on the Quality of a Project

There are any number and types of schedules on projects. Schedules include those in which the design leads the construction significantly. There are fast-track design-and-build projects that significantly increase the risk to quality by their very nature. In understanding the effect of quality and its relationship to scheduling, one should understand the basics of an A/E&C project. Three interrelated factors directly affect every A/E&C project: quality, cost, and schedule.

Since these three factors are not isolated from each other, it is known intuitively that

- During the project, when costs are controlled too strictly, quality and/or the schedule can suffer.
- When quality is explicitly controlled without regard for anything else, cost and the schedule of the project can be adversely affected.
- When schedules are too closely adhered to, there is a risk of incurring cost overruns on the project and the quality of the completed facility.

The best mechanism for visualizing the relationships of these three factors is the mathematical graphical theory known as Venn diagrams.[9] (See Figure 4.5 for a Venn diagram for cost, schedule, and quality.)

Investing in Good Quality Rather Than Paying for Poor Quality

In actual cost and schedule terms, what does investing in good quality mean? How significant an impact should control of quality make on a project?

As stated in the preface, the A/E&C community operates worldwide and is among the foremost in size, scope, and economic magnitude, with capital assets exceeding those of all the stocks listed on the New York Stock Exchange (more than $1 trillion). Any concerted application of quality improvement techniques can help achieve significant savings for the industry.

In addition, the A/E&C community is part of a competitive and global market. It should be clearly understood that these fundamental principles of quality are not only being used but advanced by certain global competitors. There is a strong need in the United States to learn and get better from the quality management methods currently being implemented by A/E&C firms in Europe and Japan. Europe has embraced the more traditional quality

Figure 4.5.   Venn diagram for cost, schedule, and quality.

methods associated with QA.[10] On the other hand, Japan has embraced those associated with TQM.[11]

Numerous studies have shown that more than 25 percent of the costs can be cut from most constructed facilities through the use of a good, sound quality program. In the United States, there is a national award competition that has developed into an excellent model for a sound quality program. This is the MBNQA program. The criteria for the MBNQA are designed to enhance quality within companies. However, they can easily be adapted to projects.

Established by the U.S. Department of Commerce in 1986, MBNQA is becoming a highly competitive achievement among U.S. companies. It is notable that Granite Rock, Watsonville, California, won the MBNQA in 1992; it was the first A/E&C company to do so. Granite Rock has practiced the methods of good, sound quality management and has reaped the benefits.

This company is a supplier of construction materials, including aggregate and concrete, in a localized region near San Francisco. The company has 15 locations, thousands of customers, and several major suppliers. It is in a market that has felt the effects of both foreign competition and the U.S. recession in a significant way. Through implementation of a sound quality program, Granite Rock has not only overcome these factors, but significantly increased its market share—at a higher price. The company's materials are far superior in quality, and customers recognize its added value in selecting Granite Rock over lower bidders. This company and its customers have reaped the benefits of high quality and high productivity.

The major thrust of the MBNQA is TQM; however, traditional quality improvement tools are also effective means of improving performance in A/E&C projects. Many factors affect proper use and application of such tools. However, specific, measurable benefits accrue through use of a proven quality system in the following three areas.

1. Earlier project completion and reduced costs accrue from improved productivity.
2. Innovative project analysis and development of more efficient work patterns can be used to introduce a new means of measuring progress and quality.
3. Contractual incentive techniques can minimize litigation and preclude the owner's use of retainage. This should improve control of construction and, therefore, project quality.

Earlier Project Completion and Reduced Costs Accrue from Improved Construction Productivity

The early conceptual activities in an A/E&C project greatly influence the installation sequencing and subsequent project productivity. If one again considers the game of dominos (discussed in chapter 2), one can understand the functional description of an A/E&C process.

Here is an example of the potential savings that can be achieved. In this case, a medical mid-rise building was constructed from a basic frame of an existing building in a northern climate.[12] An independent estimate was performed prior to construction, and a full account of direct and indirect costs was performed after construction was completed. The basic work-breakdown elements were analyzed to determine the construction elements that were most important to customer focus and satisfaction. Pareto analysis was performed to separate the significant few from the trivial many work-breakdown elements. A full-scope TQM program was applied to only the significant few elements. Table 4.1 summarizes the savings in each area.

In this case, even though paving was a borderline significant work element, a 12 percent cost improvement was achieved. The TQM quality methods of project teaming played an important role. This team building and partnering included consultants, contractors, and subcontractors.

Table 4.1.   Example of savings possible through use of a quality system.

Construction Work-Breakdown Element	Percent Savings Achieved Compared to Expected Performance Results
Specialty work	14 percent
Clearing /grub/utilities	0 percent
Earthwork	19 percent
Vertical enclosure	28 percent
Elevator system	35 percent
Finishwork	15 percent
Flooring	42 percent
Structure	5 percent
Hardware	21 percent
HVAC with mechanical	12 percent
Insulation materials	11 percent
Job direct billings	7 percent
Inside coatings	18 percent
Hard and soft landscape	8 percent
Paving	12 percent
Plumbing	0 percent
Drywall	8 percent
Other mechanical	12 percent
Roof enclosure	0 percent
Windows/glazing/doors	15 percent
Closing/management work	(11) percent
Aggregate average improvement from expectation	28 percent

The Arizona Department of Transportation in Phoenix has made a significant impact in the organization it initiated 24 months ago.[13] Improvement was accomplished through partnering. The department estimates direct savings of $11 million in the last fiscal year covering 120 projects. In future years, it expects to save $20–$25 million per year. In addition, the department completed more than 80 projects without any litigation or lawsuits. In prior years, it would not have been unusual to have $30 million budgeted for legal actions on $250 million in capital projects, with 40 to 50 contractors involved. Team building and partnering was effectively accomplished irrespective of the public bidding process. An important part of this process was the execution of a joint agreement. Even though it was not legally binding, these significant results were achieved. This agreement focused on the important quality issues between the contractor and the department that were identified during early alignment sessions.

In addition, the department accomplished consistency by revising its processes and procedures. The resulting benefit was the distinct lack of rework on its projects. In addition, a new procurement process significantly decreased delivery time for materials. Payments to contractors were made in a timely manner. Improvements also occurred in the design process. Today, the organization is working on a quality improvement process team to better process advance engineering work to the best possible project definition and scope.

In another A/E&C success story, encouraging innovation and rewarding individual quality contributions were effectively used to complete a project on time.[14] The direct benefits to this A/E&C project included cost savings exceeding $11.6 million (more than 6 percent below budget), on-time completion, and better-than-expected quality.

In a final success story, the Los Angeles County Transportation Commission (LACTC), Rail Construction Corporation (RCC) are realizing significant quality improvements (10 percent) on an important portion of a $1 billion a year set of projects that will take 30 years to complete.[15] The cumulative savings here is resulting from the implementation of both a traditional QA program and a TQM effort.

As mentioned before, the result of a quality cost analysis is based on improving a particular quality attribute in one isolated case. As these examples make clear, the analysis is worth the investment.

The design and construction process contains work-flow items that are interdependent and that have a great influence on other work-flow items for the project. The objective of this text is to present methods and then to show the results and benefits of using these methods. To accomplish this, one has to start with quality fundamentals. This is the cost, schedule, and quality triangle, previously shown in Figure 4.5.

The objective on any project is to hit the mark in the center of the Venn diagram in Figure 4.5. Remember, there is an overlap between each pair of factors; however, it is important to strike a balance between factors. Too often, this diagram does not represent the actual relationship between cost, scheduling, and quality. Many times, cost or schedule considerations overwhelm quality on A/E&C projects.

Remember, the scheduler cannot forget about cost and quality. The estimator or cost engineer cannot forget about the schedule and quality. The quality engineer cannot forget about cost and schedule, although they each, indeed, have a primary function.

Therefore, the following section discusses different types of A/E&C schedules and schedule phases and addresses the potential risks to quality inherent in each type and what can be done to minimize them.

Fast-Track Design-and-Build Project

A fast-track design-and-build project involves compression of the schedule by starting construction before the design is complete. This project type affords the greatest potential reward if the schedule is achieved; however, it carries one of the greatest risks to quality and costs. If the design is not sufficiently ahead of construction, quality problems can arise. A significant amount of investment in prevention methods must be made early in the project. If this is not done, the project may quickly get to a point where significant harm has occurred to quality and cost.

Begin by calculating the quality risk and recognize the realistic rewards. Decide whether the costs of implementing a prevention method exceed the costs of rework and, if so, to what extent. Will the implementation of a quality program eat its profits? Will rework eat the profits? If the answer to the first question is yes or the answer to the second is no, then chances are good that not enough significant few work items exist to worry about.

Keep in mind that there are significant rewards for developers, for example, who let contracts remain a fast-track schedule. However, they must recognize the potential adverse effect on quality and take an early, strong posture on the issue of prevention methods to enhance quality.

Cost-Plus-Fixed-Fee (CPFF) Project

The schedule is not the only variable that drives a project. Often it is cost. A cost-plus fixed-fee project offers benefits in terms of quality. Although somewhat schedule driven, a fixed fee will have less value as time progresses unless there is an escalation clause in the contract or no inflation in the economy.

This type of project is a safe mechanism for quality. In addition, contractors have less incentive to cut corners if actual costs are billable. Quality, which often suffers on schedule-driven or cost-driven contracts, is more easily incorporated into CPFF projects. Recognize that there is a potential risk in the creation of a system that does not necessarily produce cost-effective or schedule-efficient projects. A good balance, however, can be achieved through the use of strong fee incentives in the contractual process.

Hard-Money, Lump-Sum, or Fixed-Price Project

This type of contract is designed to ensure that there will be no cost over-runs (although this often happens through change orders). Schedule and quality can suffer if care is not exercised. On this type of project, the owner or client had better be a "Philadelphia lawyer." Many contractors will attempt to increase profits by nickeling and diming the owner through change orders. A contractor may also skimp on personnel and materials to meet the price. A scope of work, drawings, specifications, and schedule should be explicitly defined. Remember, there is no such thing as too much detail under this type of contract.

Qualification of the potential contractor is of utmost concern in this type of contract. Extreme care should be exercised before selecting the low bidder. How much did that bidder leave on the table? Is there a large difference between the low bidder and the next two bidders? Why? Did he or she understand the scope of work? Again, be careful! Schedule and quality can be destroyed if these questions are not acceptably answered. (Hard-money and CPFF are discussed further in chapters 18 and 19.)

Notes

1. Uncovering concerns is sometimes not easy. Quality tools such as failure modes and effects analysis (FMEA), fishbone diagrams, and process flow diagrams may be helpful in this task.

2. A publication on the use of Pareto analysis, its principles, impact, and construction of a Pareto diagram is available through the A/E&C Division of ASQC, 17595 Harvard, Suite C215, Irvine, Calif. 92714.

3. The Western Electric Company. *Statistical Quality Control Handbook*, Fourth Printing. New York: Western Electric Company, 1970.

4. American Society of Testing Methods. Testing Standards. ASTM, 1916 Race Street, Philadelphia, Pa. 19103.

5. The American Society of Mechanical Engineers. Boiler and Pressure Vessel Code (BPV), American National Standard, current addenda. ASME, United Engineering Center, 345 East 47th Street, New York, NY 10017.

6. American Welding Society, 2501 Northwest Seventh Street, Miami, Fla., 33125.

7. "Sampling Procedures and Tables for Inspection by Attributes" is available through the U.S. Government Printing Office, Washington, D.C. 20402.

8. This technology is changing rapidly. While 386 or 486 computer technology was sufficient a few years ago, 786 and 900 series are on the drawing boards and will be available shortly.

9. Anderson, R. L. *Statistical Theory in Research*, 1st ed. New York: McGraw-Hill, 1952.

10. ISO 9000-1987, *Quality Management and Quality Assurance Standards—Guidelines for Selection and Use*, ISO 9001-1987, *Quality*

Systems—Model for Quality Assurance in Design/Development, Production, Installation and Servicing; ISO 9002-1987, *Quality Systems—Model for Quality Assurance in Production and Installation*; ISO 9003-1987, *Quality Systems—Model for Quality Assurance in Final Inspection and Test*; and ISO 9004-1987, *Quality Management and Quality System Elements—Guidelines.* To obtain a copy of the standards, please write to: ANSI 1430 Broadway, New York, NY 10018. 712-642-4900.

11. National Institute of Standards and Technology. *1993 Malcolm Baldrige National Quality Award Criteria.* Gaithersburg, Md.: National Institute of Standards and Technology, 1993.

12. Hart, Roger D. "Quality Measurement in Engineering & Construction." 46th ASQC Annual Quality Congress Transactions, 1992.

13. Hart, Roger D. "Putting TQM Theory Into Practice." Transportation Research Board (TRB) Conference. Washington, D.C., January 19, 1993.

14. See note 12.

15. See note 12.

5   Quality in Relation to Industry Codes and Standards

Codes and Standards

- Written Quality Programs to Meet Codes

Regulatory Agencies and Jurisdictions

Quality Standard References

- Matrix of Current References (Table 5.1)

Quality References

- Quality Programs That May be Required for Working in Certain Industries (Table 5.2)

Every A/E&C organization desires to provide for architectural/engineering (A/E), construction, and maintenance services that are in full compliance with applicable regulations, codes, and client contractual requirements. Project management should be responsible for establishing a project quality system that is consistent with the project requirements and achieves the quality objectives of the project. Compliance with this quality system should be a requirement of the project team.

Codes and Standards

A/E&C as well as operational maintenance must satisfy the criteria of specified codes and standards as well as the customer's contract requirements. Customer requirements many times exceed codes and standards.

Early definition of quality requirements for each major step of the project is essential. The identification and compliance with applicable codes, standards, and customer requirements should be addressed early in the conceptual-design phase of the project. Identifying requirements early in the design phase can significantly influence the final design, fabrication, construction, maintenance, and operation processes, and can substantially reduce rework. The design should be clearly communicated to suppliers and subcontractors through contract documents, drawings, and specifications.

Codes and standards are normally related to the regulatory agencies that have jurisdiction over the project (see chapter 12 for further explanation). Local and regional codes are common and are usually modified versions of national codes. A design based solely on a national code probably will not satisfy local municipality requirements.[1] The latest version of the applicable codes and standards should be checked and personnel should be trained to adhere to this latest version. A newly revised or adopted code can significantly influence the A/E&C outcome.

Design-output documents such as drawings and specifications should be reviewed for compliance with codes, standards, and customer requirements prior to submittal to the customer for approval. This review should also include any subsequent issues. The review should be conducted by a representative who is technically competent in the applicable codes and standards and the customer's special requirements.

If codes, standards, and customer requirements conflict with one another, the conflict should be resolved by agreement between the contractor and the customer. Procedures should be established for review and coordination of these activities.

Written Quality Programs to Meet Codes

In general, A/E&C organizations should maintain written quality programs that are accepted by code authorities for construction, fabrication, and repair activities in accordance with such codes as the ASME BPV Code and provisions of the National Board of Inspection Code or their international equivalents (See Figure 5.1). In addition, there are numerous other codes, including

- Uniform Building Code (UBC) and National Electrical Code (NEC) developed by the International Conference of Building Officials.
- The Building Code developed by the Building Officials Code Administrators (BOCA) International.
- Standard Mechanical Code developed by the SBCCI.
- National Fire Code developed by the NFPA or international equivalent.
- AWS D1.1, Structural Welding Code, developed by the AWS or international equivalent.

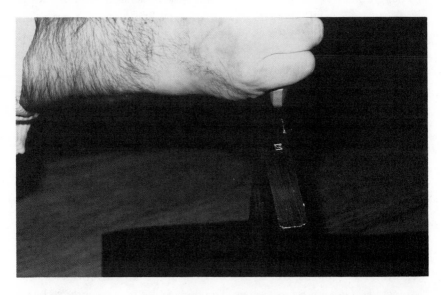

Figure 5.1.   Many codes require the stamping of completed structures, systems, or components with an identifying mark. This mark provides proof of a level of quality recognized by the code authority. ASME has a code-stamping system to identify conformance to the fabrication of mechanical items to the ASME BPV code.

Certificates of authorization can be issued by ASME, the National Board of Boiler and Pressure Vessel Inspectors, and others. Compliance with these codes may be subject to verification by an authorized representative. This verification may be performed by the code authority or by an authorized inspector.

Deviation from the accepted program is not normally permitted without a program addendum issued by an authorized inspection agency. It is the responsibility of the certificate holder to maintain the program procedures current to the applicable codes. Any revisions to the program procedures must be acceptable to the authorized code inspector.

Regulatory Agencies and Jurisdictions

Early in the conceptual design phase of a project, the applicable regulatory agencies (local, regional, state, or federal) should be identified and their jurisdictions established. Their requirements should be considered when the codes and standards are reviewed for project applicability. Since the agency review time can greatly affect the overall schedule and may have an impact on quality, particularly at the beginning of construction, it is advisable to meet with the agencies early in the design stage to discuss how their requirements may affect the design.

Any contract with the customer should identify the persons or functions responsible for obtaining agency approvals and permits. If it is the customer's responsibility to obtain them, the contractor should get copies for the project records. The permits should be reviewed to confirm that no additional requirements have been imposed by the various agencies, particularly those with local jurisdiction.

Quality Standard References

The A/E&C industry must conform to numerous customer-mandated or industry-recognized quality-related codes and standards. It should be an A/E&C organization's desire to satisfy (within its own guidelines and implementation programs) the quality requirements mandated or recognized by its customers and their industries. Table 5.1 offers examples of applicable industry or customer standards. (This list is not exhaustive and is intended only as a general guideline.)

Table 5.1.   Matrix of current references.

Customer or Industry	Requirements or Standard
Aerospace/Department of Defense military	MIL-Q-9858A; MIL-I-45208A; NASA NHB 5300.4 (1B)
Australian customers	AS 2990 standards guidance
Canadian customers	CSA Z-299 standards
Computer/electronics industry customers	DEC or IBM standard; IEEE validation standard and specifications
Department of Energy	DOE/RW033; ASME NQA-1; DOE Order 5700.6C
Environmental	U.S. DOD and/or U.S. EPA QAMS-5 (Draft) ANSI/ASQC E4-1992
Hotel industry	Hyatt or Ramada quality standards
Hydrocarbon	Customer Specifications; ISO 9000 series; API Standard
International nuclear power	IAEA standards and guidelines
Other federal agencies	U.S. GSA or U.S. DOS standards
Other international customers	Country standard and/or ISO 9000 series standards
Other industrial customers	Customer specification or Malcolm Baldrige National Quality Award (MBNQA) criteria and application latest year
Pharmaceutical/ biotechnology customers	U.S. FDA, GMPs, and Code of Federal Regulations (CFRs)
State and local building customers	BOCA or UBC Codes, as required by the state or local jurisdiction
Transportation	Washington Area Mass Transit Authority (WAMTA) or Los Angeles County Transportation Commission (LACTC)/RCC guidance Note: UMTA (FTA) guidelines available
U.S. automotive industry	Ford Q1 or GMC Quality Standards
U.S. commercial power Nuclear Fossil Hydro/nonconventional	10CFR50 (App. B); ASME NQA-1&2 Utility specification, ASQC E-7, and other ASME section V Utility specification, U.S. Federal Energy Regulatory Commission (FERC) regulations

Table 5.2.   Quality programs that may be required for working in regulated industries.

Program	Document Needed	Regulatory Guidance
Nuclear regulated	QA systems manual	Responds to NQA-1, et al.
Construction practices	Field QC system manual	Field QC guide conforming to ISO 9002
Quality standard	Quality standard	Overall corporate document (ISO 9001)
Power industry	Power QA manual	Responds to NQA-1 and 10 CFR 50, Appendix B
Supplied structures and components	Supplier surveillance manual	Procurement inspection methods (ISO 9002)
A/E&C work	Quality procedures	Typical project manual
Piping construction	QC system B&PV code work	Repair and alterations (ASME B&PV Code)
Nondestructive testing	NDE procedures manual	NDE (SNT-TC-1A)
TQM program	Work process improvement manual	Continuous performance improvement method (MBNQA criteria)
International program	Quality manual	Full scope procedures manual ISO 9001, BS5750, Part I (1987)
Company training program	Indoctrination and training manual	Quality training (MBNQA criteria)
Australian program	Quality manual	AS 2990 Category A, AS 3901/ISO 9001
Environmental services	QA project plan	Environmental services draft ANSI/ASQC E-4-1993

Quality References

Table 5.2 is a general list of unique programs that A/E&C firms may have to develop in response to the requirements of regulated industries (see chapter 12 for further explanation).

Notes

1. This process can be enhanced by using quality function deployment (QFD), meeting with the customer, and brainstorming during the design process. Refer to Akao, Yoji. *Quality Function Deployment (QFD): Integrating Customer Requirements into Product Design.* Cambridge, Mass.: Productivity Press, 1990.

6 Quality System Elements I: Leadership, Organization, and Responsibility

Leadership

Organization

A/E&C Senior Executive Leadership

Management for Quality

Public Responsibility

The Responsibility of Managing Quality

- Affecting Quality
- Assuring Quality

The Responsibilities of Managing Quality at the Project Level

- During the A/E Process
- During the Construction Process

A Typical Project Quality Organization

- Exhibit X—Functional Positions/Responsibilities

Leadership

The key to a quality system lies in providing quality leadership, developing an organization, and defining responsibility. In this text, the term *leadership* refers to a take-charge attitude toward the quality of work. Proactive, not reactive leadership enhances quality effectiveness. For leadership to be translated into every aspect of a quality management plan, there must be the support of senior management, adherence to quality guidelines, proper advisement by a quality organization, and the empowerment of every employee to perform quality work.

This text provides guidelines on a quality system for the A/E&C— including support services—of structures, systems, components, and materials. An A/E&C organization should provide quality measures of operations for all customers. These measures should define the organizational structure, responsibilities, procedures, processes and resources for implementing an effective quality program. These guidelines should be a standard for quality excellence.

An A/E&C organization's quality system should comply fully with most external requirements and, in particular, be based on the requirements of such standards as the International Organization for Standardization (ISO) quality standard ISO 9000 (ANSI/ASQC Q90) series and the MBNQA criteria. The system should provide for policies, procedures, and instructions for planning and implementing quality programs to ensure that services exceed customer expectations.

Overall responsibility for the quality system should lie with the most senior executive, usually the CEO. This person should empower a manager in the quality organization (if one formally exists) to be responsible for the overall assessment of the quality system. Project managers should be responsible for developing and maintaining the necessary control to satisfactorily affect quality.

Further, the CEO or equivalent should believe significant gains can be made by implementing sound preventive practices. The elements of these preventive practices should be based in defined guidelines. The manager of a quality organization should have the authority to assess all business entities to ensure that the A/E&C organization is exceeding customer quality expectations. The term is commonly referred to as *delighting the customer.*

All personnel should perform work in a manner consistent with a specific quality plan based on a quality system. Personnel should familiarize themselves with this system and all implementing procedures in their quality plan. The CEO should fully support the implementation of the company quality guidelines for all personnel.

Organization

In an effective organization, delighting the customer can vary significantly from project to project. This is particularly true in the A/E&C community due to the large diversity of business lines or sectors. However, any organization in the A/E&C business should have certain of the attributes described in this section.

The team or organization should maintain an industry leadership role in the implementation of TQM throughout its interlinked operations. This leadership role can be achieved through

- A fully integrated TQM program and organization that should be results oriented and directed to providing excellent value for customers. This includes the implementation of such standards as the ISO 9000 series and using the MBNQA criteria.
- Effective quality programs specifically tailored for those operations managing the quality process. (A typical QA program is specifically described in chapter 7.)

Senior executive managers should support TQM and other effective quality programs and should use advisers or consultants to help implement TQM. The A/E&C organization should implement a consistent TQM program in every aspect of its operations, from early conceptual activities through design, operations, and turnover of the project upon completion. This program should be based on the following TQM leadership criterion.

- Executive leadership should be provided by the CEO or equivalent as TQM sponsor and the leader of the TQM team board with the TQM executive and directors. (If the organization is sufficiently complex, a consultant can be used.)

The TQM process should be institutionalized and ingrained in any A/E&C organization and on every project. To illustrate the importance of this idea, Table 6.1 shows the interrelationships of various TQM methods

Table 6.1.   A/E&C and O&M TQM processes and relationships.

Early conceptual	Design phases	Bidding activity	Purchase activity	Work execute	Turnover completion	Operate maintain/ decom.
Alignment		Alignment	Alignment	Alignment		
	QA	QA	QA	QA	QA	QA
		Approved supplier's list	Approved supplier's list			
			QC	QC	QC	QC
Quality plan		Quality plan		Quality plan		
					Customer feedback	Customer feedback
		Reliability		Reliability		

(see chapter 3). It also depicts application to A/E&C and quality O&M processes.

The essence of the TQM program should be the requirement that each project have a comprehensive quality plan. This plan should integrate the TQM methods noted in Table 6.1. It should be orchestrated or facilitated by a TQM alignment facilitator who has determined statistically significant work-breakdown elements important to quality.

Any A/E&C organization implementing TQM should lead this effort for the A/E&C community. This can be accomplished by a fully functioning quality program over a period of several years which results in significant documented savings and added value to its customers. A/E&C organizations should

1. Provide leadership in a sufficient number of work-breakdown tasks by encouraging and disseminating the precepts of quality and TQM throughout their organizations. These precepts should consist of

   • Sustaining clear and visible values
   • Information analysis of quality
   • Management of the quality process on projects
   • Human resource management and development

- Quality and operational results
- Customer value through focus and satisfaction

2. Provide consistent quality and TQM policy throughout their activities, and issue policies that fit or tailor standard industry policy to quality and TQM.
3. Interact with competitive and world-class organizations through the process of benchmarking (see chapters 10 and 11).

- Permanently institute TQM steering committees, with subsequent quality action teams, to act as the mechanism for focusing on quality methods.

Senior executive leaders and managers should have strong backgrounds in quality, and the organization should have an attitude of public responsibility for its actions. There should be personal involvement, visibility, focus on the customer, and an environment for quality excellence. There should be a clear indication of the integration of these values into the sustaining day-to-day leadership by all facets of the company.

Typically, a successful A/E&C organization has many of these traits. However, it is important when implementing an effective quality program to be able to differentiate one's organization from one's competitors by delighting the customer. To achieve this, managers must objectively and pragmatically assess the organization's strengths and weaknesses. This requirement applies as much to A/E&C business as to any other. The following paragraphs list common strengths and weaknesses of A/E&C businesses.

A/E&C Senior Executive Leadership

Strengths: Senior executives in A/E&C organizations are typically involved in quality-related activities. There is usually evidence of sound values communicated throughout companies. There is usually continuous and demonstrated communication of these quality values through A/E&C organizations.

Typically, A/E&C organizations try TQM initiatives such as customer advisory councils, corporate quality councils, quality steering committees, sometimes SPC support teams, and quality implementation committees. Managers may participate in several organizations espousing quality improvements. There is normally good integration of improvement in effectiveness of personal leadership in quality-related activities.

Areas for improvement: Although senior executives get involved directly in quality-related activities, the manager of quality (or equivalent) does not usually have direct access to the CEO. Although an organization chart may indicate direct access, in practice this relationship does not exist. In addition, the CEO may have an open-door policy to foster direct, proactive leadership in quality-related activities. Employees, however, may not be aware of or clearly understand this policy.

Although a company's quality improvement process may have some track record, many of its activities may have occurred in just the last year or two; its process, therefore, is still in its infancy. The A/E&C organization may have had a major quality event recently, but management does not yet clearly understand the event's impact on the firm's quality.

The duties and responsibilities of the various quality committees and councils should be clearly detailed. There may be potential for conflict and redundant activities.

Management for Quality

Strengths: Organizations in the A/E&C community normally have good ongoing training programs, with the basic concepts of quality being understood at all levels. There normally is good focus on the customer in terms of cost and schedule values, but quality focus usually needs improvement. Goals are normally established to meet customer requirements. There usually appears to be sound integration of business goals and plans into day-to-day operations. A/E&C organizations normally use training, quality awareness communication, and upper management visitations as the methods to evaluate and improve awareness and integration of quality into the workplace.

Areas for improvement: When problems associated with quality training are found, clear action is normally taken. It is, however, not clearly understood normally how such problems are fed back into quality education and training programs. CAs taken as a result of A/E&C operations need improvement. Benchmarking against competitors and industry leaders to improve the organizational structure is usually not addressed or understood. There also need to be clear, specific benchmarking methods and indicators.[1]

Public Responsibility

Strengths: Organizations in the A/E&C community normally have low accident rates and maintain them through incentive programs. A/E&C organizations normally promote quality awareness in areas of environmental and safety issues through participation in various national organizations. This posture is usually one of strict environmental and safety compliance. However, this is usually only a reactive posture.

Areas for improvement: It frequently does not appear clear how A/E&C organizations identify potential environmental risks, analyze them, and minimize them in their quality policies and practices. There are discussions on responsibilities to the public for health, safety, environmental protection, and ethical business practices, yet these discussions need to be backed up with concrete quality policies and improvement practices. A review should be made of how to go from simply strict compliance with environmental and safety regulations to a more proactive involvement in compliance matters.

The Responsibility of Managing Quality

Every A/E&C organization should provide for an integrated organizational system, at a corporate level and a project level, that assures and affects quality. This section prescribes an internal structure for the quality functions, defines the responsibilities and authority at an executive level, and establishes policies and objectives.

A typical organization chart should depict the overall interaction of quality-affecting entities and quality-assuring organizations. Each operating manager should be responsible for providing an organization chart that addresses internal operations, including specific projects, on a project-level basis.

Affecting Quality

Line or operating management is responsible for directly affecting the quality of all projects. Effective and adequate quality can be achieved only through the cooperation of various operating management personnel. The responsibility for affecting quality should not be confined within one group or department; the critical path should be from top management to the architect/engineer, or constructor. The roles affecting quality should be also delineated in standard operating procedures (SOPs).

Assuring Quality

Quality is assured in the A/E office and the construction site at various levels. The first level of assurance should be the responsibility of the checker, whether in the office or the field. This level may be performed by line supervisors or their delegated representatives. The second level of assurance may be performed through the inspection, test, or surveillance functions. Depending upon the nature of the project, the independence of the organization performing second-level assurance may vary. Chapters 12–17 and appendices F–I contain descriptions of typical inspection, test, and surveillance relationships. The third and final level of assurance is achieved by quality evaluations through audits, reviews, or assessments. Quality evaluations are independent activities designed to review or audit samples of A/E&C activities, for addressing improvement opportunities in the system or process. Personnel performing this third-level assurance have to be independent of the A/E&C process activity that they are assigned to evaluate.

The subelements of an organizational quality system require A/E&C activities to

- Clearly define quality objectives, responsibilities, and accountability.
- Review and assess the status and adequacy of quality (periodically by executive management).
- Establish the responsibilities and authority of individuals who perform the A/E&C work and verify conformance to quality requirements.
- Ensure that persons performing first- or second-level assurance have the appropriate organizational independence from the A/E&C work activity.

In addition, the policy of any A/E&C organization should be to establish a TQM process that affects quality within work activities through

- Instilling a TQM culture for quality-affecting activities
- Providing a system to encourage quality performance through empowerment of employees, individually and in teams
- Providing a system to encourage training and education in quality-affecting activities, with appropriate recognition and concrete rewards

A suggested TQM program is discussed further in chapter 7.

The Responsibilities of Managing Quality at the Project Level

As just explained, A/E&C projects may have three or more levels of QA. The extent of this assurance is normally contingent upon such factors as the complexity of the project, the importance to safety, and time. This should be clearly defined in the early stages of the project, preferably prior to contract award. The extent of assurance is commonly established during the initial contract or kickoff meetings, or during the initial alignment process for the project.

During the A/E Process

Managing quality at the project level should begin with designating a project quality manager to provide primary second-level assurance to the extent defined in an operations quality plan. Depending on the size and complexity of the project, the project quality manager may perform his or her function on many projects simultaneously. The project quality manager should help develop a project quality plan that will describe project organizational control of first-level assurance. This plan should include the following activities, as applicable: design (conceptual or baseline), validation and verification of calculations and computer codes, overall design verification and qualification testing, design output documents and their change control, quality records management, QA personnel qualifications, and constructability reviews. This quality plan is commonly called a QA manual, a design quality manual, a QA program description (QAPD), or a QA program plan (QAPP). Further clarification of these organizational quality activities should be included in the SOPs.

During the procurement segment of the A/E&C process, the project quality manager should again help develop a quality plan. At this point, he or she may include in first-level assurance the following activities, as applicable: QC of purchasing and subcontracting activities, verification of identification and traceability, supplier inspection and test (including equipment and status), control of nonconformances, shipping, and receipt inspection. The project quality manager may rely on the support of first-level assurance from a central procurement organization defined in procedures.

During the Construction Process

Managing process quality at the project level may also be assured by a field quality manager. Again, the quality plan should define the first-level assurance of the field quality system. It should define the means for determining quality requirements, field inspection and test, quality problem reporting of the construction work process, verification of identification and traceability, and start-up or preoperational quality punchlist activities. Construction quality practices should include a typical site quality organization.

As a general note, third-level assurance is continuously applied by independent parties as coordinated by the project. (This concept is further explained in chapter 9.)

Up to this point, the text has addressed the subject of quality enhancement in a conceptual way through discussions of leadership, organization, and responsibility. It is now time to discuss the application of these concepts to a project in the A/E&C community, at least in a procedural sense.

How does one apply these concepts to a project in terms of primary responsibility? Again, it depends on the nature of the project, which can be simple (building a single-family dwelling) or extremely complex (a billion-dollar hazardous-waste-remediation project). The balance of this chapter uses a simplified project as an example of a typical organizational quality procedure. It must be recognized that (1) it may be somewhat oversimplified, (2) it may be too elaborate for some small projects, (3) it may be insufficient for certain regulated industries, (4) it may not be designed for self-performed type work with hard-money contracts, and (5) it requires more in-depth treatment of many of the soft quality issues of TQM related to alignments, action teams, steering committees, and the like.

A Typical Project Quality Organization
Purpose
This model procedure describes the positions, responsibilities, and qualifications for the A/E&C quality organization that is in conformance with jurisdictional regulations and industry codes.

Scope
This model procedure applies to all members of the project involved with internal and direct external interfaces.

Responsibility
Project management is charged with informing a customer of all changes in the responsibilities, qualifications, and directives of the

A/E&C organization's project quality group. Further, project management is responsible for reviewing, coordinating (which could be through consultants), and obtaining senior executive approval of all design changes.

Procedure
Organization chart. The organization chart should graphically depict areas and levels of responsibility within the project. Overall project organizational and functional responsibilities are used to provide guidance and control of quality-affecting activities, thereby ensuring proper execution of their provisions in all designated areas. These provisions include the following:

• Detailing the requirements for A/E&C activities in contracts, inspections, procedures, identification of items requiring special documentation, handling, and installation.
• Establishing the implementation quality plan for the requirements of a quality program.
• Executing the day-to-day management of the project A/E&C activities by enforcing the quality provisions of the program and requiring subcontractors and suppliers to adhere to the intent of the quality program.
• Performing the quality tasks on designated areas. Each area requires its own emphasis, as delineated in the technical specifications of the contract. Factors of complexity, type, and location must be considered when determining the levels of quality monitoring, surveillance, and inspection to apply to each area.

Functional responsibilities. Functional responsibilities of various positions within the organization that affect quality are identified and explained in the descriptions of functional positions and responsibilities contained in an organization chart. The positions normally addressed in this chart are listed here, and a detailed description for each of these positions follows this list.

• Comprehensive responsibility
    —Project manager or superintendent

- Field operations
  —Earthwork and civil subcontractor
  —Electrical subcontractor
  —Mechanical subcontractor
  —Building subcontractor

- Support operations
  Main office personnel
  —Data processing
  —Financial/accounting

Staff qualifications. Qualifications of individual members (noted previously) of the staff should be on file or retained.

Exhibit X—Functional Positions/Responsibilities
This exhibit describes functional responsibilities. Each position is referenced to a particular subparagraph under paragraph.

Project Manager or Superintendent
General. Under technical direction of the senior executive or CEO, the project manager or superintendent should

- Be aware of all aspects of the quality-assuring and quality-affecting activities of the personnel performing under the scope of work, through contract documents, and within the structures, systems, and components to be inspected or tested
- Establish and implement a quality program for controlling the work required by contract documents
- Assure approval of any design changes through appropriate project control systems
- Assure the training, supervision, and evaluation of assigned personnel
- Monitor and review project and management reports as to their effect on the quality program
- Make reports on quality activities, and assess the effectiveness of any recommendations and actions taken
- Assure the development of adequate project control procedures

- Provide resolution of possible and actual problems during A/E&C activities
- Actively participate in project management meetings
- Exchange information with customer representatives
- Ensure the continued adequacy of the quality program and the field effort

Authority. The project manager or superintendent should be given the authority and organizational freedom to identify quality-related problems and to initiate actions for correcting them, thus assuring quality workmanship and products as well as helping to preclude problem recurrence.

Specific functions. Specific functions of the project manager or superintendent include the following activities and such others as may be assigned by the senior executive or CEO.

- Provide overall management coordination with the jurisdictional officials' (such as building inspectors') inspections and tests
- Assure subcontractors' material control, electrical, mechanical and building work (including structural work) complies with contract documents
- Assure the early and timely correction of faulty work
- Assure the proper conduct of all life-safety testing specified by contract documents or jurisdictional authority
- Assure the proper receipt of all work, materials, and equipment delivered to the site, including materials and equipment furnished by others
- Assure that any past repetitive or significant problems are immediately corrected, and assure the customer or owner that they will not recur in the future
- Coordinate project quality activities to assure timely execution of the work

Earthwork and Civil Subcontractor
General. Under the direction of the person managing earthwork and civil activities, the subcontractor should be required to

- Keep fully informed of all aspects of the work, the drawings, specifications, and material to be inspected or tested
- Establish and implement a program for inspecting, testing, and controlling all of the work required by specifications
- Review and approve material substitution
- Ensure that construction control reports are issued on a timely basis
- Train, supervise, and evaluate assigned field personnel
- Execute duties outlined in control procedures or as assigned
- Maintain communication with the project manager or superintendent, including regular reports on relevant quality activities and information and recommendations for improved quality activities
- Maintain communication and cooperate with counterparts from the jurisdictional authority

Authority. Earthwork and civil subcontractor personnel are assigned authority and organizational freedom within the earthwork and paving efforts to identify quality-related discrepancies and notify personnel so they can initiate actions to correct them. This helps to assure quality workmanship and products.

Specific functions. Specific duties of the earthwork and civil personnel include the following activities and such others as may be assigned by competent authority

- Exercise overall direction of inspection and testing (I&T) of earthwork and civil operations
- Coordinate testing requirements
- Assure that all earthwork and civil work are constructed to the design plans and profiles, all embankments and fills are compacted to the specified densities, and all drainage channels and structures are properly located, constructed, and backfilled
- Provide soil testing to ensure that the moisture content of embankments, backfill, and the like is controlled in such a manner as to obtain proper densities, and provide timely and accurate field data to construction personnel so that work may proceed on schedule

- Schedule all asphalt and concrete placement activities, and inspect all asphalt and concrete pavement construction
- Review and certify the results of the previously listed activities

Electrical Subcontractor

General. Under direction of the person managing the electrical subcontractor, the subcontractor should

- Keep fully informed of all aspects of the work, the drawings, specifications, and material to be checked
- Establish and implement a program for inspecting, testing, and controlling all of the electrical work required by specifications and directives
- Review material substitutions prior to submittal to the customer and for final approval
- Execute duties outlined in control procedures or assigned by the project manager or superintendent
- Make regular reports on electrical quality activities with information and recommendations
- Help the project manager or superintendent revise control procedures when necessary
- Coordinate any required certification of electrical and I&C installations
- Assure that installed life-safety protection systems are operating properly during interconnections
- Assure that required tests of electrical-related devices are made
- Coordinate with other contractors to work out construction configurations and interfaces that will minimize electrical installation interference problems while maintaining optimum operational capability
- Participate in project staff meetings to assist project management, field engineering, construction, and other support and control groups when required

Specific functions. Duties of the electrical contractor include the following activities and such others that may be assigned by the project manager or superintendent.

- Exercise overall supervisory control of activities of all electrical and
  I&C installations, including alternating current (AC) power, electrical
  lighting systems, life-safety protection systems, interior communications systems, and lighting-protection systems.

Mechanical Subcontractor

General. Under direction of the person managing the mechanical contractor, the contractor should

- Keep fully informed of all aspects of the mechanical work, the
  drawings, specifications, and material to be installed or tested
- Establish and implement a program for installing, testing, and con-
  trolling all of the mechanical work required by specifications and
  directives
- Review material substitutions and submit them for approval to the
  appropriate manager
- Assure that construction reports are issued on a timely basis
- Monitor and review mechanical activities generated by assigned personnel
- Execute duties outlined in these control procedures or assigned by
  the project manager or superintendent
- Make regular reports on mechanical activities
- Inform the project manager or superintendent of actual problems
  and assist in their resolution
- Participate in project staff meetings to assist management, construc-
  tion, and support and control groups when required
- Maintain communications and cooperate with counterparts in the
  client organization

Specific functions. Specific duties of the mechanical contractor include
the following activities and such others that may be assigned by the project manager or superintendent.

- Exercise overall supervisory control of installation and testing of all
  mechanical systems, including welding, plumbing, HVAC; gas systems; and the fire sprinklers portion of life-safety equipment

- Assure that welders are properly qualified for their duties, by testing or other means, in accordance with contractual and code requirements
- Inspect plumbing and HVAC systems facilities to assure systems meet contract requirements
- Inspect all boiler and tank installations
- Witness pneumatic and hydrostatic leak tests of piping systems
- Assure sanitary piping tests are performed satisfactorily
- Assure piping, fixtures, equipment, hangers, and insulation comply with design criteria

Building Subcontractor

General. Under direction of the manager coordinating through the project manager or superintendent, the building subcontractor should

- Keep fully informed of all aspects of building work, the drawings, specifications, and material to be tested
- Establish and implement a program for installing, testing, and controlling all of their building work required by the contract, drawings, and directives
- Assure that their construction status reports are issued on a timely basis
- Monitor and review the work activities generated by assigned personnel
- Execute duties outlined in their control procedures
- Inform personnel of possible and actual problems and assist in their resolution
- Maintain communications and cooperate with counterparts in the jurisdictional authority's organization.

Specific functions. Specific duties of the building subcontractor include the following activities and such others that are assigned by competent authority.

- Assure that all scales and other measuring and test equipment (M&TE) devices are properly calibrated and adjusted at specific intervals

- Assure that temperature control devices, thermometers, pressure control devices, pressure measuring devices, and pressure applicators are calibrated at specific intervals and when their accuracy is suspect
- Conduct tests as required to assure that dispensing devices, mixing devices, moisture control devices, and other designated equipment are functioning properly
- Assemble a reference collection of applicable materials data
- Assure that all work activities are carried out according to the applicable specifications or authorized procedure
- Exercise overall supervisory control on construction and testing of all aspects of building construction
- Assure that line, grade, and base preparations comply with drawings and specifications
- Assure that concrete cast-in-place (CIP) forms are properly placed and of correct dimensions, or assure proper concrete masonry unit (CMU) placement
- Assure that rebar and embedments are of adequate quality and are properly placed with necessary ties and that proper weldments are made
- Assure that waterproofing, waterstops, and expansion media are properly installed
- Assure that structural masonry work is installed as specified by contract drawings
- Assure that architectural and finishwork are installed as specified by contract drawings
- Assure that concrete is properly placed
- Maintain accurate and complete records of all field activities
- Generate and distribute all required reports
- Assure that required work samples are taken and processed
- Cooperate with personnel to resolve discrepancies and to preclude repetition
- Develop and assure appropriate NDE is performed satisfactorily through visual testing (VT), MT, PT, and the like.

Note

1. National Institute of Standards and Technology. *1993 Malcolm Baldrige National Quality Award Criteria.* Gaithersburg, Md.: National Institute of Standards and Technology, 1993.

7 Quality System Elements II: Programs, Procedures, and Strategic Plans

Quality Programs

- The Quality System
- Customer-Mandated Quality Programs
- Internal Programs Without Customer Requirements

Procedures and Instructions

- Preparation and Implementation
- Instruction and Procedure Preparation and Approval
- Instruction and Procedure Revision
- Documentation
- Indoctrination and Training
- Training Levels
- Contractor and Supplier Training

General Background on Programs and Procedures

Strategic Quality Planning

Quality Programs

If an A/E&C organization desires a long-standing initiative to improve management effectiveness and quality by the use of a participative management philosophy, the remainder of this text will help the organization obtain a distinct competitive advantage. A good quality program should incorporate a variety of successful techniques from within the A/E&C organization that lend themselves to a quality improvement process. This philosophy is becoming more popular with the advent of such quality advocates as W. Edwards Deming and the phrase *total quality management* (TQM).[1]

This philosophy, when properly employed, allows an effective quality improvement process to correct problems through the use of highly experienced personnel, the motivation of all personnel, and the measurable improvement of systems and products. The system makes TQM (the philosophy) and the techniques of the quality improvement process (QIP), which include quantified solutions, integral parts of each other. A quality system should incorporate these two concepts and include the following criteria.

- Unqualified support by highest-ranking persons. This support should be clearly given to the QA organization; for projects, this should be accomplished through a project quality manager and a project director.
- The integration of quality philosophy and measurable quality improvement through a performance measurement program to be implemented on a project basis.
- Understanding and motivating the organization through various methods that empower the employee and that are supported by a comprehensive recognition and reward programs.
- Clear and effective quality feedback through an organizationwide trend-analysis system that identifies problems and provides CA.
- Adequate preparation for the implementation of quality change processes through procedural change systems.
- The support of quality improvement through training, assimilating information, providing guidelines, and the R&D of quality improvement through a QA organization.

The principles of the quality system should stress giving employees the knowledge and the proper conditions needed to do a quality job. The principles should start with the development of correct criteria for recognizing and rewarding employees, promoting sincerity, encouraging peer interactions, and improving education and training. On projects, a training person should be responsible for these duties.

A quality system employed on a project should

- Establish a quality management and cultural environment by developing vision, long-term commitment, and wide involvement in an annual strategic development, training, and planning event.
- Continually update the missions of every organizational component to clearly state their goals.
- Set quality improvement opportunities and priorities.
- Through annual planning and development, establish improvement projects and action plans.
- Implement and subsequently evaluate projects using methodology on an ongoing, even a daily, basis.
- Provide continuous feedback, through standardized mechanisms, of the results of the A/E&C projects as a part of the QA program.

An A/E&C organization's culture should instill a program for many years successfully by managing a quality improvement process. This should pave its way through current quality thinking into the innovative quality system of the next century. A successful program is visionary. Implementing this program is time-consuming and requires a long-term commitment.

The Quality System

An A/E&C quality system should provide an array of specific quality programs to meet the needs of the types of projects undertaken. Whether the customer, law, or regulation mandates a specific quality program, this system should provide a structure to manage it at the project level.

The system used to apply a quality program on a project can be categorized

- When adapting this quality system to customer-mandated quality programs

- When there are only internally directed quality programs on projects without a customer-mandated program

Customer-Mandated Quality Programs

Although one should maintain a consistent quality system based on the principles described in this text, the system should be flexible enough to meet the needs of customers. To develop a quality system with this capability, one has to understand the overall quality system document hierarchy (for example, programs, procedures, instructions, and so on). First, an overall system description should be documented as the top-level quality document and be divided into two sections: policy and criteria, and model quality program and general practices.

Second, project quality implementation manuals should be derived from the system description. The system description should be considered minimum documentation (the baseline); additional requirements from each project should supplement the basic package.

In large A/E&C organizations, exceptions to a system are sometimes necessary. Review and approval of exceptions by the responsible person approving the higher-tier package should be required for the lower-tier document.

Prior to contract award, a review should be made of the customer's or other external requirements to determine their effect on the A/E&C organization's normal procedures as they relate to quality. A mechanism should be instituted whereby, for example, supplemental sheets can be inserted into a program manual to specifically tailor it for that project. If the customer mandates a major change to the quality program, the change should be reviewed and approved by top management and contain, as a minimum, the quality implementation requirements.

During the execution of the customer contract, when specific quality issues are identified, further supplemental changes may become necessary. These changes should receive the same review and approval.

Internal Programs Without Customer Requirements

If the system described in this text is followed, one should exceed most customer expectations. Exceeding customers' expectations, or delighting the customer, is the ultimate goal in any good TQM system. In any case, every project should include a quality program or plan (defined later in this chapter) that is based on the quality document hierarchy. Since the requirements of A/E&C projects vary widely (nonnuclear/nuclear, government, medical, traditional building construction, high-rise/mid-rise, environmental restoration), each project quality program should be tailored to cover the requirements of its project. In the absence of mandatory requirements, the following project quality plan structure may be adapted for use.

- Purpose and scope
- Responsibilities and authority
- Project quality strategic objectives
- Project quality management
  - —Quality strategic planning activities
  - —Quality organization
  - —Quality matrix of project activities
  - —Control of programs, instructions, and procedures
  - —Document control and changes
  - —Indoctrination and training
  - —Nonconformance control and CA
  - —Quality documents and records
  - —Quality evaluations and audits
  - —Quality costs
- Quality of design
  - —User quality alignment and conceptual analysis
  - —Specification and drawing checking
  - —Design verification through review and test
  - —Design and environmental data validation
  - —Control of field-identified concerns
- Quality of suppliers and subcontractors
  - —Precontract activities (supplier or subcontractor)
    - Preaward qualifications
    - Quality engineering bid analysis
    - Approved supplier's resource
  - —Contract activities
    - Quality specifications
    - Quality engineering contract reviews

—Fabrication activities
  Procurement source inspection
  Site receiving inspection
- Quality of construction, maintenance and operation, or decommissioning, demolition, and restoration
  —In-Process QC of site activities
  —Material and equipment handling, storage, and maintenance
  —Control of site special processes
  —Site inspection and test
  —Control of M&TE

It should be the organization's policy that the quality system be regularly and systematically reviewed and assessed to verify its continuing suitability and effectiveness. This review, as a minimum, should include the following criteria.

- Routine and detailed management reviews and assessments of the quality system conducted by senior management at least once per year
- Quality reviews of SOPs for compliance with quality requirements
- Planned, systematic, and regular quality audits (see chapter 9)
- Project audits that cover, project quality system audits, project technical audits (carried out by discipline management) and reviews and audits of suppliers
- Appropriate customer satisfaction analyses

An A/E&C organization should have assessment procedures that are used for quality audits carried out by quality staff and that cover such items as CA and audit-record retention.

Specific quality procedures and practices may vary from project to project; however, the quality system description should apply to all projects as detailed in the project quality manual. Even in the case of small projects, it should be company policy to pursue an appropriate and active quality program.

In addition to or integrated into the overall quality system should be a policy to establish a TQM program that is based on the following principles (see chapter 6).

- Identify barriers to continuous improvement and remove them. Enhance teamwork throughout the organization by working together in mutually beneficial supplier/customer relationships.
- Any activity or work process can be improved. Concentrate on the quality of work processes and not on individuals.
- Significant quality improvements are not instant solutions.
- Use the basic tools and practices of quality for analyzing, measuring, and improving the performances of work processes.

Quality-related documentation should confirm adherence to key policy, procedural, and regulatory guidance by describing a system of controlled documentation designed to verify document review, approval, update, issue, and recall. This system should be described in SOPs. A records-management system should be described as indicated in chapter 9 in the section "Document and Record Quality."

The quality system should be communicated to staff in the following ways.

- New employees—New staff should be indoctrinated by the human resource department. This indoctrination should include statement descriptions of (or references to) quality policies and procedures. It may also include a written commitment to quality and a definition of the basic responsibilities of the employee.
- All personnel—The organization's quality system description should be distributed to discipline and project managers, and to applicable QA staff. Statements of quality policy should be prominently displayed on the premises.
- Procedures—Education and training of personnel, including temporary staff, to understand and implement the quality requirements embodied in the procedures should be the responsibility of department and project managers.
- Project quality—Program orientation and training in project-specific subsystems should be the responsibility of project discipline managers.

Procedures and Instructions

The A/E&C community is a service industry, and quality lies with the people in that community. Work procedures and instructions are necessary for the successful accomplishment of any project. This section is a general description on how to control and use this quality tool.

Preparation and Implementation
Activities affecting and assuring quality should be described as a system in instructions, procedures, or other suitable means of a type appropriate to the circumstances. A documented program should be established at the earliest time consistent with the schedule for accomplishing the quality activities and should be approved and available before the activity begins. The system should be structured and adapted to the product or service of the project, and its scope and function organized to provide confidence that

- The system is understood, effective, and up to date.
- The system is complete and prescribes the objectives and performance of the various activities (development, design, procurement, construction, production, and project management) having an impact on quality.
- The system is clear, unambiguous, and understandable and indicates methods to be used and criteria to be satisfied.
- The products or services satisfy customer requirements and expectations.
- Emphasis is placed on problem prevention rather than dependence on detection after occurrence, while not sacrificing the ability to respond to and correct failures, should they occur.

Instruction and Procedure Preparation and Approval
In the preparation, review, and approval of instructions and procedures, project management, with quality management, should determine the need for a document or revision, develop the scope, and assign an originator. In addition, management must coordinate with the originator the assignment of control numbers, amendments to the index, and so on.

The originator initially should research other instructions, procedures, and requirements necessary to develop an understanding of the effort needed to produce a document or revision to an existing document. The assignee should then coordinate with other project personnel whose input to the document or revision is needed, write the instruction or procedure, effect a review by project individuals who can supply knowledgeable comment, resolve comments, and prepare the final draft to be submitted for approval.

Project management should approve the distribution of the final draft to the applicable organizations.

Prior to initiation, revision, and issuance of an instruction or procedure, project management must decide if training or retraining is required for personnel who will implement the procedure.

Instruction and Procedure Revision

Documents may be revised at any time to reflect changing project conditions or to improve the document process. Such revisions should be prepared, reviewed, and approved in the same manner as the original document. A section should be reissued whenever a revision is made. All pages of a revised procedure should carry the latest approved revision indicator. A revision or acknowledgment system should be employed to provide proper assurance that the latest revision is implemented. Follow-up of delinquent responses should be part of the program.

Documentation

The original master of each instruction and procedure should be kept in a location that will provide protection to minimize damage, loss, or deterioration. The quality system description and SOPs should be controlled in part using standardized forms. Minor revisions may be made using simpler methods.

Indoctrination and Training

Project personnel performing or managing activities affecting quality should receive initial indoctrination and periodic individual training to achieve and maintain a high level of proficiency. Initial indoctrination should be conducted to provide orientation to program and technical requirements. Refresher training should be provided periodically or whenever there is a significant change to the quality program requirements.

The extent of indoctrination and training should be commensurate with the scope, complexity, and nature of the activities, as well as the education, experience, and proficiency of the personnel. The organization should provide for a detailed development program for management and salaried personnel and provide qualified and trained field craft personnel. The need for qualification and subsequent certification of personnel performing specialized activities, operations, tests, or inspections should be evaluated by project management in light of contract and industry codes.

Training Levels

The need for training should be identified, and a method for providing training should be established. Methods include formal presentation of the required material, reading lists of appropriate manuals, plans, instructions and procedures, and on-the-job training (OJT) by the supervisor.

Executive and management personnel: Training should provide executive management with an understanding of quality activities together with the tools needed for full management participation in the operation of a quality program. Management should also understand the tools available to evaluate the effectiveness of the quality system.

Technical personnel: Training should be given to technical personnel to enhance their contribution to the success of the quality system. Training should not be restricted to personnel with primary quality assignments, but should include assignments such as procurement inspection, process and product engineering QA, and construction QA or QC. Particular attention should be given to training in quality measurement techniques.

Supervisors and craftspeople: All supervisors and craftspeople should be thoroughly trained in the methods and skills necessary to perform their assigned tasks, that is, the operation of instruments, tools, and machinery; the use of quality-related documents; and the relationship of their duties to quality and safety in the workplace.

Contractor and Supplier Training

Contractors and suppliers providing services or equipment should establish and maintain procedures for identifying training needs, and provide for training of personnel performing activities affecting quality. Personnel performing specific assigned tasks should be qualified on the basis of education, training, or experience. Records of training should be maintained and, where applicable, certifications should be made available for project review upon request.

General Background on Programs and Procedures

An important issue in today's work environment is the MBNQA. This prestigious award program, founded in 1987, is fast becoming a significant influence on the business world in the United States. This award encompasses seven basic criteria as bases for selection. Each criterion is weighted differently, with greatest emphasis placed on leadership, customer focus and satisfaction, and human resource management. A copy of the application, which contains details on the criteria, can be obtained at no charge from[2]

United States Department of Commerce
Technology Administration
National Institute of Standards and Technology
Route 270 and Quince Orchard Road
Administration Building, Room A537
Gaithersburg, MD 20899

Upon careful review of the material contained in this text, one should note that key quality factors have been incorporated into descriptions of quality programs on A/E&C projects. The MBNQA criteria appropriate for the A/E&C industry, beyond leadership and human resource management, include the following:

- Information/analysis: Competitive benchmarking, trend analysis, and CA feedback.
- Strategic quality planning: Short- and long-range measurable planning; A/E&C tasks should be accomplished using established strategic planning mechanisms integrated throughout.
- Managing the quality process: Through numerous QA and QC programs, a supplier surveillance program, leadership in project management in several disciplines, quality reviews, value engineering (VE), reliability, and others.
- Measurable results: Project-by-project measurements are identified and factored into automated and computer-assisted feedback mechanisms for improvement of current and future projects.
- Customer focus and satisfaction: Weighted in a TQM program using an extensive alignment system and process with continuous customer feedback at focal points delineated as Pareto-significant work items during workshops.[3]

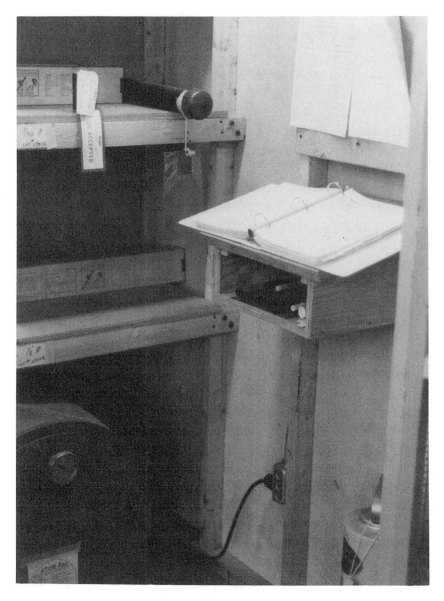

Figure 7.1. Quality programs, procedures, and plans should be located at the job site or office right at the workplace. Whether the procedures are at the job site or office, strict revision and maintenance control is mandatory. The inadvertent use of outdated or obsolete drawings or specifications is an all-too-frequent problem during the A/E&C process. Superseded documents should be positively recalled and destroyed to prevent their inadvertent use.

Many factors go into the development of an effective quality program for a firm, a division, or a project. Economics play an important role in determining the level of detail.

The following items should be considered when reviewing each TQM element.

- Proving the need for TQM on the project with cost and risk analysis
- Identifying direction and path forward through alignment and ROI analysis
- Defining TQM project organization with a steering committee
- Quantitatively identifying potential problems in the process
- Determining better ways to execute the work through lessons learned
- Providing a feedback plan on actions taken to paths forward
- Providing systems for reliability, availability, and maintainability (RAM)
- Providing root-cause analysis with QA and trending
- Defining mechanisms for obtaining measurable quality results
- Determining action plans for customer focus and satisfaction
- Tailoring the use of work process improvement
- Determining limitations of the TQM economic/quality model

Strategic Quality Planning

An organization should have quality strengths as identified in strategic quality planning and quality and performance plans. There should continue to be personal involvement, visibility, focus on the customer, and an environment for quality excellence. There should be a clear indication of the integration of these values into the sustaining day-to-day program by all facets of the organization.

What are the strengths, and what are the weaknesses of an A/E&C organization's strategic quality planning systems affecting quality? Following is a list of common strengths and areas for improvement in strategic quality planning in the A/E&C business.

Strategic Quality and Company Performance Planning Process
Strengths: There usually are well-developed mechanisms for planning strategically in the short term (within one year) for quality and leadership

in customer satisfaction. Such excellent tools as a customer advisory council and corporate quality councils are used to translate overall plans to all work units. Some A/E&C companies use software programs that give them a sound approach to obtaining objective customer and process feedback for quality planning purposes.

Areas for improvement: Long-term (three years or more) planning for quality and for customer focus and satisfaction in many cases requires enhancement. Technology innovations usually are reactive rather than proactive (usually not developed within the industry). The quality manager of an A/E&C organization in many cases does not participate in a quality steering committee or a corporate quality council. SPC techniques have only recently been considered in the industry.

Quality and Performance Plans

Strengths: Cost and scheduling programs have been developed into a pricing model that can reduce cycle time, improve accuracy, assist in meeting performance objectives, and produce greater customer satisfaction. An account information management system may also enhance performance, particularly at field locations. There usually are short-term goals and objectives relative to quality and performance.

Areas for improvement: Aggressive quality goals are usually stated in terms of having zero defects within x years for a complete, intact, on-time, and accurately billed project. How these goals are accomplished is not always clear. A/E&C organizations state some of their goals in short-range objectives only and do not display an understanding of their positions relative to their competitors.

Summary on A/E&C Quality Programs, Procedures, and Plans

This text blends quality ideas with fundamental industry concepts to help readers fully understand quality in the A/E&C community. By comparing industry quality standards (periodically footnoted in the text) and this text, readers will note similarities. This text has integrated several industry quality standards into a uniform system for the A/E&C community. Further, there is a distinct correlation between this text and two common standards used in the industry: the ISO 9001 standards and the MBNQA criteria. The relationships among these two standards and this text are detailed in Table 7.1.

Table 7.1. Comparison of this text by chapter, ISO 9001 (ANSI/ASQC Q91), and MBNQA criteria.

Text (By chapter; section)	ISO 9001 Standard (By element)	MBNQA (By criterion)
Chapter 1	NA	NA
Chapter 2	NA	2.0
Chapter 3	4.1.1	NA
Chapter 4	4.20	NA
Chapter 5	4.3	NA
Chapter 6	4.1.2	1.0, 2.0
Chapter 7	4.2	3.0
Chapter 8	4.3	8.0
Chapter 9, subsection 1	4.4	5.1
Chapter 9, subsection 2	4.5, 4.16	5.3
Chapter 9, subsection 3	4.6, 4.7	5.2, 5.4
Chapter 9, subsection 4	4.8	5.2, 5.4
Chapter 9, subsection 5	4.9, 4.19	5.2
Chapter 9, subsection 6	4.10, 4.11, 4.12	5.2
Chapter 9, subsection 7	4.13, 4.14	5.2
Chapter 9, subsection 8	4.15	5.2
Chapter 9, subsection 9	4.1.3, 4.17	5.5
Chapter 10	4.18	4.0
Chapter 11	4.20	6.0
Chapter 12	All	All
Chapter 13	All	All
Chapter 14	Selective	All
Chapter 15	All	All
Chapter 16	Selective	All
Chapter 17	Selective	All

Notes

1. National Institute of Standards and Technology. *1993 Malcolm Baldrige National Quality Award Criteria.* Gaithersburg, Md.: National Institute of Standards and Technology, 1993.

2. See note 1.

3. The term *alignment* is a controlled meeting with an unbiased and trained facilitator whose purposes are to focus brainstorming and produce paths forward.

8 Quality System Elements III: Assuring External Quality Requirements, Customer Focus, and Satisfaction

Assuring External Quality Requirements

- Implied Quality Requirements
- Explicit Customer Expectations
- Regulatory Requirements
- Industry Codes and Standards
- Competitive Situations

Customer Focus and Satisfaction

- Customer Value
- Alignments
- Internal and External Customer Interface

Assuring External Quality Requirements

External quality requirements come in many forms in the A/E&C community. These requirements may be implied or explicit, contractual or regulatory, created by industry codes and standards, or imposed by competitive situations. Each one of them may require an A/E&C organization to change, tailor, or adjust its standards or quality program to fit the project. Although each project requires a focus on the customer's needs, an A/E&C organization should set minimum standards in its model program and conform to them as a matter of operating policy. These situations are carefully examined here.

Implied Quality Requirements

Quality requirements may be implied through the course of meetings, telephone conversations, letters, alignment sessions, and the like. It is important to identify implied requirements as customer expectations. These expectations should be promptly evaluated by project management to understand the true effect on quality, cost, and schedule. They should then be communicated to the customer in the form of a contractual evaluation. Differences of opinion should be resolved clearly, contractually, and in sufficient time so as not to adversely affect the project. Changes to A/E&C projects have an almost exponential adverse effect on the work as the project progresses. It is imperative that resolution be made early in the project.

Explicit Customer Expectations

These expectations are usually stated in the Request for Proposal or Bid Qualification Announcement, at pre-bid meetings, during contractual negotiations, during project meetings with the customer, or during focus and satisfaction alignment meetings. These mechanisms may be formal, informal, written, or oral. An important attribute of a quality system is that it be flexible enough to integrate the customer's expectations and policies no matter which direction they are coming from (assuming they are legal and within reason). These expectations may be translated with a standard contract format, documented, and evaluated by their personnel.

Regulatory Requirements

The A/E&C organization must conform with certain laws and regulations in the area of quality, whether they are mentioned in the contract or not.

They become increasingly more stringent as the potential effect of a project on the general safety of the public becomes greater. Because of the importance of this topic, it is discussed separately in chapter 12.

Industry Codes and Standards

Again, because of the importance of this subject to the A/E&C community, an entire chapter is devoted to this subject (chapter 5). The complexity of this issue is not necessarily a matter of public safety, but a matter of jurisdictional boundaries. In many cases, local, small, and inherently safe projects sometimes have many more codes and standards with which to conform than billion-dollar projects with less jurisdictional boundaries.

Competitive Situations

This is the most interesting situation. This text is intended to provide readers with a distinct competitive advantage. By implementing the quality ideas in this book, the readers A/E&C organizations will be able to offer projects with markedly better quality at distinctly competitive prices. How do readers know that this will be the case? They need to focus on particular quality elements and determine what works and what does not. How can this determination be made? Through measurement? (These are simple questions, but hard to answer.) As discussed in previous chapters, measuring quality in an industry that produces a product at the conclusion of the industrial process creates an interesting dilemma. If one uses the techniques of identifying significant work-breakdown items and measuring true quality costs, one will be able to quantify the effect of particular actions on the quality of one's project.

It is important to begin by performing competitive benchmarking by using the MBNQA criteria as they pertain to information and analysis. Simply comparing one's results with competitors' or noncompetitors' work-breakdown items will give one a distinct advantage over one's competition. As is commonly known, this information is sometimes not easy to get; it is often vague and inaccurate. Information in the public domain sometimes will not provide a clear picture. A good quality engineering professional can earn his or her weight in gold if assigned this task and empowered the authority and resources to accomplish it. Remember, to achieve a competitive advantage and markedly improved value requires an investment. Numerous studies have shown that, in the present state of the A/E&C community, an investment in the up-front quality techniques discussed throughout this text can be returned manyfold at the conclusion of a project.

Customer Focus and Satisfaction

Sometimes in the day-to-day activities of a project, customer focus and satisfaction can get lost in the woodwork. But, in reality, customer focus and satisfaction should be the most important considerations in any quality system and should never be taken for granted.

Let it be clearly understood that this does not necessarily mean the customer is always right. What it does mean is that all A/E&C projects' personnel should have a clear understanding of the true project value to the customer, focus on this project value, and satisfy the customer with a long-term effort. The customer sometimes knows more than project staff members, but simply does not have the resources to communicate effectively to them. One must indeed look to the end user to understand the conceptual criteria of the project, and not rely solely on the information given by the customer (the customer's customer).

In every element of any quality system, customer focus and satisfaction must never be removed. The balance of this chapter is devoted to methods that the A/E&C community can employ to ensure this focus and satisfaction.

Customer Value

Customer focus and satisfaction is given the most importance in a TQM program through an extensive alignment system and process with continuous project and client feedback at key focal points. These points can be denoted as Pareto-significant work items during TQM alignment workshops. To enhance customer value, recommendations should be made on the formation of a TQM steering committee. There should be associated action teams relative to employee and supplier empowerment, and a focus on future customer expectations. The committee should reconvene routinely to plan a detailed course of action for the teams.

Alignments

When the alignment process is introduced in an A/E&C organization or used on a project, a presentation should be made to management on all alignment steps. This process must include a qualified facilitator during the early stages of an A/E&C project. Periodically, an A/E&C organization should review TQM techniques being used on all projects. Doing so can provide a more consistent approach through cross-pollination of these techniques and will serve to enhance the overall quality effort.

Internal and External Customer Interface

The quality system should promote development of a quality network among both internal and external customers. Alignment meetings should be ongoing between the external (customer) and internal (project management) workers and decision makers. In some cases, a joint business plan can be prepared by the two groups, fostering the concept of a partnership. In any of these cases, to monitor the continued progress of the alignment process, one should establish a customer satisfaction and survey feedback system.

An organization should have quality strengths in customer focus and satisfaction in terms of

- Managing the customer relationship
- Committing to the customer
- Determining customer satisfaction
- Objectively obtaining customer satisfaction results
- Comparing different customers
- Perceiving future customer requirements and satisfaction

There should be personal involvement, visibility, focus on the customer, and an environment for quality excellence. There should also be a clear indication of the integration of these values into the sustained day-to-day activities of the project by all facets of the A/E&C organization.

As mentioned before, a typical successful A/E&C organization has many of these traits; however, it is important when implementing an effective TQM program to be able to differentiate oneself from competitors. What are an A/E&C organization's strengths and weaknesses? The A/E&C business, like all others, has strengths and weaknesses that affect quality and, in turn, customer focus and satisfaction.

9 Quality System Elements IV: Managing Process Quality

Design Quality

- Design Planning
- Design Documentation
- Design Criteria
- Design Verification
- Design Change Control
- Introducing and Designing a Quality A/E&C Project

Document and Record Quality

- Document Quality
- Quality Records

Purchased Items and Service Quality

- Control of Purchasing Quality

Quality Identification of Items

- Item and Identification and Traceability Implementation

Quality of the A/E&C and O&M Processes

- Special A/E&C and O&M Processes
- A/E&C Processes
- A/E

- Purchasing Process
- Construction Process
- O&M Process
- Product and Service Production and Delivery Processes

I&T and Its Status and Equipment

- I&T
- Inspection, Testing, and Operating Status
- Measuring and Test Equipment

Nonconforming Items and CA to Assure Quality

- A/E's Role in Nonconformances
- Corrective Action

Quality in Handling, Storage, and Shipping

- Quality Issues in the Purchasing Process
- Quality in Handling and Storage for Construction

Quality Audits and Assessments

- Quality Audit Methods
- Evaluations, Audits, and Assessments

Design Quality

During a complete A/E&C or O&M project, the designing organization should be responsible for quality, coordination, and technical accuracy for A/E services. In a globally competitive marketplace, the consequences of design deficiencies, even ones that a few years ago would have been insignificant, can be disasters, both economically and legally. Therefore, design personnel should strive for flawless documentation, which simply assures uniform adherence to time-tested processes and procedures. These processes and procedures should be established, documented, and maintained on all projects involving design activities to ensure that the design should comply with requirements.

Design Planning

The purpose of design control is the successful integration of all technical requirements to produce quality project design deliverables. To achieve this purpose, an A/E plan needs to be prepared to identify and define the responsibilities of each design—and R&D—discipline. Also, this plan should address the use of labor and staff and the provision for adequate resources. Design concepts need to be translated into design output instructions, procedures, specifications, and drawings that include tolerances and acceptance criteria with a look toward acceptance testing. In addition, organizational and technical interfaces should be identified, documented, and managed in project design procedures.

Design Documentation

The beginning of the design process is the clear understanding of the design inputs (for example, design concepts, codes and standards, client criteria directives, regulatory rules, site environmental characterization) upon which the final design will be based. These inputs should be defined and reviewed for precision and accuracy. Incomplete, ambiguous, or conflicting design inputs should be identified, documented, and resolved with the customer as soon as they are uncovered.

The design process should also include documented instructions and procedures covering development activities (for example, methods, data collection systems, assumptions, formulations, and calculations used to develop the detailed design), independent design review practices (such as efforts to verify compliance with design objectives, goals, and initial design criteria), and administering the design process (for example, approval, issuance, revision, and storage aspects).

The design process ends with the approved design output documents (drawings, specifications, or other design documents translating requirements and scope of service). The design output needs to

- Conform to design input
- Specify acceptance criteria
- Comply with regulatory requirements
- Incorporate critical and appropriate concept characteristics

Design documentation must be clearly documented, reproducible, retrievable, and high in quality.

Design Criteria

The assurance that all applicable criteria have been used in the design process should be paramount to the success of the final design. The validation of design criteria should be equally important. If possible, established, time-tested design criteria should be used. This not only increases the quality of the final design, but doing so is cost and schedule effective. When new or unique design criteria need to be developed, design efforts need to include documented peer reviews or other controls to assure the validity of the design.

Environmental considerations and their effect on the design effort need to be addressed very early. This can include site environmental assessments or investigations, sample collection, and risk assessment. The issue of long lead times on regulatory reviews involving local, state, and national jurisdiction is an important design criterion. The evaluation of the results and restrictions of or limits invoked by environmental review can significantly change the design concept.

Design Verification

Design verification should be an independent evaluation of the design basis and features and should confirm the adequacy of the design and project performance. Such verification activities should be performed by qualified individuals (other than the person who developed the original design) in the appropriate A/E disciplines.

Figure 9.1. As the requirements for sound, environmentally strategic plans on A/E&C projects increase, the design process will have to include environmental characterization. In the twenty-first century, this design criterion for constructing facilities will become the primary consideration in the early conceptual phases.

Design verification should be established such that the design output documentation meets the validated design input by one or more of the following means:

- Holding independent design reviews such as a formal, comprehensive, and systematic examination of a design to evaluate the incorporation of all design input
- Performing qualification tests and demonstrations
- Performing alternative or simplified calculations
- Analyzing the design against a similar proven design, if available
- Assessing the usability or acceptability of design acceptance data

In some cases, VE may be contractually part of the overall design effort. In these cases, one should address these requirements in a quality plan or in design control procedures.

Design Change Control

All changes to information or output documents should be processed in a manner that will require the same control as applied to the original design (such as, documented procedures for the identification, review, approval, issuance, and storage of all changes and modifications). This type of control should apply from the commencement of the design activity through and including the processing of field design changes. Design procedures should identify the process of design modifications to ensure that changes to the original design receive the same level of attention as the original design.

Introducing and Designing a Quality A/E&C Project

An organization should apply quality strengths in introducing and designing a quality A/E&C project. There should be personal involvement, visibility, focus on the customer, benchmarking of the best of similar designs, and an environment for quality excellence. There should be a clear indication of the integration of these design values into the sustaining day-to-day design activities in all facets of the project organization.

As with other quality system elements, what are strengths of the design organization, and pragmatically what are its areas for improvement? The A/E segment is no exception. Below are some points that apply specifically to design quality.

Strengths: Several A/E&C organizations use design input techniques such as customer advisory councils, customer contact employees, and customer surveys to define customer requirements. In addition, a number of A/E&C companies use a variety of factors in the design input, such as government regulations, agency guides, field test reports, contractual details, and supplier's cut-sheets (or manufacturer's specifications from a catalog). Design verification and validation may be performed by the previously listed techniques and the A/E disciplines. The results of periodic customer surveys may be reviewed with appropriate A/E&C organization operating units or divisions.

Areas for improvement: In A/E&C quality programs, the specific tasks that should be done relative to design tend to be unclear, particularly when a significant amount of the design may be subcontracted. The concepts of design verification and validation may require more formality than now practiced in the design process as related to design reviews. In addition, unless specifically prescribed and paid for by the customer, R&D is normally not undertaken.

Before proceeding far into the design stage, one should investigate the actual aspects of the design process being performed. In some respects, it is not so important what others (such as a subcontracted design) do, but how one manages the design process. One should also determine whether the capabilities of current suppliers or subcontractors are to be evaluated as part of the designer's responsibilities. If not, one must determine whether any controls have been imposed to assure their quality. Somehow this must be accounted for in a timely fashion. (This issue may need to be addressed in an alignment session with the customer, for example.)

In some cases, feedback from the customer is not always sought after project completion on lessons learned for future projects. In other cases, feedback is obtained but not well documented. This creates a major weakness in the overall quality system, which, to be effective, relies on the cumulative knowledge gained on all projects, good and bad.

Document and Record Quality
Document Quality
The System

One should define and maintain procedures to control the methods of developing, filing, and retrieving in such a manner that quality requirements are assured.[1] These procedures should be reviewed and approved for adequacy by authorized personnel in one's organization prior to issue. Further, these procedures should assure that

- The critical and necessary quality documents are available at locations where operations essential to the effective functioning of the quality system are performed.
- Obsolete documents are removed from the workplace (or identified from all points of use) in a timely manner to prevent their inadvertent use.

Changes to documents should be reviewed and approved by the same organization that performed the original review and approval. Where practical, the nature of the changes should be clearly identified on the document. A master list or equivalent tracking procedure should be established to identify the current revision in order to preclude the use of out-of-date documents. A procedure should be established for changing and reissuing documents.

The A/E or Construction Project Office

An initial evaluation should be required when establishing a document control system. This evaluation should determine which documents are to be controlled to assure the correct information is available to those implementing the project's quality program and to those designing, building, or operating the facility. A review of the documents based on types to be controlled should be made and a list developed, starting with documents that are to be subject to document control. Consideration should be given to each document, weighing the need to have current, correct data against the cost effectiveness of the control mechanism.

Drawings and specifications should be controlled to assure that the constructed or operated project is built to the latest approved and, most important, correct design. Policy manuals and procedures should also be controlled to be certain that project employees have the latest information concerning project implementation and direction.

At the start of each project, A/E&C management should specify in writing which working quality records are to be captured in a permanent record system. Quality procedures for field activities should specify the same information for control of field documents. Training should stress the document-control features established and the criticality of using only the latest document to perform project activities.

The key to document control pertaining to design deliverables, as with other controls, is the contract or contract-referenced standard, plus supplemental agreements the customer has established as a baseline. When subcontracting, document-control measures that are consistent with those already established should be clearly specified in the subcontract or purchase agreement. Remember, a project or construction manager is only as good as the subcontracts managed. The subcontractor's quality program should be reviewed to assure that controls have been established and that follow-up surveillance and audit activities will be employed to assure effective implementation of the specified document control measures.

A/E&C Project-Level Document Control

As mentioned earlier, one should implement a document control system to control project documentation that prescribes activities affecting the quality of design, construction, or operation. Documents controlled by this system should include the following:

- Project documents (project procedures manual, quality plan, client criteria, drawings, and specifications)
- Process control documents (drawings, sketches, travelers, work orders, specifications, standards, and reports)
- Procurement documents (material requisitions, purchase orders, contracts, subtier documents and drawings)
- Work instructions (procedures, standards, checklists and other reference documents, whether from one's organization or from external sources).

One should establish on each project a system for the control of documents (at all stages) that provides for the following:

- Uniquely identifying documents by numbering and titling
- Identifying each revision by a number, letter, or date
- Formally checking and approving each revision
- Maintaining registers or logs of documents
- Maintaining record and archive copies of each revision of documents
- Establishing standard document distribution (master distribution list) and records of issue

The previously listed provisions should apply at both the precontract and contract-execution stages. The document control system should be defined in a procedure that should have provisions for

- Reviewing and approving documents, such as instructions, procedures, drawings, and specifications, and changes thereto, prior to release, to assure that the applicable requirements (including quality requirements) are sufficiently, clearly, and accurately stated and authorized.
- Identifying individuals responsible for the previously listed tasks and issuing documents and revisions.
- Assuring that review and approval of changes to records are subjected to the same process as the original.
- Implementing a unique numbering and revision status system for application to documents (usually developed to meet client requirements).
- Assuring registers of documents are established and the current revision status of each document is identified. The registers or logs

should be updated and issued on a regular basis thereby allowing obsolete documents to be identified, marked superseded, or withdrawn (segregated or destroyed).

Document Change Control

One should specify that changes to approved documentation be documented, reviewed, approved, and recorded and that the affected organizations be advised. Requests for changes may be initiated by the customer, project team members, suppliers, or contractors.

To initiate a change, a change request should be prepared to describe the nature of the change. The change request should be distributed to the affected organizations, including those involved in the review and authorization of the original requirement. These affected persons then should assess the charge and report to project management on its impact on quality, cost, and schedule.

When details of the proposed change are agreed to and approved by the customer and the project manager, the approved change order authorization should be issued, allowing the affected engineering or project functions to implement the change. Affected documents may then be modified and promptly issued to those responsible for further processing of work.

Quality Records

Formal Quality Records

When a formal quality records management system is necessary, the first step in establishing a formal quality records system should be to carefully examine the contract and its work scope with the customer. The requirements for the system may be in the statement of work or in a reference. Commercial contracts typically delineate the minimum requirements in the body of the statement of work. Government contracts (Department of Energy, Transportation, and others) typically invoke the requirements of existing codes of federal regulations (CFRs).

Once the contract has been reviewed, a designation of each record type should be made to delineate those that fit the definition of quality records. A document should be created that lists the types, such as correspondence, purchase agreements, drawings, specifications, discrepancy reports, audit reports, as-built, test reports, inspection logs, and so on. As

Figure 9.2. The filing system for quality records should follow the logical pattern of a complete A/E&C process: conceptual design, detailed design, early construction, mechanical work, electrical work, finishwork, system testing, turnover, operation, and the like (see chapter 2).

explained in the following paragraphs, the body of the document should contain a means of identifying whether the document is a formal record.

For records to be designated *formal records*, a system must be maintained to retain and retrieve project files. This system of capture may vary from record to record. The copy-to method may be suitable for correspondence or transmittals. Other records, such as reports or specifications, may simply be copied. It is essential that the capture includes timely submittal to the project files. Since only completed records are quality records, it is important that records designated for such submittal be captured after the final entry or signature. Such records are typically termed *authenticated.*

When a record is received to be retained, the first stage should be to perform a check of the incoming document to assure its legibility, authentication, and completeness. Records that are acceptable should be organized for ease of retrieval. Many standard electronic imaging systems are available, but special features may sometimes be needed because of the uniqueness of a document.

Use of a records locator is termed *indexing*, which consists of designing a locator data base with fields such as record type, date, origin, and location in file. If computer data imaging or microfilming are used for storage, the locator should specify how to retrieve the record.

Protection and storage is another consideration. Original hard-copy records may be retained for use on a day-to-day basis. Protection requirements and management prudence may demand that records are protected from vandalism, theft, fire, damage, and loss.

Another decision that should be made involves the length of record retention. The contract may specify the time, project management may decide with customer concurrence, or a combination may be advisable. The considerations that should be made are as follows:

- Should records be kept for the life of the project?
- Should there be identification codes for records?
- Should records be turned over to the customer at the end of the project or periodically? Which ones and when?

Access to records storage should be limited to authorized personnel. Compliance is usually accomplished through maintenance of a list of individuals who can have access. The list should be distributed and posted in storage areas. A positive means of checkout control should be defined and implemented with a log. Software is available to perform these tasks.

Retrieval should be based on an index system. Retrieval from hard-copy files is usually a straightforward withdrawal by an authorized person. A sign-out card is a standard control device. Retrieval from digital image or microfilm records requires that the requester supply information in the data fields of the locator index.

Record changes should be controlled to the same degree as the initial record. When the changed record is in the record system, the index should cross-reference the baseline to its change and vice versa. Hard copies may be updated by lining through the wrong data and entering the correct data, followed by dated initials.

It is essential that procedures be established and followed to maintain a quality records system. Consequently, it is imperative that personnel be trained to follow these procedures and that training records are maintained.

Informal or Working Quality Records

Informal, or working, records are related to the formal records system. Many working records will provide a basis for formal records or will evolve into them. Requirements for working quality records may be specified in terms of the types of documents to be included in the formal quality records system.

Usually, working records are protected in interim files. Key storage considerations include damage or loss from fire, rain, flood, theft, and other disasters. If working records can be reconstructed, there may not be a need for extraordinary protection. If they cannot easily be replaced or recon-structed, or are designated to become formal quality records, then they should probably be submitted for interim storage on a frequent basis to preclude the problem of replacing destroyed, damaged, or lost originals.

The legibility and integrity of working records are important consider-ations. Oil, mud, rain, and snow can cause recorded inspection, test, or surveillance notes to be rendered unacceptable as quality records. Inspection logs, concrete strength records, discrepancy, and surveillance reports are examples of records particularly susceptible to such problems, and care must be exercised to safeguard them.

Corrections to entries in quality records should be made with a single line through the erroneous information, careful addition of the correction, and the adjacent dated initials of the individual who noted the change. A

Figure 9.3. Quality records storage is controlled in many ways for protection and safekeeping. In some cases, fireproof filing cabinets are necessary; in others, physical separation of duplicate copies is necessary.

correction procedure, frequently part of the quality instructions, should be developed and implemented, and personnel should be trained as to its provisions. A record of the training should be retained.

Record control measures of subcontractors must be clearly specified in subcontracts and purchase agreements. Subcontractor procedures should be reviewed to ensure their adequacy, and surveillance or audits should be employed as measures to ensure implementation. Specific instructions should be provided for records being retained by the subcontractor.

Purchased Items and Service Quality
Control of Purchasing Quality
The System

One should define and maintain a system to ensure that items are procured to specified quality requirements throughout the entire procurement process, whether the items are structures, systems, components, materials, or services. In addition, both the procurement process and the quality system that goes with it should be implemented consistently in both the headquarters procurement office and at the site.

Purchasing

The success of any project depends in part on the control of purchased items and services. Consequently, a great deal of emphasis should be placed on associated activities. The purchaser should start the task early in each project and perform the planning that will control each project purchasing activity to help assure quality in materials and delivery. This should be accomplished through the definition and implementation of a supplier control program. The program should be tailored to the needs of the project and the unique features of the procured item. Also, it should define the procurement review and verification methods that will be applied to assure quality.

Preparing for the procurement process requires establishing many criteria. These criteria include those associated with implementing procurement methods, document preparation, selection of sources, bid evaluation and award, and the measuring of supplier performance that is normally established in a procurement or contracting plan.

One should define and maintain working teaming (partnering) relationships with repetitive sources of quality items and services for A/E&C

projects. This should be reflected in an approved suppliers list (ASL) which may be used to track performance histories of active and potential suppliers, and should be used when requesting a proposal or bid from the supplier or subcontractor.

Bid evaluations should determine the extent to which suppliers or subcontractors can conform to procurement documents. Bid evaluations should also assess technical considerations, QA requirements, supplier personnel, supplier production capacity, supplier past performance, alternatives, and exceptions. Unacceptable conditions identified during the evaluation process should be resolved prior to award of a contract.

Principal procurement administration related to quality should be detailed in SOPs. Methods should be employed to directly assure the quality of purchased items and supplies. These methods should take the form of preaward quality surveys, supplier quality manual approvals, supplier surveillance, and shop inspection. Detailed implementation of these methods and specific implementation and standard shop-inspection procedures should be procedural in nature, clearly defined, and consistently deployed.

Subcontractors

Subcontractors may be selected on the basis of many factors, including their past history and their ability to satisfy the contract requirements. A formal contract control system may be employed to select and assure performance of the subcontractor and to establish review and verification methods that will be applied to further control performance and assure quality.

Evaluation of subcontractor bids should be performed to assess a subcontractor's ability to perform to the design output requirements specified in procurement documents. Project management should start early to plan quality and to assure that specific project considerations and requirements will be met. Planning, including subcontractor plans, should establish the program and procedures required to meet task objectives with high standards. A program of planned audits and surveillance should be established to monitor the subcontracted work and to assure that potential problems are corrected early in the life of the project, thereby avoiding any adverse consequences.

A successful A/E&C organization must control suppliers and subcontractors, thus the saying, "You are only as good as your 'subs.'" Selecting the right subcontractor is the key. A bad subcontractor, no matter how one controls it, causes problems. There should be personal involvement, visibility, and focus on selecting the supplier and subcontractor. All subcontractors should demonstrate a quest for excellence in their sustained day-to-day performance. As with other quality system elements, what are a supplier's or subcontractor's strengths, and pragmatically what are its areas for improvement? Following are some points that apply specifically to supplier and subcontractor quality.

Strengths: Most A/E&C organizations have a system for evaluating their suppliers, including an excellent means of tracking costs and schedules that is used on a routine and ongoing basis. Specific design and specification requirements are communicated directly to existing and potential suppliers. Inspection is usually performed on receipt of the major materials and equipment prior to their integration into a construction site. This procedure covers affiliates and partners, such as engineering consultants, marketing and business development personnel, and suppliers of materials and equipment.

Areas for improvement: There often is no actual material supplier surveillance or audit procedure. There may not be contractual control of supplier quality. A review is often necessary to control the quality of suppliers contractually and to determine whether there is a need to provide actual surveillance or conduct an audit in the supplier's facility.

Quality Identification of Items

The System

One should define and maintain procedures for identifying items from applicable drawings, specifications, or other documents. This should be done throughout the various stages of manufacture, delivery, and installation. Identification should specify where, and to what extent, contractual traceability is appropriately maintained. Each item or batch should have a unique identification. A procedure for traceability of the item should be part of the quality system.

Item and Identification and Traceability Implementation

It is important that proper items be procured, and it is equally important that those items be controlled so that they are available and easily located for installation in their proper locations. A quality system should assure that only correct and accepted items are used or installed. Certain items (such as predefined and configured rebar) should be identified from the time of their manufacture through site receiving. That identification should be maintained until the item is installed or used and should trace the item to appropriate drawings or other design output records.

Physical identification (for example, tagging or labels) should be used to the maximum extent possible. Where this is either impractical or inappropriate, physical separation, specific control, or other means are used. Markings should be applied using methods and materials that provide a clear identifier. These markings should not detrimentally affect the item.

When required by regulations, codes, or standards, specify either item identification and traceability requirements in specification or grade of material (batch, heat, part, lot, or number) on test, inspection, or other documents. A good quality program should define an item's implementation and use.

Items with limited shelf life should be controlled through proper identification. One should use identification consistent with the planned duration and conditions of storage. Control should include protection of item markings subject to environmental deterioration and provisions for updating existing records.

Quality of the A/E&C and O&M Processes
The System
Project management should define and plan the A/E&C and O&M work processes that directly affect quality and should assure that the processes are carried out in a controlled manner. These steps include

- Documenting work instructions defining the manner of A/E, construction, and installation where the absence of such instructions would adversely affect use of suitable equipment, or of suitable working environment and compliance with reference standards, codes, and quality plans
- Monitoring and controlling process and product characteristics during the process
- Approving work processes
- Stipulating that criteria for workmanship should be, to the greatest practical extent, in written standards or by means of representative samples

Special A/E&C and O&M Processes

Special processes are defined as those that produce items whose quality cannot be fully verified by first-level assurance and where continuous checking and comparison with requirements should be performed to assure that quality is achieved. These processes should be qualified (formally tested, validated, and verified) and comply with the conditions noted previously. Records of qualification testing of materials and equipment should be maintained, as well as records of the qualifications and certifications of the personnel doing the testing.

A/E&C Processes

The following are examples of A/E&C processes and special processes subject to quality controls.

- A/E: Calculations, verifying software, data validation, design reviews, drawings, specifications, and as-built items
- Purchasing or procurement: Requisitions, bid evaluations, supplier qualification, purchase orders, contracting, performance evaluation, shop inspection, and receipt inspection
- Construction: Solid, earthwork, civil work, welding, paving, enclosure, mechanical, electrical, finishwork, remediation, and NDE.

The control of these practices uses standard guidance when self-performing. Examples of these practices are included in such industry standards as those from CSI, ASTM, ASME, and TRB. [2-5]

A/E

A/E project management should define and use procedures to control and verify design activities and thus assure that specified performance is achieved. Particular attention should be given to assurance of the following activities.

A/E Conceptual Planning

Project management should develop plans that identify the responsibility and authority for each design development element. The plans should describe these elements and should be changed as the design evolves.

- Activity assignment: The design and verification activities should be planned and assigned to qualified staff equipped with adequate resources.
- Organizational and technical interfaces: Organizational and technical interfaces among different groups should be identified and the necessary information documented, transmitted, and regularly reviewed.
- A/E during design input: A/E requirements relating to the project should be identified and documented, and their selection should be reviewed by the customer for adequacy.
- Incomplete, ambiguous, or conflicting project requirements: Issues should be resolved with those responsible for drawing up these requirements.
- Coordination of design criteria: Attention should be given to coordinating the design criteria with the customer to assure design output will meet the intended use. The TQM alignment process is an excellent tool for this purpose.

A/E Process

The production of specifications, drawings, and other output design documents should use the following process tools:

- Design calculations and testing
- Computer data and codes
- Conceptual design specifications and drawings
- Existing design specifications and drawings
- Data validation processes
- Design discipline interfaces
- Readiness reviews during design phases

Designers should use these tools during the design input stage. First-level and second-level assurance should be maintained during the process. (See chapter 7 for details on this approach to assurance.) The extent or depth of this assurance should be clearly delineated in the design input stage with a quality system description and SOPs that further describe the activities associated with the design review process.

A/E Work Product

The work product should be expressed in terms of drawings, specifications, studies, calculations, and analyses. This product should

- Meet the design input criteria
- Contain acceptance criteria
- Conform to regulatory requirements
- Identify those characteristics of the design that are critical to the safe and proper functioning of the facility (or other end product)

A/E Verification

Design products and any changes thereto should be verified. Design management should plan, define, document, and assign to qualified personnel the responsibility to verify the design products. Verification should be made to assure that the products meet the criteria requirements through such design control measures as

- Holding and recording complete design reviews
- Undertaking qualification and acceptance tests and demonstrations
- Carrying out alternative or simplified calculations
- Comparing the new design with a similar proven design (also see the section on design quality in this chapter)

Purchasing Process

Controls should be defined to assure that project management and the quality organization collaborate early in each project—prior to initiation of purchasing—to perform planning that will assure the achieving of specific requirements. A supplier control program should be established, implemented, and tailored to the needs of the project and to the specific items being procured. This control program should also define review and verification methods to be applied to assure quality.

Quality planning in the purchasing function involves many factors, including those related to the definition of methods, preparation of documents, selection of suppliers, bid evaluations and awards, and control of performance. One should maintain relationships with only the most reliable suppliers. These relationships should be reflected in an approved supplier resource that is used to select and track performance histories on active and potential suppliers, as discussed previously.

One should work closely with suppliers to verify their performance. The methods used include coordinating with the suppliers to ensure that they understand the purchasing documents and requiring supplier identification of techniques and processes to be used. Other methods employed may include planned audits, surveillance, inspection activities at supplier facilities, and reviews of quality records.

One should also recognize the importance of adequate packaging and shipment. Therefore, one should expend considerable effort during the planning and implementation of each procurement to assure that items arrive at the job site in a manner that precludes damage or loss.

The quality process should be controlled through the use of process tools described in a purchasing procedure. The purchasing quality process should be described in the quality system description.

Construction Process

The construction quality process should be organized into stages: mobilization or preconstruction, construction, and finally, start-up, turnover, and demobilization. It is important that resources, field deployment, and personnel are clearly planned prior to installation of structures, systems, and components. It is essential that the need for environmental remediation studies and investigations be evaluated before the start of any field activity, including the erection of any engineered environmental systems.[6]

Construction attributes that clearly should enhance quality include

- Increased site supervision, particularly subcontractor coordination
- Consistent use of checklists on a daily basis and travelers to verify completeness and clear status of the work
- Qualification of personnel directly affecting the work quality
- Delivery of materials, structures, systems, and components to installation locations using the JIT philosophy of minimizing stocking and excessive supplies to assure reliable system performance
- Using open-item or punch lists to assure construction completeness

Figure 9.4.   The construction portion of the A/E&C process begins from the bottom up with earthwork. Although the use of track backhoes are basically the same as they have been for the last 30 years, the equipment technology is continually being improved.

Figure 9.5. A good concrete foundation is another early phase in the construction portion of the A/E&C process and one of the most important to a project. Extra care in this phase will produce a quality facility with comparatively little repair and rework to the facility in later project stages.

The quality process should be controlled by a site construction organization using process tools described in the project construction practices. The quality process should be assured by the QA organizations through the use of assurance tools described in the field quality system.

O&M Process

O&M Activities

O&M quality activities should begin with early planning before a planned outage or a routine maintenance shutdown. The success of the O&M process is directly a function of the extent to which quality is planned early on. Planning should be centered on the initial A/E activities. Someone should be assigned the responsibility for the quality management functions associated with each outage or maintenance activity.

A/E interface with the customer before execution of the A/E activities should consist of identifying customer needs, such as operational quality problems or concerns, routine O&M scheduled activities, and facility upgrades and renovations.

Operational quality problems or concerns. O&M A/E quality activities should be improved by working with the historical data from related work activities and from the client. One should identify the important problems using standard analysis methods (see chapter 11). Once these needs or problems have been identified and agreement reached as to their significance, one should determine the CA to be taken to preclude repetition. After an in-depth predesign evaluation, which includes the effect on environmental quality, the A/E activities may begin.

Routine O&M scheduled activities. In this case, O&M A/E quality activities can be improved by facilitating good communication between the client and the A/E&C organization through a TQM program (for example, quality teams or a work process improvement program). At the conclusion of planning activities, a decision analysis technique may be performed.

Facility upgrades and renovations. The work begins with the planning actions noted. In this case, the work is involved in a major one-time outage. Because of this, additional planning should be directed to the customer's ultimate quality purpose for operating the renovated facility. A common pitfall in trying to improve quality occurs when changes are designed during the outage/shutdown. This may appear to improve quality but may, in fact, have an adverse effect. A designed facility has complex interactions.

As a result of changing the design during the outage, there may be a probability that the upgrade may in fact not meet upgrade objectives.

Prior to the A/E process and based on using set design criteria and a baseline, a detailed matrix should be completed that identifies the quality elements noted in this text. The extent of quality coverage includes consideration of conceptual design, site mobilization, facility shutdown, field work activities, facility startup, and operational follow-up verification.

A quality plan should also be prepared, as described in chapter 7, to meet the following quality needs.

- Continued conformance to contracts, codes, and standards (see chapter 5)
- Sufficient, intensive, and early quality inspection, surveillance, and audit before the outage
- Focused quality activities in terms of early quality coverage, efficient performance during the outage, and minimizing facility downtime

A good quality program should include checklists completed prior to contract execution, preferably at the bid stage. The purpose of these checklists is to provide proper QA on every outage. Major outages may require more extensive checklists. These include such outages for major nuclear plant modifications, large-scale petrochemical facility expansions, and large megawatt fossil plant upgrades. Technical support during both field surveillance of the outage and field work activities is essential to the success of the outage.

O&M Purchasing

The purchasing function during the O&M process should usually focus on inspection for acceptance of items. This task should take place sufficiently prior to facility shutdown. Purchase orders should require the supplier to furnish acceptable items. How that objective is met by the supplier is largely dependent on the effectiveness of the supplier's quality program.

Purchasing should be sufficiently planned to assure the following factors.

- Procuring long-lead structures and JIT procurement of materials and components. These will minimize the impact on the schedule and optimize storage space, thereby enhancing quality.

- Minimizing often hurriedly field-procured items during the outage, to eliminate unexpected adverse conditions.
- Determining availability of qualified suppliers of critical structures, systems, materials, and components.

When it is necessary for materials to be subjected to destructive testing to determine acceptability (hardness, tensile and compressive strength, bending, and so on), consideration should be directed to using prototypes for these tests.

O&M Facility Shutdown

The effectiveness of O&M quality activities will depend on the timing and adequacy of planning. This plan should be formulated by quality management as early as possible after receipt of the work authorization. In addition, a close interface should be made with the customer. It is essential not only for definition of initial requirements, but also to provide for coordination of schedules denoting planned outages or maintenance shutdown. Factors that may affect planned activities include other nearby activities that may interfere with space or accessibility, availability of support crafts to move material or equipment, I&T operations to assure the acceptability of work performed, and availability of utilities and services (electrical, water, ventilation).

Facility activities should be classified as either routine O&M or facility upgrades or renovations. The primary goal of routine O&M should be to prevent significant malfunctions. Such activities (for example, repacking of pumps) subsequent to a defined operational period are associated with preventive maintenance. Although routine O&M is repetitive in nature, review of these activities may indicate a deteriorating condition which may be corrected during a future outage for modification.

Facility upgrades or renovations can contribute to improved performance or increased reliability. (These activities may include tasks such as replacement of motors with more energy-efficient motors.) They tend to be one-time occurrences, although they can be repetitive for certain customers.

O&M activities should be controlled by instructions, procedures, drawings, checklists, or travelers. Document identification and revisions should be provided for travelers or checklists, along with space for reporting results at fabrication or installation checkpoints. Further, the traveler and inspection documents should include space for customer's or one's own hold points. Fabrication, inspection, and testing should be performed by qualified and certified personnel using calibrated equipment, qualified procedures, and previously accepted materials. After completion of the O&M activities, startup and turnover should occur expeditiously.

Product and Service Production and Delivery Processes

A/E&C organizations appear in some cases to have in-depth and comprehensive nonconformance control systems in several quality process areas. Performance standards are usually measured against requirements, and root-cause analysis appears to meet normal expectations with an ultimate goal of CA to preclude repetition. A common root cause seems to be the need for simplifying the process by a procedural change or by computer support.

SPC as it relates to out-of-control occurrences is not often used as a tool in the A/E&C community. It is normally necessary to follow a quantitative assessment of the actual quality processes in various areas to gain additional confidence in A/E&C work.

I&T and Its Status and Equipment

I&T

The System

I&T should be a normal quality method for examining the work. It should be associated with first-level and second-level assurance under normal circumstances (see chapter 7). One should verify the adequacy of an item by a planned, documented, and authorized system of I&T. This system should include the following I&T types.

- Receiving
- In process
- Final
- Record

Receiving I&T. Incoming structures, systems, materials, and components should not be processed or used in construction (except in the circumstances described in the next paragraph) until they have been inspected or otherwise verified as conforming to specified requirements.

Figure 9.6. Procurement, construction and operation include special processes within their phase of the overall A/E&C process. These processes require specific controls. (See the definition of *special process* in Appendix A.) Welding technology is one such subprocess. It is controlled through the use of essential and nonessential variables. In-process (rather than final) inspection is an effective tool for this special process which can significantly reduce the amount of rework and repair.

Verification should be made according to the quality plan and approved procedures.

When incoming items are released to construction prior to receipt inspection, they should be positively identified and recorded using a method that permits immediate recall and replacement in the event they are found to be nonconforming. A quality plan and procedures should address the controls required to release inspected material. In determining the intensity of the inspection, consideration should be given to the control exercised by the supplier and any formal evidence of the supplier's quality performance.

In-process I&T. In terms of in-process I&T, a quality program should provide for the following:

- Inspection, testing, and identification of structures, systems, materials, and components
- Definition of conformance of items to requirements by use of process-monitoring and control methods
- Placement of items on hold until all I&T have been completed and reports verified, except when products are released under positive-recall procedures
- Identification and segregation of nonconforming material
- Provision for formal I&T records

Final I&T. The quality plan and procedures for final I&T should assure that all I&T, including those specified either on receipt of the item or in process, have been performed and that I&T data meet predetermined, specified requirements. No item should be turned over to the customer until all I&T specified in the quality plan and procedures have been satisfactorily completed, or completed with exceptions and associated data and as-built documentation are available.

I&T Records. One should define and control records that provide evidence items have passed required I&T. Exceptions should also be documented.

Inspection Implementation
Details of the inspection systems of the A/E&C organization and its suppliers and subcontractors should be documented in a quality plan or in

approved procedures. Inspection of activities affecting quality to verify conformance with documented instructions, procedures, specifications, and drawings should be controlled by the quality plan and quality procedures. Inspection should be done by individuals who are independent of those who perform the activity. Peer inspection may be acceptable. Both inspection and process monitoring should be provided.

Inspection procedures should provide for the following:

- Identification of the inspection characteristics
- Identification of individuals performing the inspection activity, including any special agencies
- Acceptance criteria
- A description of the inspection method, including special equipment
- Documentation of inspection activities
- Maintenance of quality records

Where a sample is used to verify acceptability of a group of items, the sampling process should be defined in the inspection procedure.

Inspection of a subcontractor at the work site or at the supplier location. Site inspections should be performed by qualified personnel in accordance with field inspection procedures. Inspections at the supplier's shop generally are referred to as *shop or field inspections* and are performed by an inspection group in accordance with a shop or field inspection manual (this will be explained later in this chapter). Where they are applicable, sampling procedures should be approved before inspection begins.

Inspection Status. Procedures should be written and approved that define *inspection status* so that personnel can use the term in a consistent manner. SOPs should have provisions for item identification by one of the following means:

- Tags or labels
- Inspection documents
- Location and segregation in approved areas
- Approved process control methods such as travelers

Testing Implementation

Material, in-process, and final tests should be conducted to assure that an item will perform as specified. This testing may include NDE and destructive methodologies, start-up testing, in-service testing, and others. Requirements and performance specifications, including acceptance criteria, should be identified in test procedures. *Note: The same basic implementation methodology described for inspections also applies to testing.*

The extent of testing should be specified in the design documents. This information should be assembled early by the organization assigned the responsibility for performing the tests. This will allow sufficient time for test planning and scheduling to be integrated into the schedule. No structure, system, material, or component should be installed, used, or turned over to the customer until the testing has been satisfactorily completed and exceptions documented and approved. A defined, controlled record system should provide evidence that structures, systems, material, or components have passed all testing and meet acceptance criteria. Various detailed test methods and requirements should be described in the following (as well as subtier) documents: NDE procedures, field test procedures, and shop test procedures.

Inspection, Testing, and Operating Status

Status During Procurement

Inspection, testing, and operating status should be positively controlled throughout the procurement cycle. Measures for identification, and the extent of definition, depend in part on the complexity of the procurement. These measures also depend on such items as the importance to safety and the preclusion of adverse consequences. Inspection, testing, and operating status control should be part of the supplier's control system and continue through receipt at the purchaser's site. Provisions for such controls and their implementation should be specified in the purchase order or contract contained in the assessment or audit conducted at the supplier's facility and included as part of the receipt inspection procedures.

Flexibility should be allowed in determining the device to be used in identifying status. Batch- or heat-number tags might be suitable for traceability information for raw materials. Marking on the material is typically used for identifying specification and type. Color coding should be used

Figure 9.7. Testing is performed by quality inspection personnel who are technically qualified and certified and can produce precise, accurate, and reproducible results. Here, MT is being performed. This test can be somewhat qualitative and subjective if the qualifications of inspection personnel are not controlled.

in use-life control applications and for type differentiation of items such as welding materials. Tagging as *accept, reject,* or *hold* is typical for quality status. Associated shipping documents should also reflect status. Tagging or marking techniques provide visibility and are a reinforcement to the accompanying paperwork. Procedures should provide for placement and removal of identification only by authorized individuals.

Status During Construction
I&T should be performed under the supervision of a field quality manager who is responsible for ensuring the completion of these activities to meet

Figure 9.8. A sound testing program is an important part of a good quality system. This testing program should be based on the latest testing technology available. In this photograph, a six-head ultrasonic-test (UT) fixture integrates the individual images into one three-dimensional image of the pipe weld using the latest computer technology.

standards, client requirements, task-specific procedures, and other requirements. Status should be controlled for inspection, testing, and operating of systems and subsystems during construction, testing, and startup. The following paragraphs outline the basic status requirements for conducting field activities. These requirements should be general in nature and should be modified or augmented by procedures to comply with local, state, federal, or client requirements.

Construction activities may take the form of self-performed or subcontracted projects. The following discussion addresses self-performed projects, but may be readily applied to subcontracted projects.

Procedures describing control of inspection status should be defined and included in an I&T manual and in the plan for each construction site. These procedures should address the inspection disciplines involved in the work. Some of the more common inspection disciplines may relate to

- Environmental remediation
- Civil and earthwork
- Concrete and masonry
- Structural work
- Mechanical equipment
- Welding
- Piping and supports
- Insulation and coatings
- Instrumentation
- Electrical; HVAC; and fire protection
- Vessels and tanks
- NDE and destructive evaluation

Provisions describing tagging, checklists, travelers, and the like in field procedures should require that activities associated with each discipline be inspected at various stages and should identify witness or hold points for critical functions or systems (such as concrete prepour, pressure test, underground conduit and piping, and final inspection of a vessel closing).

Each quality activity should normally be documented in inspection reports designed for the item being inspected. These documents should become part of the site quality records and should be authorized by the quality representative prior to inclusion in the site records file.

Test Status During Construction. At various stages throughout construction, individual elements, systems, or subsystems should be tested prior to continuing with the installation or erection. Some testing should be defined in procedures designating hold points for field testing. Such tests should be witnessed by a site quality manager or his or her designee.

The testing program should make provisions for positive status of structures, systems, materials, and components requiring testing (that is, testing required, testing in process, testing completed, test failed, retesting required).

The results of field testing activities should be documented on forms and validated by the assigned quality representative, with A/E acceptance, prior to closure of the site records.

Status During Startup and Operating Tests. Start-up procedures generally include checklists to assure proper sequencing of the start-up process. During startup, detailed inspections and tests should be performed. One should include provisions within a quality plan to identify, control, and document inspections, tests, and operating status during this start-up phase.

M&TE

The System

One should calibrate and control inspection, measuring, and test equipment, whether owned, on loan, or provided by the suppliers or the client, to demonstrate the conformance of an item to the specified requirements. Equipment used should be selected to assure measurement accuracy consistent with requirements and traceable to a known standard. An M&TE quality program should

- Identify the measurements, the accuracy required, and the M&TE to be used.
- Identify, calibrate, and adjust all M&TE that affect product quality at prescribed intervals, or prior to use, against certified equipment

having a valid relationship to nationally recognized standards; where no such standards exist, the basis used for calibration should be documented.

- When results are unsatisfactory, define, document, and control calibration instructions, including details of type, identification number, location, frequency, methods, acceptance criteria, and action
- Assure M&TE is capable of being precise and accurate to the degree necessary.
- Control calibration records for M&TE.
- Assess the validity of previous inspection and test results when M&TE is found to be out of calibration.
- Assure that environmental conditions are suitable for calibrations, measurements, and tests.
- Assure that the handling, preservation, and storage of M&TE is such that fitness for use is controlled.
- Safeguard measuring and test facilities, including both test hardware and test software, from adjustments that would invalidate calibration.

Where test hardware (for example, fixtures, jigs, templates, patterns) or test software is used for inspection, it should be checked at prescribed intervals to confirm its capability to verify the acceptability of product. One should define the extent and frequency of such checks and establish records as evidence of control.

M&TE Procurement
Planning for M&TE must be accomplished early. Long lead items for special equipment that the purchaser may be specifying must be planned for well in advance of anticipated need.

Supplier selection requires attention. Sources for M&TE should have a history of supplying items meeting quality requirements. If equipment is to be produced to design, the source must have a positive track record with comparable items. The purchasing function must be explicit regarding standards and technical requirements. Standards used should be nationally traceable. Certification attesting the validity of M&TE should be specified in the purchasing document and constitute a prerequisite for acceptance.

M&TE Implementation

A system should be implemented to control M&TE for self-performed activities and for assuring the acceptability of supplier and contractor M&TE activities. When under the control of the supplier or subcontractor, M&TE should be used in a manner to assure measurement accuracy that is known, consistent with requirements, and traceable to a known standard.

The M&TE system should be accomplished with procedures described in an SOP manual. The identification of M&TE requiring calibration and the corresponding calibration requirements may be included in these SOPs.

Procedures for the control of M&TE should include a description of the following:

• Calibration services obtained from the client, self-performed, or sub-contracted to a qualified supplier; this requirement is not intended to imply a need for special calibration and control measures on rulers, tape measures, levels, and other such devices if normal commercial practices provide adequate accuracy

• Control of calibration technique, calibration frequency, issuance for use, maintenance and control of instruments, tools, gauges, fixtures, reference and transfer standards, welding machines, and ND equipment (to be used in measurement, inspection, and monitoring)

• Identification of M&TE and traceability to the calibration test data, including attachment of an easily visible calibration sticker or tag that identifies the equipment and the date of calibration as well as the date the next calibration is due

• Calibration and maintenance at intervals based on the accuracy, purpose, intensity of usage, stability characteristics, and other conditions affecting measurement accuracy

• Calibration on or before the designated use date

• When M&TE is found out of calibration, conducting and documenting an investigation to determine acceptability of those items previously inspected, including repeating original inspections or tests using calibrated equipment

• Accuracy requirements of calibration standards less than the error of the production M&TE

• Maintenance of records to indicate the complete status of all items under the calibration system

• Certification and traceability of reference and transfer standards having known valid relationship to nationally recognized standards; where national standards do not exist, provisions are defined to document the basis for calibration. The laboratory standards against which calibration or recalibration of measuring and testing devices are measured, controlled, calibrated, and used in an environment compatible with the required accuracy and operating characteristics

Nonconforming Items and CA to Assure Quality
A/E'S Role in Nonconformances

The architect or engineer should make provisions within each quality plan to identify, document, and correct conditions adverse to quality or deficiencies discovered during the design phase of a project. These conditions (deficiencies) typically will be discovered during review of the A/E and design documents and their calculations. Two elements are essential for successful completion of this task: the architect or engineer responsible for the design should contribute to the correction, and senior A/E management should review design nonconformances periodically to discover trends.

A/E Involvement During Procurement and Construction. The architect or engineer of record should play a vital role in the disposition of nonconformances identified during purchasing, construction, testing, and start-up activities. It should be the responsibility of the architect or engineer of record to review, evaluate, assess, and approve, in a timely manner, all dispositions affecting engineering and design documents. In doing so, that person must consider technical, physical, and economic factors that could affect the project when he or she is evaluating nonconformance dispositions.

Nonconformances During Purchasing

Purchasing documents should clearly state that purchased items and materials are expected to meet specified acceptance standards. This information should be included in the standard terms and conditions on the purchase order. At the discretion of the buyer, a form may be included in the purchasing package to permit the supplier to describe a nonconforming condition that he or she wants the purchaser to consider for acceptance. Such forms are typically titled, *Supplier's Discrepancy Action Request.* This request is usually limited to complex purchases for which the purchaser

Figure 9.9. Physical separation is a positive method for controlling nonconformances. If the nonconformance relates to a special process, special controls will be necessary.

has specified the design, and when schedule urgency suggests such considerations. It amounts to a remote materials review board. The discrepant condition should be described clearly for consideration by the purchaser. The purchaser is under no obligation to accept such items.

One should ensure that the supplier has an acceptable quality system in place to address nonconforming items. The purchaser normally performs receiving inspection to detect any nonconforming items. In important-to-quality purchases, or when designs are specified by the purchaser, supplier surveillance by the purchaser (or in some cases assigned resident inspectors at the supplier's facility) provides assurance that purchase requirements are being met. The right of access to the supplier's facility should be a standard provision of the purchase. Inspection hold or witness points should be specified.

Nonconformances During Construction

Provisions should be made within the quality plan to control structures, systems, materials, and components that do not conform to requirements. This control should provide for identification, documentation, segregation, disposition, CA, reinspection, and notification to affected organizations. The nonconformance system should be documented (including standardized forms), approved by management, and reviewed and concurred by all affected organizations.

The system should provide definitions of nonconformances, including when and for what conditions nonconformance reports should be generated. Typically, a nonconformance is generated when work or a process has been completed, found to be unacceptable, and rework within original guidelines or in a timely manner is impossible.

Identification at the site involves easily recognizable markings or tags. All site nonconformances should be documented and included in a *discrepancy event record*. These documents should be serialized and include adequate traceability to the requirements, quantity, description of nonconformance, disposition instructions, date, and approvals (including the jurisdictional and client approvals).

Another priority of this system should be to identify which dispositions require approval of the architect or engineer of record and which need concurrence or approval from the customer. SOPs or construction practices should contain descriptions of acceptable deviation from requirements.

CA

The System

When an item or service is determined to be nonconforming, rendering its quality unacceptable or indeterminate, it should be documented promptly and controlled as already discussed. Conditions adverse to quality, causing or contributing to nonconformances, should be identified promptly and corrected as soon as possible. The root cause should be identified and actions taken to preclude or minimize recurrence. A CA system should assure timely detection and correction of conditions adverse to quality. Types of conditions that may cause or contribute to adverse quality include

- Structure, system, and component deviations, failures, malfunctions, deficiencies, and discrepancies
- Defective materials, equipment, or services
- Supplier problems and deficiencies
- Inadequate procedures and records
- Procedural noncompliance
- Design and construction practice deficiencies
- Inadequate control over the work being performed
- Insufficient training of personnel
- Quality problems associated with scheduling and costs

The CA system should inform levels of management of the existence of important quality problems and of the CA taken. Problem details and their causes—along with CA taken to preclude recurrence and the date of correction—should be documented. In addition, the system should ensure that there is a process to assess the effectiveness of the CA and to apprise management of follow-up evaluations. The CA system should include an integrated information management system to track root causes on several projects with the goal of creating a positive impact on future projects (see chapter 11).

Project CA

The project quality organization should be responsible for defining and using a CA system that is responsive to the conditions that adversely affect quality. The project CA system should be implemented through the use of project quality program procedures, which should include

- Timely detection of conditions adverse to quality, using prompt feedback systems to assure conformance
- Systematic analysis of deficiencies and evaluation of nonconformances to determine the need for CA
- Analysis of processes, work operations, changes, records, service reports, and customer concerns to detect and eliminate potential causes of nonconforming products or services
- A means to determine the cause of the nonconformance and prompt assignment of actions to preclude recurrence

- A mechanism to verify completion (closure) of specified CA
- Confirmation that changes to procedures resulting from specified action have been implemented and documented
- Documentation and reports to appropriate levels of management that identify significant conditions adverse to quality, analysis, cause of the condition, and the CA taken
- Technical reviews to verify conformance to the design basis when CA affects the design of structures, systems, materials, or components
- Completion (or closure) of CA documentation verifying proper implementation

How does one apply the concepts of nonconformance and CA (at least in a procedural sense) to a project? Appendix B provides simplified examples of typical nonconformances and CA procedures. It must be recognized that these typical procedures may be (1) overly simplified, (2) too elaborate for some small projects, (3) insufficient for certain regulated industries, and (4) not designed for self-reformed work with hard-money type contracts. In addition, a good recognition and reward system may do a lot of good in preventing the nonconformances, but nonconformances will still occur. One needs to know how to dispose of them and, more important, how to prevent them from occurring again. Appendix B contains descriptions of four different nonconformance and CA systems, each with a different purpose.

- The first type of nonconformance and CA system described in Appendix B is a system for regulated business environments where no nonconformances are acceptable. This system is usually associated with environmental remediation projects.
- The second type of system is designed to review and determine nonconformances during the completion of major tasks. This is known as the readiness review process.
- The third type of system is one for design-and-build small commercial projects.
- The fourth type of system is for either a large civil work project or a transportation project.

Quality in Handling, Storage, and Shipping
These Issues in the Purchasing Process

Requirements for handling, storing, and shipping structures, systems, components, and materials should be addressed in the purchasing document. Special consideration must be given when the purchase involves items that require protection from crushing, shock, abrasion, and the like, or when items are age-sensitive (such as elastomers or epoxies) or must be protected from the atmosphere. Welding materials frequently require sealing to provide protection from moisture or other contamination. Special coatings may be specified (for example, a rust preventative, plastic wrappings, and so on) for items that require protection from rust, dirt, or dust.

Reputable suppliers with quality systems typically are aware of and will provide proper protection for off-the-shelf items they supply. Still, the purchaser must define such precautions in the purchase order to ensure adequate protection.

For complex or purchaser-designed items, it may be necessary for the purchaser to provide special packing and packaging instructions for the supplier. Instructions of this type describe materials, methods, and configuration of protective materials and crating. Diagrams or drawings are usually part of such instructions. Typically, they are produced by a packaging engineer on the purchaser's staff.

Requirements must be specified in the purchase order or contract for treatment of damaged items and associated claims. Damage to items themselves or to packing, packaging, or crating should be detected during receipt inspection and should be reported immediately, through the purchasing agent, to the supplier. A standard form, completed to record and report shipping damage, is frequently specified in the contract.

Suppliers may be monitored, and at times shop inspection should be initiated to assure execution of these requirements. The method of performing shop inspection (or supplier surveillance) should be described in a shop inspection program manual.

Quality in Handling and Storage for Construction

As mentioned in other sections of this text, project quality activities should fall under the direct supervision of a field quality manager. The following section discusses the receipt and control of materials on site and describes methods to ensure that the materials are correct as purchased and are properly stored and handled. Each construction site should augment these methods, as required, to comply with local, state, or federal contract requirements.

Site Material Control. Materials received at field locations should be subject to inspection by both materials personnel and QC inspectors. The detail, depth, and documentation requirements of receipt inspection are dependent on the type of material or equipment being received. (For example, ASME Code materials and important-to-safety, bulk, or commercial-grade materials or components should be inspected carefully against code requirements.)

All materials or equipment received should be identified using a method described in the organization's field procedures. Identification may include

- Heat number traceable to original material certificates
- Material specification and code type (such as ASTM A-336)
- Color coding used to identify the various steels that resemble carbon steel, but have different chemistries
- Prefabricated pipe spools and equipment or vessels with piece marking or equipment number as part of the identification

Receiving inspection documentation should be controlled by a site materials group or a site inspection entity. When required, an authorized inspector's validation should be included as part of the required documentation.

All material or equipment that does not pass receipt inspection should be kept in a secured holding area until proper disposition directions are received from the architect or engineer of record. Upon receipt of an engineering disposition, the subject materials or equipment should be removed from the holding area and disposed of as directed. Records of such activities should become part of the complete package for the system or subsystem involved.

On-Site Handling Methods. Depending on the job site, several methods of material handling and movement of equipment may be available. Field procedures should detail the requirements of on-site movement and handling of materials and equipment. These procedures should address such items as the following:

• Minimizing the use of wire ropes for the lifting or positioning of any heavy material or equipment. The exception to this requirement may be for heavy vessels or equipment skids that are equipped with lifting lugs designed to use wire ropes and shackles.

• Whenever possible, use of fabric slings or straps for lifting and moving materials and equipment. Fabric slings or straps should be used in the lifting or movement of stainless steel materials.

• When forklifts are employed in the movement of stainless steel materials, forks must be fitted with a nonmetallic covering to protect the material from contact with the forks. (This method should be used whenever any exotic materials or equipment with high luster finishes are lifted or moved.)

• When lifting or positioning heavy equipment packages, approved rigging procedures should be followed that cover the methods to be employed to ensure the safety of personnel performing the work. These procedures should be prepared prior to field move-in and each lift planned in advance to ensure that all construction quality activities are properly reviewed and evaluated. Scale models may be employed on some sites, as required, to verify the safest rigging possible or to develop new methods for a particularly heavy lift.

Quality Audits and Assessments
Quality Audit Methods
The System

Quality assessments should be started preferably just after contract award because the effectiveness of the quality program will directly relate to an early planning effort. Consequently, considerable energy should be expended early to define a viable program that will not only assure meeting objectives, but identify potential problems so they may be anticipated and possibly avoided.

At the beginning of the project, the project manager and a project quality manager should perform a detailed contract review to determine the specific requirements that must be met. This review should be used to develop a tailored program and to identify milestones. Included with the definition of milestones should be the definition of the review and assessment processes to be applied from conceptual design and environmental remediation through construction and turnover to the client.

A quality plan, QA procedures, or operating procedures should be defined. The line organizations affecting quality should be responsible for developing operating procedures for activities affecting quality. Each procedure addressing quality-affecting activities should be reviewed for compliance with quality needs.

Readiness reviews should be completed at project milestones defined during the early planning stage by technically qualified individuals who are independent of the work being reviewed. These reviews should be systematic, independent, and documented to properly assure that each critical quality need has been met. In addition, readiness reviews should be defined and scheduled, their procedures implemented, and training provided on their use.

Management assessments should be performed periodically to evaluate the effectiveness and management controls of the quality program. An independent body should execute these assessments, evaluate organizational adequacy, assure effective implementation of the quality program, plan procedural controls, and evaluate the nonconformance and CA systems.

The findings should be reported to management and CAs tracked to completion. The amount of reporting to executive management is normally defined in the quality system description. A good quality program will assure that corrections are identified and changes in the work activities made in a timely manner.

Evaluations, Audits, and Assessments

A planned evaluation and audit program should be developed early to assure compliance with contractual and technical requirements. The audit program should also evaluate incorporating quality needs into the project quality program as well as implementing the resulting program. Project audits should occur at frequencies consistent with customer needs, program needs, and previous audit history. Performance-based audits can also be used to evaluate the program in greater depth. These audits are sometimes more effective than traditional compliance-audit techniques. Performance-based auditing uses the witnessing of work in progress, the checking of calculations, the interviewing of key personnel, and the referencing of past surveillance.

Audits should be scheduled on a defined, periodic basis, but increased when necessary to reevaluate previous findings, and to address procedure changes, requirements changes, work scope, and management direction. Supplier quality programs should also be audited on a specific cycle and reviewed annually, increasing the frequency as required.

Audits should always be executed under the direction of lead auditors who are independent of audited activities. Technical experts should also be used on the audit team to provide knowledge in specific areas. Organizations scheduled for audit should be notified in writing in a reasonable amount of time before the audit. The audit team leader should work with the audited organization to schedule the audit to minimize impact on work activities. The audit itself should start with an entrance meeting conducted by the audit team. This meeting should cover the audit's purpose and scope with the organization to be audited, organizational interfaces, and audit schedule.

Audits should be performed using approved checklists or an equivalent. When concerns are identified during the course of the audit, the auditor should bring them to the attention of the organization being audited and the audit team leader (ATL). This provides the organization being audited with an opportunity to provide constructive input into those concerns. An audit exit meeting should be conducted to discuss the results. The audit is considered complete when a report documenting the results and observations is given to the audited organization and other interested parties. The audited organization should be given time to provide a written response to the report. Where significant findings are identified, the audited organization should be reaudited to address that specific area and to assure that CA has been taken.

Surveillance

Surveillance should be employed to monitor quality program implementation and, most often, assess performance-based activity in the shop or field. Typically, surveillance is performed to monitor critical activities during procurement or construction phases to assure that the quality program has been implemented and the required quality has been attained.

Surveillance should be performed by qualified auditors or technical specialists who are independent of the work activity under review.

Surveillance, announced or unannounced, should be documented in a report to the organization being reviewed and to other responsible parties. Surveillance should be planned with a defined scope, and results reported, including follow-up actions taken. Descriptions of surveillance programs usually are contained in the supplier surveillance or field quality systems procedures.

Assessment of Quality
An organization should have quality strengths in the practice of performing assessments. There should be personal involvement in, visibility of, and focus on performing quality assessments that ensure both customer satisfaction and an environment for quality excellence. For any quality system to work well, there must be a clear indication of the integration of these values into the sustaining assessment program by all facets of the A/E&C organization.

In addition, there are numerous other methods for assessing quality. Whatever methods are employed, one should evaluate the assessment results and determine their importance and value to the customer. This should be based on a desired performance level. These methods should be further defined in SOPs.

Often, a successful A/E&C organization will possess many of these quality traits. However, it is essential when implementing an effective quality system to be able to differentiate oneself from competitors. Below are some common strengths and areas for improvement in the A/E&C business as they pertain to assessments of quality.

Strengths: There are normally sound compliance-type assessments in the A/E&C community, particularly in the regulated industries. In addition, there usually is involvement of senior executives in quality assessments. There appears to be a continuous mechanism set forth in evaluating quality measurements which are reported regularly.

Areas for improvement: Quality assessments normally should take the form of quality management review and assessment, surveillance, or audits. This does not always appear to be the case in the nonregulated industries supported by A/E&C organizations. Further, these assessments should be independent of the work performed in order to provide objectivity. This does not always appear to be the case.

See Appendix C for an example of an audit and audit report which covers a management audit of a main A/E office.

Notes

1. The system explained here is in hard-copy form. Today's personal computer, compact disk, read-only memory (CD-ROM), and scanning technologies give an added dimension to this method. In any case, whether it is on paper or electronic media, this system should be followed.

2. See note 4 of chapter 2.

3. See note 4 of chapter 2.

4. See note 5 of chapter 2.

5. National Research Council, Transportation Research Board, 2101 Constitution Avenue, Washington, D.C., 20418.

6. Refer to ANSI/ASME E-4 Standard, 1994.

10 Quality System Elements V: Motivational and Human Resource Management

Facilitating and Focusing the Project Team

Ensuring Excellence Through Qualification, Education, and Training

- Qualification of the Project Team
- Education and Training Programs

Empowering Project Team Members

- Employee Involvement
- Employee Performance and Recognition

The human factor as a key to an effective quality system in the A/E&C community cannot be overly emphasized. Most organizations involved in project quality management in the A/E&C community clearly are service organizations. People are the process and create the product. Therefore, this element of an effective quality system—people—is probably one of the most important.

All elements of the quality system deal with the human factor to one degree or another. These attributes of an effective project team should be enhanced to directly affect the quality of projects.

- Ensuring the qualifications, education, and training of the project team.
- Facilitating and focusing the project team early in the life of a project.

Figure 10.1.   An important element of the quality system is human resource management and development. The best written and documented quality system is of no value unless A/E&C personnel are informed, trained, developed, and empowered. In addition, they must be given positive incentives, recognition, and meaningful rewards. Success of an A/E&C project depends on having a team trained in and dedicated to the quality system.

- Benchmarking an organization against a world-class organization (see chapter 11).
- Empowering project quality team members to use all of their true capabilities for development of innovative technology. This should create a project that is correctly focused, effectively uses its people, motivates them through meaningful recognition and reward, and increases their technical excellence.

This chapter addresses three of these elements independently. However, it must be clearly understood that they are all interrelated, and they each directly affect the others. Sometimes there are no black or white answers when dealing with the human equation. Nevertheless, any A/E&C project can be dramatically improved if the following four factors are honestly and pragmatically addressed early in any project.

Facilitating and Focusing the Project Team

This part of TQM is a substantial management motivational technique. It can make a significant impact on project excellence in execution. TQM uses modern quality enhancement techniques to significantly improve excellence and client satisfaction. The application of these techniques is normally orchestrated or facilitated by an alignment facilitator. There are many courses that teach one how to perform or act as a facilitator, including how to form a steering committee and a management support group, develop action teams, and so on. Each project should have means for facilitation. This should be tailored by the facilitator to meet the needs of the individual project. This is further discussed in chapter 6 (organization) and chapter 7 (strategic planning). The facilitator will assist in the development of a TQM plan based on the elements discussed in chapter 11.

Facilitation should employ decision-making and problem-solving analyses. These analyses are based on TQM modern management statistical methods discussed also in chapter 11.

Ensuring Excellence Through Qualification, Education, and Training

The qualification, education, and training of the project team are essential parts of the quality system, depending on the size, scope, and breadth of

A/E&C projects. All the good training programs at the latter stages of a project cannot change the initial qualifications of the project employees. On the other hand, all the good qualified employees cannot make a project successful without timely project training on pertinent points.

Qualification of the Project Team

During the formative stages of the project, management should effectively and honestly review the team's credentials and qualifications. A successful project team has to have the proper qualifications to perform its tasks effectively. One should review these tasks and assure that team members have the necessary qualifications: academic background and experience. Good candidates for getting the job done have experience in design and in the field.

Training and development TQM steering committees are often established in large companies to enhance personnel growth, which helps assure people's development and increases their contribution to the A/E&C organization. Cross training of personnel will assure well-roundedness. Therefore, training is an issue that should be addressed both on projects and organizationwide.

Education and Training Programs

The following section provides guidelines for a customer-oriented program to train and indoctrinate project personnel in activities that affect or assure quality. The program is designed to help assure that specific curricula is established for personnel being trained, that trained personnel attain appropriate skill levels, and that skill levels are measured.

Applicability

These guidelines apply to all activities pertinent to managing the transfer of information during training of project personnel. They involve descriptions of training methods to assure that records are maintained, completed, and verified. These training methods should be applied to the subject matter as defined in a training matrix. Finally, these guidelines apply to personnel who perform or manage activities affecting and assuring the quality of the facility.

Sources and Reference
- Quality system description.
- Customer's QA plan
- Customer's employee development and training program

Responsibility
In terms of training personnel who assure or affect quality, the project manager is responsible for

- Appointing a training coordinator (TC)
- Appointing a training advisory board (TAB) when necessary
- Implementing the customer's procedures and directives that identify the personnel, in general, who require orientation
- Periodically reviewing the status and adequacy of the training and indoctrination program described in project procedures

The TC is responsible for

- Developing and maintaining the training matrix
- Scheduling the various training and indoctrination tasks in accordance with the training matrix and the trainee's records
- Maintaining the indoctrination and training records, including the customer training-assignment sheets; coordinating this activity on training records with customer personnel, including those that list OJT and reading assignments
- Obtaining qualified training instructors (TIs), when necessary, to provide classroom instructions and coordinating this activity with the customer
- Reviewing and approving the TI's classroom material and examinations
- Providing periodic reports to the customer's project manager, apprising him or her of the status and adequacy of the training and indoctrination program, and making recommendations to improve its effectiveness
- Periodically monitoring classrooms to assure the adequacy of the TI's presentation

TIs are responsible for

- Developing lesson plans, course notes, and audiovisual aids based on the purpose and scope provided by the TC and obtaining approval on these from him or her
- Instructing the trainees and providing effective interaction in the classroom
- Developing mechanisms, such as exams, for determining the proficiency of the persons who have received the training, and administering the same
- Assuring attendance sheets are completed and transmitted to the TC

Trainees are responsible for

- Completing the training assignments and attending the classroom training as scheduled
- Learning the assigned subject matter and applying it effectively
- Providing evidence of the completion of any outside training to the TC

Training Guidelines
General Requirements. The indoctrination and training should concentrate on subjects related to position requirements. These include all codes, standards, programs, plans, procedures, and instructions; all structures, systems, and components; all administrative and supervisory requirements; all project design and construction requirements; and specialized job knowledge and performance requirements. The indoctrination and training should be focused to assure suitable proficiency in selected activities. It should be documented that this proficiency has been measurably achieved and maintained.

The extent of this indoctrination and training should be a function of the nature and complexity of the project and its significance to affecting or assuring quality. The background, education, experience, and other credentials of the trainee also must be taken into consideration.

Training should be documented and include the course objectives, content of the program, attendees, the date, and the instructor's name.

Periodically, the TC should review the curricula and personnel records with the various line managers to assure that a program adequately covers the needs of the project. Training records should be maintained by the TC and include classroom attendance sheets or certificates, completed training assignments, and completed examinations.

Assignment and Appointment of Training Personnel. The project manager should assign a TC whose function is to assure the implementation of training. The project manager may also appoint a TAB. The board, headed by the TC, should, as a minimum, consist of at least one member each from project management, engineering, and QA. The team should meet as requested by the TC to develop and update the training matrix, develop and update the training tasks, and review any possible changes in the training and indoctrination program.

Formulation and Development of Training Material. Assisted by the TAB, the TC should formulate a training matrix. It should be designed to specify the instructional tasks necessary to perform the following:

- Indoctrination of new personnel in terms of both general introduction and job function
- Indoctrination of personnel changing positions in terms of both OJT and training assignments
- Routine training of personnel for positions required for a project
- Training of personnel in nonroutine matters when changes or important issues are raised

After completion of the training matrix, the TC assisted by TAB should work to develop individual training tasks. These tasks should include the TI's name, purpose and scope of the task, and the date by which materials are to be completed. At times it may be helpful to prepare a lesson plan (schedule of tasks) and format as well. Assignments should be subdivided and can include video, classroom material, reading material, and other training media.

Trainees in the quality field will need indoctrination and training at various stages of their work. These stages can be categorized as follows: prerequisite to their position function (indoctrination) and ongoing to maintain their position function (training).

TC Scheduling of Training Tasks. The TC should notify the individuals being indoctrinated or trained of the course schedule. Unless a legitimate schedule conflict exists, the trainee is expected to attend classes or keep up with reading assignments. The TC also should notify trainees when routine or nonroutine training is scheduled.

The TC should provide the trainee's supervisor with a schedule of activities and planned scope of the training. The TC and the supervisor should try to resolve schedule conflicts prior to the trainee's participation.

Trainee Participation in Indoctrination. New employee indoctrination should consist of a general module and a module related specifically to the job function. Usually, the general module will include both a videotape pertaining to projects or the company and a list of mandatory general readings. The specific module related to the new employee's job function should consist of a mix of OJT supervised by the employee's supervisor, further mandatory readings, and classroom work as specified on an assignment sheet. This indoctrination should be concluded with an examination conducted by the TC and reported to his or her supervisor.

An existing employee may change his or her position or function, requiring an indoctrination into his or her new role. The indoctrination for this new role should consist of OJT supervised by his or her immediate supervisor and classroom modules developed specifically for his or her new role. This indoctrination may be concluded with an examination (depending upon the function) conducted by the TC and reported to his or her supervisor.

Execution of the Training Function. Training should be conducted by various TIs, depending upon the subject matter. The trainee is expected to keep up with the reading assignments, attend required classroom training, and pass required examinations. The completed assignments should be initialed by the trainee, dated, and returned to the TC. The TC should keep track of assignment completion and examinations, and notify supervisors of delinquencies. External training may be used in lieu of other training tasks. It should be approved by the TC, and proof of the trainee's successful completion should be supplied to the TC.

Routine training should be maintained, when required, for the jobs affecting or assuring quality and when there is sufficient interest in a subject that contributes to improving the project or the headquarters organization.

As a matter of course, periodic classroom training and assigned readings should be tailored to specific customer work functions. The trainee should receive announcements concerning scheduled classroom training as a reminder of his or her scheduled participation.

When training on a specialized topic becomes available, it should be scheduled if there is sufficient interest or if it contributes to improving the project or the headquarters organization. This training may be internal or external, or may consist only of reading assignments. In this case, examinations are usually not used.

In some cases, additional training may become necessary as the project progresses due to changes in the scope of work. This may involve having selected personnel attend internal or external training classes or assigning mandatory reading.

Examinations. Some training and indoctrination classes will require examinations upon their completion. Assignment sheets should specify whether a course includes examinations to avoid misunderstandings. The TC should immediately notify a trainee of test results and advise if a retake is necessary.

Records. Individual or packaged training records and copies of any related correspondence should be handled carefully. These records include quality system element guidelines and subsequent revisions, training matrixes, lesson plans, and the trainees' training records.

Maintaining Records. When satisfied that the trainee has an adequate understanding of the assigned material, the TC and the trainee's supervisor should sign and date the bottom of the form that verifies this. The TC should keep the form for safekeeping. The TC should continually update the training data base, noting readings completed, courses attended, and examinations passed.

Update of Training Tasks. As the project progresses, invariably conditions, procedures, programs, and hardware change and improve. These changes must be effectively transmitted to the personnel responsible for implementing them. Training is an effective tool for aiding in this transmission, although by no means should it be used as a replacement for other mechanisms. When a change occurs, the TC should assure that it gets factored into the training matrix and therefore into the training tasks.

Empowering Project Team Members

Empowering A/E&C project team members is an important ingredient in a project's success. This can be an extremely useful technique in motivating individuals and improving the quality of the project. But what exactly is empowerment?

Empowerment is the delegation of authority to employees, allowing them to make important decisions that directly affect the quality of the A/E&C project. Delegating authority to employees is an interesting concept. How far into the organization does one go? Where does one stop? These decisions have to be made on a case-by-case basis. However, certain criteria can be established. The following can be used as empowerment criteria.

- Delegate the authority as much as the responsibility.
- Delegate the authority until it hurts organizational control, then back off slightly. In other words, there reaches a point when problems start occurring. This point needs to be found by trial and error.
- Delegate and then test effectiveness.
- Coordinate the delegations and check for inconsistencies.
- When delegation first occurs, frequently assess its adequacy.
- Take a proactive approach to listening to project employees when they voice their desire for authority to accomplish their tasks.
- Delegate authority on projects, and recognize and reward actions in a manner directly proportional to the size, complexity, and success of the effort. Realize that the carrot and the stick go only so far.

There are many empowerment tools available to manage human resources on A/E&C projects. Several of them are discussed here. Effective motivational tools, meaningful human resource training, and a recognition and incentive system provide the foundation for empowerment. Participation is particularly important. The use of a people development TQM committee is one such empowerment tool. A quality practitioner can assess and recommend a course of empowering action during a project, particularly during its early stages. Recommendations may be made on the establishment of such techniques as a TQM steering committee and action teams relative to benchmarking, customer feedback, strategic quality planning, employee and supplier empowerment, and a focus on future expectations. The committee may convene to plan a detailed course of action for employee action teams.

Establishment of an employee total quality recognition and reward system ensures that employees' ideas are reviewed in a consistent and timely manner. For example, a suggestion answering machine might be used to provide feedback to the employee including casual labor. A record-keeping system should be used to keep track of all ideas. Most important, the system must allow implementation of good ideas. Such empowerment techniques noted previously should be well established to ensure employee incentives are implemented in a sound approach.

Objective interviewing of employees, particularly recent hires, can go a long way toward determining the extent to which an organization can delegate both in the office and on the job site. This should be true in both an open shop and a union environment. For example, a site visit can include an investigation of what human resource management activities are accomplished beyond what the union provides for the A/E&C organization.

The A/E&C organization should continually improve empowerment through its management annual review and assessment process (see chapter 9). This event should include a careful review of the effect of empowerment on the project.

Employee Involvement

There should be a significant amount of employee participation through the use of such concepts as project quality improvement teams. A quality improvement committee or team should be responsible for involving employees. The overall management structure should be relatively flat, otherwise employee empowerment efforts will not be successful.

The concept of empowerment should be examined in light of the organizational structure (flat or vertical), and the effect of structure on employee empowerment should be documented. This examination should relate to the exact nature of the type of quality required and the effectiveness of employee involvement from past efforts.

Forms such as error, cause, and removal forms can be an effective mechanism for identifying quality improvement by employees. The A/E&C organization should consider the use of quality audits as a tool to go beyond simple quality assessment. They might be used to recommend employee empowerment. One should also rely on the organization's QA professional for support in empowering employees.

Employee Performance and Recognition

One should have a sound performance and reward compensation program. The quality improvement team or recognition teams should present recognition awards. Quality performance and recognition tools should include

- Departmental team recognition
- Safety awards
- Office-performance awards
- TQM team-recognition awards
- Project-performance awards

The concept of internal customers should be a key method for improving job performance and increasing recognition. It should be noted that marketing, sales, accounting, and safety are areas where performance can be clearly recognized within the A/E&C organization. One would tend to question the amount of recognition and incentive for employees in the operations segment of the A/E&C organization that measures them meeting quality objectives. Human resource and quality management personnel should resolve any concerns about the amounts and types of employee recognition.

Empowering employees through delegation of responsibility and authority for quality and quality-related actions will strengthen the organization. As mentioned in previous chapters, there should be personal involvement, visibility, focus on the customer, and an environment for quality excellence. There should be a clear indication of the integration of these values into the sustaining day-to-day empowerment actions exhibited by all facets of the A/E&C organization.

Many successful A/E&C organizations rely heavily on employee empowerment. Often, however, empowerment efforts can be developed further. Improvement will tend toward an organization's competitiveness as it sets the stage for enhanced motivation and production and increases the chances for top-quality innovation. The following list offers suggestions for improving the employee empowerment process through human resource management.

- Consider an individual professional development plan for each employee
- For the long term, consider the professional development of employees as a group
- Emphasize cross training of employees in several job functions
- Create a roundtable meeting of supervisors and an executive committee to discuss areas where employee empowerment may be viable
- Create a try-a-job program to enhance employee empowerment by establishing an open policy in which any employee, within certain restrictions, can try a job for a period of time
- Create a company "university" to aid employees in increasing their knowledge

11 Quality System Elements VI: Quality Results and Statistical Methods

Motivational and Statistical Methods

- Quality Management Motivational Techniques
- Additional Management Situation Analysis Methods

Reliability, Availability, and Maintainability

Quality Trend Analysis and Other Methods

Information and Other Quality Analysis

Motivational and Statistical Methods
Quality Management Motivational Techniques

A substantial management motivational technique is TQM. This technique can directly enhance project quality execution. TQM uses modern management quality enhancement techniques to significantly impact excellence and provide customer focus and satisfaction. Each project should include a plan for implementing TQM. This plan should be tailored by a facilitator to meet the requirements of the project. The facilitator should assist in the development of a TQM plan based on the following:

- Scope of effort
- TQM responsibility
- General related project requirements
- TQM plan elements
  - Proving the TQM need with cost and risk analysis
  - Identifying direction and paths forward through use of an alignment process and ROI analysis
  - Identifying the TQM organization, including a TQM management support group, TQM steering committee, diagnostic task force, TQM control points along the project schedule, diagnostic sources, and value analysis and engineering
  - Quantitatively identifying potential project problems in the A/E&C process
  - Providing feedback on actions taken to paths forward
  - Providing root-cause analysis in conjunction with QA
  - Testing theories of root cause through analysis of past projects
  - Identifying significant variables in the A/E&C process
  - Employing procedures and measurements
  - Identifying limits to the TQM economic and quality model

The TQM process should be explained in a set of guidelines that can be used as an educational tool for all organizational personnel. There are various applications of modern statistical methods that can be used in TQM. For example, the mathematical analysis of decision-making and problem-solving processes is one example. TQM uses the modern management statistical evaluation analyses described here.

Additional Management Situation Analysis Methods

Here are seven methods that can be used.[1]

1. Situation appraisal. This technique requires a proactive approach. It is not intended to provide solutions, but rather to impose order. A situation appraisal should be used to evaluate the whole picture and to identify specific high-priority issues to be resolved. This analysis separates concerns into workable components and selects appropriate solutions. It assures that efforts are made to gather and analyze information.

2. Problem analysis. This tool adequately defines problems. It helps personnel avoid jumping to conclusions and taking unfocused action. Problem analysis is used to determine possible root causes and develop tests to eliminate causes that are incorrectly identified. Assumptions are confirmed and causes verified before CAs are taken.

3. Decision analysis. This method clarifies the purpose of the effort by measuring the severity of a decision on people and processes. Decision analysis lists and classifies objectives, results to be achieved, and resources to be committed. It also generates and evaluates alternatives. Finally, it is used to determine the pros and cons of alternatives before outlining the objectives to be obtained. In addition, this analysis assesses inherent risks by identifying what could go wrong. This structure allows a TQM group to make informed decisions from accurate and complete information.

4. Potential problem analysis. This method systematically reduces the risk of any undertaking by identifying obstacles to a plan or action. Potential problem analysis develops appropriate preventive actions that address likely causes, thereby reducing the probability that a problem will occur. If preventive actions are not realistic, contingent actions are developed that minimize the likely effects should the problem occur.

5. Pareto analysis. This analysis helps users determine and justify the vital few tasks that provide the maximum opportunity for improvement in failure rates, quality costs, downtime, reliability, and the like. Pareto analysis requires the collection, analysis, and interpretation of data through the use of frequency histograms or matrices. (Its use is explained in chapter 4.)

6. Test case programs. These verify that facilities and equipment are performing efficiently. Test case programs are performed prior to and during startup. The planning and implementation of such testing should follow these listed guidelines.

- Develop a statement of objectives
- Collect background information
- Design a good test case program
- Plan and carry out the experimental work
- Analyze the data
- Interpret the results
- Prepare the report

7. Benchmarking. This method measures an organization's current performance against optimum (best-of-class) performance. Benchmarking determines how to obtain levels of optimum performance and uses this information as a basis for project targets, strategies, and implementation. There are complex mechanisms for benchmarking, but benchmarking itself is based on a very simple idea. This idea is to compare an organization's operations to the best organizations in the industry. Doing this objectively often means admitting to organizational weaknesses previously unidentified or ignored. For example, an A/E&C organization may have a lot to learn in the scheduling of projects from a high-volume pizza delivery chain. On the other hand, a prison or jail system may provide insight in *leadership* that may assist any A/E&C firm.

Reliability, Availability, and Maintainability

One can maximize safety, minimize cost, and assure meeting quantitative project tasks and production goals by applying an aggressive reliability, availability, and maintainability (RAM) analysis applied to A/E&C projects.[2] This quality management statistical analysis helps predict the quality of the A/E&C process. RAM predictions let designers and builders, in pursuit of more efficient designs and quantitative techniques and methodologies, determine figures of merit to assure the most efficient facility possible for the customer. The quantitative results point the way to those improvements most needed and identify requirements that can be tightened.

RAM analyses are used to optimize a design. These analyses maximize safety through improved reliability and minimize cost by trading off capital investment for increased reliability, production, and safety considerations. RAM engineers begin by providing estimates of the optimum intermediate storage requirements needed to maintain the required production rate; determine the best configuration for units within a given process; determine

the most desirable scheduled maintenance strategy consistent with requirements; make recommendations for spare parts, diagnostic instrumentation,
preventive maintenance intervals, and accessibility for equipment servicing;
and provide assurance that production rate requirements will be met.

Quality Trend Analysis and Other Methods

A performance feedback and quality trend analysis can be established in
the A/E&C process through quality audits, surveillance, inspection, in-plant
rejection data, client feedback, warranty information, and other user
reports. Such A/E&C quality methods allow identification of adverse quality
trends, prevention of problems, and initiation of CA as appropriate. Typical
action might include changing surveillance, auditing systems, upgrading
quality requirements, changing designs, revising processes, or other such
measures. Trend analysis is employed to improve quality, resulting in a savings in cost and time.

Because trend analysis often requires large amounts of data, the use
of a computer can make it more feasible. Other quality methods that are
enhanced through the use of computer technology include

- Quality trends on projects
- Personnel and resources being applied to project quality, including
  qualifications and certifications
- Quality information resources for use on a project including applicable procedures, forms, and instructions.

Information and Other Quality Analysis

It is important on any project to measure results. Measuring results has to
occur on a project-by-project basis. These integrated results should be
documented in such a way that easy access is attainable. In the beginning
of this text, methods are described that, if used, would significantly
improve quality. For example, the use of quality cost analysis can be one
of the most effective tools for improving quality in the A/E&C community.
Costs are somewhat universal and uniform within a particular type of project from project to project. Presently, this is the best unit of measure.
(This measurement tool was further defined in chapter 2.)

In any case, the use of information and quality analysis and application of measurable results are at various stages of development in the A/E&C community. These stages have created certain strengths as well as areas for improvement for the A/E&C community.

Strengths:
- Criteria can be easily established for the proper use of quality data.
- A nonconformance system usually already exists. However, its value (its quality cost) without a price has not been determined.
- Pareto analysis can be used to create a categorical display of results to obtain trend information based on the cost of the nonconformance.
- The concept of CA to preclude problem repetition, as well as root-cause analysis, usually appears to be well understood. In addition, trend analysis appears to be performed on projects for the regulated industries relative to excess spending.
- Software quality is often verified by a third-party verifier and testing agency.

Areas for improvement: Generally speaking, the A/E&C community does not use SPC to support most projects, although this is beginning to change. SPC is becoming more accepted in several A/E&C areas. RAM (a form of SPC) is well established and used by many, but SPC methods such as $\overline{X}$, R, p, and u charts are not yet well accepted.[3]

The management role of engineering in the design of an A/E&C quality system appears somewhat vague at times. Software in QA should become standard procedure. To implement such a program, each suborganization must determine the exact nature in which quality audits are performed, documented, and closed, particularly if it does not have an internal quality practitioner. The A/E&C organization must then investigate the exact nature and integration of its existing nonconformance system, particularly in terms of evaluating nonconformances, verifying and correcting their root causes, and closing them out.

The organization should then investigate the use of SPC. Do personnel understand SPC concepts? Does the organization implement SPC fully?

If a firm is using SPC charts frequently, it must verify that personnel understand the mathematical theory. Improper applications of SPC are common if the mathematical theory is not understood. For example, some SPC techniques are based on a normal distribution—a Gaussian pdf. If one of these SPC techniques is applied to a skewed or nonnormal A/E&C process, unreliable results will be obtained.

Most A/E&C firms rarely use benchmarking. More work in this area would be helpful. One must compare internal quality improvement data to the results of competitors and applicable world-class comparisons.

In conclusion, the A/E&C community needs to improve the use of statistical processes (see chapter 2).

Notes

1. Situation appraisal, problem analysis, decision analysis, and potential problem analysis methods vary in their use. However, a common method is Kepner Tregoe. For more information contact Kepner-Tregoe, Inc., Research Road, P.O. Box 704, Princeton, NJ 08542.

2. Ireson, W. G. *Reliability Handbook.* New York: McGraw-Hill, 1966.

3. Juran, J. M. *Juran's Quality Control Handbook,* 4th ed. New York: McGraw-Hill, 1988.

12 Quality Supporting Strongly Regulated Industries

Steering the Nuclear Industry in Quality

Proud Record of Achievement in Quality

- Regulated Industry Standards in QA
- Development of Nuclear Quality Technology

A/E&C Leadership in the Quality of Regulated Industries

- Government's Role in A/E&C Quality
- QA Program for Hazardous Waste Activities

  —Hazardous Waste Quality Records and Documentation
  —Configuration Management
  —Hazardous Waste CA System
  —Qualifications
  —Introduction to a Hazardous Waste Quality Program
  —Organizing for Quality in the Environmental Project
  —Quality Policy in Environmental Remediation and Restoration
  Work
  —Technical Qualifications of Environmental Personnel
  —Technical Procedures in Environmental Restoration and
  Remediation
  —Work Similar to Environmental Restoration and Remediation
  —Construction Quality Procedures
  —Qualifications

Various regulated industries have been at the forefront of implementing comprehensive QA programs in the A/E&C community since the nuclear industry's beginning more than 40 years ago. This began with the Manhattan Project in Los Alamos, New Mexico.[1] Leadership has continued throughout the years in nuclear quality as summarized here.

The quest for quality has steered the A/E&C community to active participation with such organizations as the International Atomic Energy Agency (IAEA), U.S. Department of Energy (DOE), U.S. Nuclear Regulatory Commission (NRC) formerly called the Atomic Energy Commission (AEC), ASME, and ASQC Energy and Environmental Division. A/E&C quality professionals have worked in direct partnership with regulatory bodies to produce excellent industry-identified standards as ANSI N45.2 Series, ANSI/ASME NQA-1, 2, and 3, and most recently ANSI/ASQC E-4-19XX.[2,3]

A proud work record has been achieved during the last 25 years in terms of implementing quality programs for the design, construction, and operation of nuclear and nonnuclear facilities throughout North America and with the IAEA internationally. Industry standards for nuclear QA have been established. Industries under mandatory quality dictates have led the community in effectively implementing quality programs. This fact has been continuous throughout the nuclear industry's proud work history.

Quality technology has been successfully developed for the nuclear industry. Industries with mandatory quality procedures have developed numerous technological tools that are now commonplace in the nuclear industry. The nuclear industry will continue its leadership in QA into the twenty-first century through constant development of new technologies.

Steering the Nuclear Industry in Quality

Many significant quality-related events have occurred during the last 40 years in the nuclear industry, including

- The transition from the AEC to the NRC and the present role of the DOE in the early 1970s

Figure 12.1. Massive power-plant construction was controlled during the last 20 years with QA programs that predominantly used detection and appraisal tools. In the future, conceptual quality and preventive techniques will be the norm in projects within regulated industries.

- Development of federal regulations such as 10CFR50 Appendix B on QA in the early 1970s
- Development of the ANSI N45.2 series standards (including daughter standards) during the 1970s
- Standardization of QA programs and power plants in the late 1970s
- The major lessons learned from the accidents of Three Mile Island and Chernobyl in the late 1970s and early 1980s
- Development of new, naturally passive, and inherently safe, passive reactors in the 1980s
- Development of ANSI/ASME NQA-1, 2, and 3 in the 1980s
- Application of such techniques as TQM into this industry in the early 1990s

QA in this period has played a vital role in positively directing the deeds and actions of the nuclear power industry. This has occurred both directly and indirectly, and in some cases, has spearheaded further development of quality technology in the nuclear industry. Regulated industries have supported professional organizations (for example, the formation of the Energy Division of ASQC), encouraged adherence to standards (a major role in development of ANSI/ASME NQA-1, 2, and 3), and participated in other significant quality work achievements.

Proud Record of Achievement in Quality

The regulated industries maintain a long and proud record of achievement in quality, particularly in the nuclear industry. Throughout various trials and tribulations, this industry has been engineering and constructing substantial facilities with the utmost regard for quality. An outstanding record has been achieved on numerous projects in terms of quality, safety, and reliability with very few of the pitfalls that related industries experience. The nuclear industry has long recognized that this is a result of having effective internal QA organizations and having management commitment to quality and excellence.

The nuclear industry is continuing to improve and develop personnel, develop quality information and standards, and research and develop new quality technology. For example, *Power Engineering* magazine annually lists related nuclear facilities by the type of project and quality program in use.

Regulated Industry Standards in QA

Regulated industries are the leading contributors of industry and generic quality standards that serve as models for planning and implementing programs for nuclear projects. Many major A/E&C firms participate in the ANSI/ASME NQA code executive and main committees that address industry questions and develop periodic revisions to this important standard. In addition, many such companies assist on such committees as the Waste Producers Quality Assurance Working Group in preparing OGR/B-14 (based on NQA-1), which provides the initial QA elements for waste producers, including such U.S. DOE sites as West Valley, New York, Savannah River, Georgia, and Richland, Washington.

Several A/E&C executives hold leadership positions in nuclear QA. Many have been enlisted to perform numerous independent, third-party reviews and readiness evaluations of necessary controls and of engineering and construction management. Several projects have used these reviews, evaluations, and controls successfully. Significant quality improvements have resulted from the expertise of many A/E&C firms.

Development of Nuclear Quality Technology

Numerous quality concepts in the nuclear industry began with and were fostered by A/E&C firms. The following is a list of some of these concepts.

- Full scope procurement QA (intensive surveillance)
- In-depth and highly qualified field QC independent of construction
- Fully developed design assurance to effect significant quality impact at early stages in the project
- Use of technical personnel on QA audits
- Preconstruction QA planning and meetings
- In-depth and comprehensive inspection planning
- The use of the concept of quality accountability

Recent evidence makes clear that A/E&C firms will continue to grow along this path and maintain their leadership role into the next century.

A/E&C Leadership in the Quality of Regulated Industries

With the advent of new and innovative approaches to quality, many A/E&C firms today are reassessing their quality systems. These new approaches include

- The application and use of modern quality management methods, especially TQM, to improve all three elements of the eternal triangle of quality, cost, and schedule
- The further enhancement of safety and productivity with the goals of reducing costs and improving profits
- The quantitative measurement of QA/QC program benefits
- The application and use of emerging technology to enhance quality programs, including expert systems and AI

Many A/E&C professionals have led and will continue to lead the regulated industry into an era of significant quality enhancement. They will assist government and other customers in the management of problems such as environmental remediation and restoration of hazardous waste sites.

Government's Role in A/E&C Quality

What is government's role in A/E&C quality? Attempts have been made to address this question over the years with very mixed results. There have been numerous symposia with congressional representatives in attendance. Group discussions have occurred on federal, state, and local levels. At the center of these discussions is usually the need for governmental regulations and the need to research and develop such regulations.

One of the most pressing problems facing the A/E&C business pertains to site remediation and reclamation activities for hazardous waste. This waste can contain both high-level and low-level radioactive materials. These remediation and reclamation projects are highly regulated by legislation from various government entities. Because of the importance and complexity of this issue, this chapter examines it in detail.

QA Program for Hazardous Waste Activities

Hazardous Waste Quality Records and Documentation

Quality procedures should be used to control work and assure safety. Appropriate forms should be used to consistently document results of

Figure 12.2. The building of nuclear power plants were highly regulated A/E&C projects particularly in regard to their reactor cores. The new, massive environmental remediation projects for the removal of radioactive wastes will also be highly regulated.

assessments, audits, inspections, surveillance, reviews, and evaluations. Such "safety-related" quality records should be available for review by the governing agency prior to final sign-off and acceptance.[4] All A/E&C safety-related quality records should be reviewed to verify completeness and legibility. As a minimum, such records should identify the nature and number of observations, the acceptability of the activity, and quality system criteria.

Configuration Management

A QA program for hazardous waste activities should be established to assure compliance while providing an effective and economical tool for overall configuration management.[5] The QA program should use procedures for control of conceptual data collection and verification, design, fabrication, and remediation and treatment processes. These procedures should comply with all Environmental Protection Agency (EPA) and DOE requirements (or their international equivalent).

All technical and nontechnical portions of a hazardous waste QA program should be planned and executed to provide sufficient control such that data on the site and certain interface activities can be used to validate compliance with specified requirements. The program should be applicable throughout all areas of performance, including planning and design, development, fabrication, processing, shipping, site receipt, site installation and remediation, and turnover to the government.

The QA program for hazardous waste activities should contain the necessary controls to effectively implement tasks without quality concerns recurring. One means of accomplishing this is through solutions identified by a formal CA system.

Hazardous Waste CA System

Deviations and deficiencies to project "safety-related" quality requirements should be reported on a CA report consistent with the regulated industry's guidance. However, certain deviations and deficiencies, because of the amount of damage, repair evaluation, and effort required, or repetitiveness, may be documented on a CA request (CAR) form. A CAR procedure should be developed to identify specific requirements for generating CARs.

The hazardous waste CA system may use a design construction, or environmental review board consisting of representatives from engineering, construction, environmental engineering, and quality, which meets periodically to review the need for CARs for potential adverse trends in "safety-related" situations. Periodic reviews assure timely identification of adverse trends. Upon identification of an adverse trend, the chairperson of the construction or environmental review board will report the trend to management for action to prevent continuation of the trend.

Qualifications

Personnel performing activities on hazardous waste projects directly and subcontractor personnel performing hazardous waste work activities (for example, soils and foundations, concrete preparation, placement and testing, reinforcing systems, and prestressing systems) should be qualified or certified in accordance with the requirements of the applicable codes, specifications, and governmental standards and regulations (see chapter 5).

The qualification of process procedures pertaining to welding, data verification, and the like on hazardous waste remediation projects should be developed and used strictly in accordance with contractual requirements.[6] Such written procedures should provide clear direction to the remedial site operating-unit managers performing the production work. They should contain and describe, as required, all of the essential and nonessential variables for each environmental process used. This includes qualification of hazardous waste treatment procedures that provide instructions for performing treatment of material in accordance with the applicable standards or EPA and DOE requirements (or their international equivalents).

Introduction to a Hazardous Waste Quality Program

The fundamental objective of many A/E&C hazardous waste quality programs is for an effective system for the economical integration of those actions necessary to provide adequate control of the project so that it will perform as intended during the site investigation, data validation, design of the engineered environmental systems, site remediation, and turnover to the customer. Project quality is dependent on both a clearly defined action plan and effective communication of the plan throughout the project, from concept to completion. The extent to which any element of the project is assured is dependent on the level of essentiality of the specific element to environmental, health, and safety considerations as a whole and to the contract considerations applied to the safety-related element.[7]

The following general elements of many A/E&C hazardous waste quality plans should be considered in issuing a plan at the start of a project.

- Detailing all aspects of the quality plan
- Defining the organizational elements and interrelationships

- Establishing appropriate indoctrination, training, and qualification requirements for persons whose activities affect the quality of the environmentally engineered project
- Establishing a design-change control system that provides a mechanism for checking, verifying, and validating the adequacy of design and predesign work activities prior to release for site activities or procurement
- Establishing a document control system to provide assurance that the latest approved documents, environmentally engineered scope of work, environmental data sheets, drawings, and specifications are available prior to the start of the work
- Establishing a system to provide control that applicable quality requirements are included in documents for the procurement of materials, equipment, and services
- Establishing a system to provide safety-related control such that purchased material or services conform to specified "safety-related" procurement requirements
- Establishing a system to provide control for special environmental site processes such as the characterization of radioactive, hazardous, and mixed wastes and discharges; the assessment of treatment and remediation, environmental and ecological conditions and behavior; the collection and analysis of data; and the mathematical models of the environmental process. These processes should be controlled by qualified personnel using procedures established by governing regulatory bodies for the health and safety of the public
- Establishing a site inspection and testing program to provide adequate control such that the project design is correctly translated to and through the constructor to the remedial or treatment activities; such inspections and tests should be performed by qualified individuals other than those who performed the activity being inspected and validated
- Establishing that measures to control tools, gages, instruments, and other measuring and test devices are properly controlled, calibrated, and adjusted at specified periods to maintain accuracy to national standards within prescribed limits; traditional environmental monitoring (that is, field sampling, laboratory analyses, and data evaluation) requires specific traceability calibration requirements along with chain-of-custody requirements of all samples taken

• Establishing measures to control materials, parts, or components that do not conform to specified environmental requirements thereby preventing their inadvertent use or installation at facilities used for pollution control, waste treatment, and waste remediation

• Establishing measures to control conditions adverse to the health and safety of the public such that they are promptly identified and corrected; in addition, such adverse conditions must be documented, actions should be taken to preclude their recurrence, and all related documentation should be forwarded to the regulating body

• Establishing a system to maintain records that provide evidence of the satisfactory completion of work, characterization of environmental processes and conditions, and design, construction, and operation of engineered environmental systems

Organizing for Quality in the Environmental Project

In organizing for quality, one should describe the organizational structure for site investigation, remediation, and treatment, along with engineered environmental systems, and establish the authority and responsibility for personnel performing activities affecting quality at the site.

An environmental quality organization chart should be provided that shows direct responsibility for implementing the quality program. This chart should specify a project organization with the responsibility for site implementation of such a program.

The president and CEO of the A/E&C organization doing environmental restoration must assume the authority and responsibility for executive oversight of the quality program implementation. This person should be assisted by a manager of quality who will report directly to the CEO and be responsible for meeting the requirements of the program. The manager of quality will appoint, for each operating environmental project, a quality manager or project quality supervisor who will be independent of the project organization but procedurally responsible for and contractually capable of assuring implementation of the program.

Each project manager dealing in environmental site remediation and restoration must be responsible for carrying out the health and safety quality requirements of the project and for appointing and directing the personnel required to achieve this function. The manager of the quality function should have the responsibility to establish, direct, and assure implementation of the quality program. This individual should have the authority and responsibility to

- Establish written policies, procedures, and instructions necessary to carry out the requirements of the quality program
- Verify that this QA program complies with all applicable laws, regulations, and EPA or DOE guidance (or their international equivalent)
- Review the latest laws, regulations, and EPA or DOE guidance (or their international equivalent) and keep the quality program in compliance with them
- Appoint subordinate quality personnel, including QC technicians; this includes individuals who perform environmental quality audits and conduct surveillance of the quality program
- Confirm that quality practitioners are qualified for their assigned responsibilities, and establish indoctrination and training necessary to develop and maintain the required qualifications
- Delegate authority within the quality organization to carry out responsibilities, including specific authority to recommend the stopping of unsatisfactory work, or to limit or control further processing of unsatisfactory material
- Review and approve procedures prepared by the project quality manager or supervisors
- Review the status and adequacy of the quality program as necessary, and apprise top management of the adequacy of the program
- Resolve any quality concern that cannot be resolved at lower levels; refer unresolved cases to executive management
- Maintain proper communication with the EPA or DOE representatives (or their international equivalent)
- Control distribution of the site environmental and restoration program QA manual in accordance with standards noted in chapter 5

Project quality personnel should report directly to the manager of the quality function. They should have the responsibility for carrying out the QA program at both the site and the design office. They should work independently of project site personnel, but coordinate with them on matters affecting quality. Further, they should have the authority and responsibility to

- Direct the training and indoctrination of project quality personnel
- Develop and initially approve site quality procedures
- Verify that procurement quality requirements are met
- Notify parties of upcoming customer hold or witness points, when necessary
- Direct project quality audit activities
- Establish and maintain proper communication with the site EPA or DOE representatives (or their international equivalent)
- Review and verify quality compliance on selected site investigative data sheets, specifications, and drawings
- Identify quality problems in order to correct them and preclude their repetition
- Initiate actions and notify the manager of quality of the solutions to identified quality problems
- Verify implementation of solutions to quality problems
- Control processing, delivery, or installation and remediation to assure that nonconforming items are not installed until the nonconformances have received proper disposition
- Initiate a recommendation to stop work when required to prevent unsatisfactory work, or to limit or control further processing of unsatisfactory material
- Review and certify appropriate data reports
- Review the status and adequacy of the site quality program, as necessary, and apprise management of the adequacy of the program

Under the direction of the project quality manager or supervisor, site QA/QC personnel (such as engineers, auditors, inspectors, technicians, and clerks) may prepare checklists, inspection plans, calibration instructions, and nonconformance reports; perform supplier surveys, source inspections, site inspections, and project audits; evaluate and approve quality reports and documents; and supervise inspection personnel. The disciplines of quality personnel may vary with each project in accordance with procedures or instructions developed for the project.

Quality Policy in Environmental Remediation and Restoration Work
A/E&C firms must have an absolute commitment to quality as it pertains to the health and safety of the public. These firms should believe firmly in

their responsibility to provide a quality project. They should also realize the potential added value in terms of quality in other areas that can have positive effects on the profitability. Finally, these firms should also know that implementing quality is cost effective on each project, particularly when the focus is on satisfying customers.

Quality is controlled at many A/E&C organizations by the establishment of a project quality organization and through implementation of a project quality plan. The plan is developed from applicable provisions of many A/E&C quality standards and tailored to meet the specific requirements of that project and to comply with contract requirements. In the case of environmental remediation and restoration, the quality plan should be tailored to meet the requirements of the U.S. Federal Acquisition Regulation (FAR) clauses and special clauses, and other requirements pertaining to environmental restoration and remediation (see chapter 5).

The plan should establish guidelines, policies, and procedures for all phases of quality to assure that all items of work conform to the contract documents with respect to material, workmanship, construction, restoration, functional performance, and identification. Primary emphasis is on inspection, supplier and subcontractor surveillance (both in the plant and at the job site), and review of contract documents and supporting documentation. A comprehensive and complete quality program should be provided upon contract award in accordance with the request for proposal (RFP) and should be in compliance with the federal contract documents.

Technical Qualifications of Environmental Personnel

Many A/E&C organizations with QA/QC departments use long-established and diverse quality systems, such as contractor quality control (CQC) programs.[8] Based on the background and experience of those using these government-mandated programs, a project organization of highly experienced and technically qualified quality personnel is needed to meet program demands. Care should be taken to assure they have the necessary environmental background to respond to all quality requirements, especially site investigative activities.

Technical Procedures in Environmental Restoration and Remediation

The use of such tools as daily quality reports during site work is a conventional practice in CQC systems. Many A/E&C organizations use standardized procedures, including CQC program submittals. These procedures are based on a complete program of preparatory, initial, and follow-up inspections, along with an accurate program of construction and preoperational testing.

Work Similar to Environmental Restoration and Remediation

A/E&C organizations with an existing corporate QA/QC department usually are able to make a smooth transition to the environmental industry. A/E&C firms that exercise QC on a job-by-job basis, according to only the minimum specified QC requirements, may have a difficult time in responding to the needs of this strongly regulated environment.

In the 1980s, much of the A/E&C community actively carried out quality functions for government agencies, including the U.S. Army Corps of Engineers, the Navy, Department of State, and Air Force, and major international governmental bodies. The challenge in the future will be to implement a quality program that blends all the elements of a good system described in this text.

Many A/E&C quality programs for projects such as weapons installation, decontamination, and new nuclear production reactors should establish clear compliance with applicable regulations while providing an effective and economical tool for overall configuration management. This program should include procedures for control of fabrication and erection processes. They should be reviewed and approved by the appropriate government representative before implementation.

Each quality organization should be headed by a manager responsible for the project site and home office quality system implemented through the many A/E&C CQC program plans summarized in this chapter. This quality manager should have the responsibility and authority to control quality. He or she should take the steps necessary to assure that each item at the site and its installation meets requirements. He or she should report directly to a senior executive and coordinate with the project manager to resolve quality problems.

The quality manager should be assisted by a staff of qualified personnel to implement the quality program plan. The actual size of the staff will vary to reflect the needs of the project, but the number and type of personnel must be satisfactory to implement the plan. The quality manager may also be assisted by personnel to oversee suppliers and by personnel who review, file, and retrieve quality-related records.

Construction Quality Procedures

Quality procedures in clear, concise form should be developed to identify and control inspection, surveillance, monitoring, and testing activities, as identified in a quality program matrix. Quality procedures specify the attributes to be evaluated to determine acceptability of an activity or item and the frequency of evaluation. These procedures should also contain acceptance and rejection parameters and the following information:

Quality Organization. Identifies the organizational duties, responsibilities, authorities, and functions. The engineer managing quality possesses sole responsibility to ensure compliance with contract plans and specifications, and reports directly to executive management. Other roles are defined and may include A/E&C discipline personnel, surveyors, laboratory technicians, and construction personnel.

Shop Drawing and Other Document Submittal. Identifies methods used for submitting documents to the government representative and lists review and approval responsibilities. This follows a contractor submittal register. These submittals include material tests, samples, equipment lists, laboratory results, source approvals, performance tests, in situ tests, source surveillances, mix formulas, certificates, guarantees and warranties, laboratory approvals, prequalified procedures, material data, experience data, calculations, drawings, welder qualifications, location and installation details, site measurements, inspection records, and test plans and procedures.

Control of Material Quality. Provides instructions and checklists that meet the intent of government standards to qualify potential suppliers and subcontractors in accordance with requirements of the quality program matrix. In addition, the control of site material, structures, and components is clearly defined. This includes the disposal of unsatisfactory materials, proper storage, and handling.

Supplier Surveillance. Provides instructions and checklists that meet the intent of government standards in monitoring site fabrication, testing, and service activities by suppliers and subcontractors in accordance with the quality program matrix to ensure that suppliers conform to the requirements of the purchase order or contract.

Calibration of M&TE. Identifies the inspection and construction equipment requiring calibration. Explains the calibration control log used to track calibration status of M&TE. Several areas of the work require a calibration control system. These include various site work, testing, erection, welding requirements, acceptance tests, and equipment (such as generators, analyzers, and meters) used to test systems.

Site Quality Inspections. Identifies the fabrication, erection, storage, handling, and installation activities requiring inspection. Provides inspection attributes and frequency. Provides acceptance and rejection parameters as appropriate to the activity. Such procedures include associated structures, systems, and components. The breakdown of these procedures may be as follows:

- Quality of plant operations
- Environmental data validation and verification
- Earthwork and other site work
- CMU and CIP construction
- Structural and miscellaneous metal construction
- Finishwork and other activities
- Special construction
- Conveying systems
- Mechanical installations
- Electrical installations

These procedures may vary depending on the nature of the project. However, the flow of a project normally follows the basic pattern of the AIA or CSI specifications and requirements.

I&T Methods. Identifies activities and items requiring I&T and methods to be used. Requires instructions for performing tests, with acceptance and rejection parameters and forms used. Provides the test results required by the government for submittal and evaluation. I&T data sheets are added to this procedure as developed and approved.

Deviation and Deficiency Reporting and Disposition. Provides instructions for documenting deviations and deficiencies on the daily report by quality personnel, and subsequent evaluation and disposition by engineering on the daily report. Problem action requests (PARs) or CARs can be identified on daily reports when PARs are generated. Approved changes in design, as recommended on deviation and deficiency CA reports, are identified on as-built drawings or specifications incorporated into the final design submission.

CA System. Identifies requirements for reporting deviations and deficiencies to the appropriate level of management for evaluation and CA.

Quality Documentation and Status Reporting. Provides instruction for receipt, review, filing, and storage of quality records. Provides direction for periodic reporting of punch-list items for follow up and close out.

Qualifications

Personnel performing such tasks as the installation of A/E&C work elements for many prime contractors and subcontractors (for example, soils and foundations, concrete preparation and placement, curing and testing activities, reinforcing systems, prestressing systems, and protective coatings) should be certified in accordance with the requirements of applicable codes, specifications, and standards.

Qualification of Procedures

Many A/E&C firms will develop and prepare procedures (such as those for welding) to be used to meet contractual requirements. Written procedures provide direction to the welder for making production welds. The procedures should contain and describe, as required, all the essential and nonessential variables for each process.

Qualification of Heat Treatment Procedures

A/E&C procedures will be prepared to provide instructions for performing heat treatment of welds in accordance with applicable standards or welding procedure requirements.

Qualification of NDE Procedures

When required by the code, standard, or specifications, the NDE will be performed to a qualified procedure. A/E&C procedures will need to be written and approved by personnel certified to appropriate levels and methods. These levels and methods should, in turn, be described in a quality program and should contain

- The governing documents
- Personnel qualification and responsibilities
- Safety considerations to be taken during the examination

- Equipment requirements
- Time of examination
- Item surface condition
- Actual techniques to be used
- Postexamination requirements, such as cleaning
- Evaluation and acceptance criteria

NDE procedures should be qualified by demonstrating the capability to consistently detect defects of the types and sizes specified in the acceptance criteria.

As repeatedly stated in this text, R&D within the A/E&C community will significantly improve the quality of this industry. This statement applies equally to the segment of this community working in regulated industries. Appendix D provides an example of R&D in-service inspection related to nuclear power plants. Readers should review this example carefully to acquire a better understanding of the importance of R&D to the development of new quality technology.

Notes

1. This was the atomic project associated with ending World War II.

2. ANSI/ASME NQA-3 is an American national standard entitled, Quality Assurance Program Requirements for Nuclear Facilities, 1989 Edition, excluding addenda.

3. This standard (ANSI/ASQC E-4-1994) is currently under final draft review with ANSI.

4. The term *safety-related* is used in the CFR and is defined somewhat differently depending on the specific regulation or guidance document. Generally speaking, *safety related* refers to a potential safety problem of the structure, system, component, or service that, if left uncorrected, would adversely affect the safety and health of the public.

5. For details refer to the U.S. Department of Defense Military Standard on Configuration Management MIL-HDBK-472, U.S. Naval Supply Depot, Philadelphia, Pennsylvania.

6. The term *qualification* refers to a specific method to assure the precision and accuracy of a procedure. It may include a specific physical test prior to use.

7. The term *essentiality* in this industry is synonymous with the term *significant few* discussed in chapter 3 and elsewhere.

8. CQC programs are defined by the U.S. Army Corps of Engineers in their CQC and Design QA standards described in ER 1180 (Form 696).

13   Supporting the Petroleum and Petrochemical Industry

Project Quality Plan

Quality System Requirements

Contract Review

Design Control

Document Control

Procured Items and Services

Product Identification and Traceability

Process Control

Specialty Process Control

Inspection and Testing

Inspection, Measuring, and Testing Equipment

I&T Status

Nonconformance

Corrective Action

Handling, Storage, Packaging, and Delivery

Quality Records

Quality Audits

Training

Statistical Techniques

For A/E&C professionals, *petroleum and petrochemical industry* refers to the building, operating, and maintaining of petroleum and petrochemical refineries and various ancillary facilities. These facilities contain miles of piping and a host of mechanical equipment that usually are not restricted inside a building, although buildings are sometimes built to contain the piping and equipment. They usually are required to conform to American Petroleum Institute (API) standards (or equivalent international standards). Because of the need for continual improvements, they are often upgraded during outages.

In recent years, this industry has been requiring compliance with ISO 9000 series standards for A/E&C activities. This is partially due to the large amount of international work being performed. Therefore, the use of the quality system described in chapters 6–11 is particularly important relative to this industry. The following discussion describes the application of that quality system for A/E&C activities in the petroleum and petrochemical industry.

Project Quality Plan

A quality plan for the petroleum and petrochemical industry should identify methods and instructions that will be employed by an organization's personnel in the conduct of activities as they relate to designing, procuring, and building a petroleum or petrochemical facility. The QA of project activities by a QA/QC organization should be made in accordance with the intent of ISO 9001, Quality Systems—Model for Quality Assurance in Design/Development, Production, Installation, and Servicing.

Quality System Requirements

Project management should develop a quality policy for the project. A quality manager should facilitate the use of the objectives of the project quality policy and ensure that the policy is understood. Project management should be performed according to a project manual. A quality program should identify those projects that require quality plans, which are as important as other project plans.

A TQM steering committee led by the overall quality manager, the person responsible for supplier inspection during construction, the project quality manager (QM), the TQM facilitator, and the engineering manager should

Figure 13.1. Petroleum and petrochemical industry projects are generally international in scope; this virtually requires A/E&C suppliers to meet ISO 9000 series requirements.

periodically meet to ensure that the quality system conforms to standards, guidelines, rules, and laws and is being used effectively. Summaries of these meetings and activities should be communicated to the entire project team.

The quality manager should set an audit schedule (based on the project control schedule) that identifies what work-breakdown elements need to be checked and who will be responsible for that element. The audit results should be kept in a file during the project. A summary of findings should be reported to project management. CA should be implemented and completed in a timely manner.

Contract Review
The project manager should review customer requests and respond with a proposal to fix any problems encountered. Contract management

practices should be spelled out in the procedures of the quality system. In addition, the requirements of contract preparation, their revisions, and performance should be explained by procedure. Contract reviews should be documented and controlled by the project manager and kept in the project files.

Design Control

Design and management organizations should define and control procedures related to the design of the petroleum or petrochemical facility to assure that requirements are met.

The project manager should request the qualifications, such as certifications, of lead process engineers. Each engineering activity should be planned and implemented to the following work-breakdown elements: architectural, civil, structural, general mechanical, piping, mechanical material handling, heat transfer, rotating equipment, mechanical vessels, water treatment, process equipment, control systems, and electrical.

An engineer for each element should assign the daily design functions to qualified technical personnel. Technical personnel will need access to all standards, specifications, and criteria necessary to complete the design activities in accordance with requirements. Software used for design should be controlled by the lead engineer in accordance with information systems procedures to validate and verify their use.

Interaction on design between disciplines should be controlled by interface procedures. The function of these procedures is to identify the work activities that require design and the people responsible. A petroleum and petrochemical design office should be located to collect the design input based both on customer needs and standard A/E&C practices.

Design outputs should be consistent specifications or drawings. Design output checking should be the responsibility of the lead engineer and should include calculation checking, layout-drawings verification, detail-drawings comparisons, and specification reviews. Checked designs should be reviewed by the project engineer (PE) for compliance with all customer needs before issuance to a supplier for quotation purposes. Design changes should be monitored by the same engineer responsible for the original design. Any design changes should be reviewed at the completion of the project and included in the final project records.

Document Control

Petroleum and petrochemical project personnel should develop procedures to identify project documents that specify information or give instructions. Project documents include drawings, data sheets, specifications, purchase orders, requests for quotation (RFQ) meeting notes, bulletins, faxes, or memos issued under the contract that contain information or instructions. Project documents should be sampled for conformance to customer and project quality needs.

Project management documents, defined as meeting notes, faxes from suppliers or subcontractors, or memos, should be controlled at a central point. Traceable identification should be denoted on correspondence and listed within an index. Engineering documents should be controlled to procedure. Procedure administration is the responsibility of the document control manager. Engineering documents are defined as specifications, data sheets, A/E&C organization and supplier drawings, bulletins, and interface procedures.

Procurement documents, such as RFQ or purchase orders (POs) should be controlled according to the A/E&C organization's procurement practices. Procurement document control may be the responsibility of the procurement manager. Subcontract documents should be controlled according to the A/E&C organization's construction practices. Subcontract document control should be the responsibility of a subcontracts manager.

Construction documents should be controlled according to construction practices. Control of these documents should be the responsibility of the CM.

Procured Items and Services

An A/E&C organization should develop and control procedures to assure that procured structures, systems, and components meet contract requirements. The procurement manager, in conjunction with the project-controls person, should develop a schedule for all materials, services, and equipment to be used. Petroleum or petrochemical facility procurement activities should be executed according to the A/E&C organization's procurement practices. Contract services should develop an award schedule in conjunction with the procurement or project-controls manager. Contract awards should be conducted according to A/E&C contract management practices.

Procurement documents should describe the material, service, or equipment ordered, and should specify the grade, type, class, style, or other identification to ensure the item or service is purchased or procured. This identification can include the codes, standards, specifications, and drawings needed to meet defined criteria. They should also define the inspection level, acceptance criteria, requirements for approval or qualification of the facility, procedures, process equipment, and personnel. The quality practitioner should assure clarity of procurement documents. He or she should also assure that documents are included or referenced in the procurement documents prior to release to the supplier or subcontractor.

The quality practitioner's review records should be controlled for the duration of the project. Procurement documents should include an approval record containing, as a minimum, the approval record of the lead engineer, the quality practitioner, the procurement manager, and the responsible PE.

The quality practitioner, in conjunction with the person responsible for supplier inspection, should assure that suppliers considered for awards have systems and procedures in place to ensure the delivery of materials, services, or equipment meeting the specified quality requirements. Methods for ensuring supplier quality systems should be included in a shop inspection or expediting execution plan. The A/E&C organization should have the right to assure at the source or upon receipt that material, service, or equipment conforms to requirements. Component inspection by the purchaser should not absolve the supplier of the responsibility for manufacturing an acceptable product.

Procured structures, systems, components, and material should be accepted at the site if they are free from damage, and they should be stored in that condition until installation. The CM should be responsible for maintenance and storage until turnover to the customer. Storage and material procedures should be included in construction practices that conform to the quality plan.

Product Identification and Traceability

The A/E&C organization should establish an identification of structure, system, and component drawings or specifications. Construction materials used in the fabrication of equipment should be traceable and have some sort of identification (which should be recorded). Numbers associated with structures, systems, and components should include that of the contract, current standards and practices, and a tag number. This identification should remain constant throughout design, manufacture, and installation. If the work is in an existing facility, the tag numbers should correspond to the equipment in the facility.

Construction materials for critical structures, systems, and components should be examined by suitable methods to ensure alloy chemistry immediately prior to manufacture. Batch consumable sampling should be acceptable.

In conjunction with the quality practitioner, the person responsible for inspection should assure that supplier quality systems control identification be used in the manufacture, inspection, and testing of equipment. Material-certification documents should follow the established numbering system. The construction practices should document how the requirements should be controlled and checked. Documentation should require that installation contractors or subcontractors be aware of the critical equipment manufacturing requirements and their records related to process control specifications. The names of personnel responsible for installation should also be recorded.

Process Control

The management organization must assure that planning, cost control, engineering, contract management, documentation, and safety comply with customer needs. The project team should execute the work through interaction of the disciplines to procedures outlined in an execution plan.

A schedule should be used to monitor progress versus costs to determine overall efficiency compared to budget. Invoicing procedures should follow accounts payable practices. Subcontracts issued for construction activities should be administered according to the A/E&C organization's contract-management practices. Purchase orders issued for structures, systems, and components are controlled by the procurement practices. Personnel issues such as insurance, work hours, accommodations, and travel should be handled according to established procedures. Communication and data procedures should be administered by a coordinator as provided in an execution plan. Confidential information should be administered in a controlled manner. An organizational chart and directory should identify who has authority for procedural, technical, financial, and final acceptance of the facility.

Specialty Process Control

The A/E&C organization needs to assure that manufacturer's instructions are followed for installation. The design output must be controlled by engineering practices, specifications, drawings, purchase orders, and construction practices. Process piping, for example, should follow piping design guidelines. Specifications for identification should provide for a clear format and numbering. A quality-requirements provision should be detailed in the inspection practices. The person responsible for supplier inspection must see to it that these provisions are included in RFQ documents and POs.

A construction quality manual should be used to implement the customer quality requirements for erection. The manual should define the program, organization, surveillance activities, and documentation requirements for construction. All subcontractor activities should conform to a quality plan.

Inspection and Testing

The A/E&C supplier inspection program should ensure that the quality of the structures, systems, and components exceeds customer needs. The person responsible for supplier inspection procedures (based on shop inspection practices) should monitor materials and equipment, including receiving, in-process, and final inspection.

Hold or witness points should be defined with the supplier prior to awarding the supplier with a contract. This includes third-party inspections. Inspection practices should be presented to suppliers for coordination. Supplier records are acceptable if the information in the records is reviewed by responsible parties. The quality practitioner should approve supplier test and inspection plans before manufacturing begins.

Inspection, Measuring, and Testing Equipment

The A/E&C organization should verify that supplier and subcontractor structures, systems, and components are sufficiently precise and accurate to meet or exceed customer quality requirements. The person responsible for supplier inspection personnel should use a supplier inspection network of personnel (readily available by numerous inspection companies) to execute supplier quality program evaluation. He or she should approve bidders who have shop inspection practices. The person responsible for supplier surveys should verify control, calibration, and maintenance of the supplier's inspection equipment and that this equipment is identified to records.

I&T Status

The A/E&C organization should define structure, system, and component certification based on a criticality rating defined in the quality plan. The person responsible for supplier inspection should verify the component documentation, inspection, and testing necessary for certification. A construction quality plan should identify the requirements for site I&T certification. Subcontractor certification should conform to the construction quality plan.

Nonconformance

The A/E&C project team should ensure that inspection procedures are in place and should function to assure that the delivered facility or associated activity meets API or equivalent requirements. Quality procedures should be contained in an execution plan. All design outputs (that is, drawings, specifications, purchase orders, and schedules) should be verified to ensure that they meet or exceed customer needs. Nonconformances should be reviewed by lead personnel and CA implemented within an agreed-upon time frame.

In addition, those nonconformances that would adversely affect project progress should be reviewed and resolved before certain work resumes. The person responsible for supplier inspection procedures should verify that supplier-furnished equipment is identified, documented, and conforms to requirements. Identified nonconformances should be documented on nonconformance reports according to inspection practices. Releases of these items should occur prior to final acceptance of the structures, systems, or components by the person responsible for supplier inspection. Construction procedures for controlling nonconforming construction items should be described in construction quality practices. The CM should implement these procedures. Subcontractor procedures for nonconformances should comply with the approved construction quality manual. Subcontractor forms may be acceptable for nonconformance documentation provided minimum required data are maintained.

Corrective Action

The A/E&C organization should control CAs, including determining the cause of nonconformances and preventing its recurrence. CA procedures should be defined in a quality plan. These procedures should be implemented by the quality practitioner. CA procedures should define the cause of nonconformances so as to prevent recurrence and to ensure that actions taken are effective and appropriate. Procedural changes resulting from CA should be identified in a CA report. The quality practitioner should control CA and should assign identification to each report. The quality practitioner must verify through the person responsible for supplier inspection that suppliers' criticality ratings should be taken into account when assessing quality system records. These records must conform to the approved quality plan.

Handling, Storage, Packaging, and Delivery

The A/E&C team should assure that the processes of handling, storage, packaging, and delivery are described in project execution practices. A project plan should detail the material handling, storage, and delivery of equipment used on the project. Packaging should be controlled by specification. The delivery records are the responsibility of the procurement manager. Handling procedures should detail the methods and means to prevent damage or deterioration to structures, systems, components, or material. The project plan should list the storage locations for items prior to erection at the site. The plan also should include provisions for maintenance (such as the rotating of electrical equipment) and climate control of the storage facility.

Upon final I&T, delivery requirements should control the condition of procured items through delivery at the site. The construction portion of the quality plan should specify conditions for accepting items at the site and for assuring that damage or deterioration has not occurred in handling, storage, packaging, or delivery prior to accepting the item.

Quality Records

The A/E&C organization should assure the identification, collection, indexing, filing, storage, maintenance, and disposition of records. A record can be a specification, drawing, computer datum, procedure, schedule, purchase order, contract, or subcontract needed to complete the facility. Records should be identified by a contract number or other method. Supplier documentation should be identified systematically. Records should be clearly marked to identify commodity, petroleum and petrochemical facility item, or service. Records should be centrally stored and easily retrievable in a way that precludes damage and loss. Issuance of documents should be controlled through interface practices.

Quality Audits

The A/E&C organization should appraise and assure activities associated with project work-breakdown elements through the use of quality audits. These audits should address the facilities, processes, and systems needed to complete the work. The quality practitioner should perform quality audits according to established procedure; an audit schedule should be provided. The customer may participate in some audits to ensure that the quality practitioner's conduct meets customer needs.

The quality practitioner should designate the person responsible for supplier quality surveys. The quality practitioner should review the survey with this person and concur that the survey verifies that the quality system being used will conform to customer needs. This person and the customer should both be on the survey team for critical items if an acceptable survey is not available. Otherwise, audits should be conducted according to quality audit practices coordinated with customer needs. The quality practitioner should designate someone to be responsible for field construction activities and construction subcontractor audits. This person should ensure that these activities are performed according to established procedures. Audit activities conducted during construction should follow procedures in the construction quality plan. This plan should also meet customer needs.

The audit results should be reported to the customer frequently. The project team should correct nonconformances to customer needs in a timely manner. Audits should be performed to assure that CA has been completed satisfactorily.

Training

The A/E&C organization should train project personnel who are performing activities that affect the final facility's quality. This training should include indoctrination. Personnel should know the responsibilities, policies, and goals of the quality plan, and the quality plan should incorporate training practices.

Training plans should anticipate the training requirements when changes are introduced. Training plans should exist to instruct personnel in safety. Training records should be controlled by instructors. Personnel should have the proper education, training, and experience to undertake the assigned tasks. Certification may be required on some activities. The quality plan should spell these out.

Statistical Techniques

The A/E&C organization should apply statistical analysis techniques in determining the effectiveness of quality, safety, cost, and scheduling programs. Contract milestones should be defined. Findings generated by audits using trend analysis should determine the effectiveness of the quality program.

Other quality statistical methods to identify out-of-control occurrences include reliability, availability, and maintainability (RAM) analysis; other quality trend analysis; management situation analysis; and various information quality analysis described in chapter 11.

Safety procedures shown in execution practices should use statistical techniques, such as accidents per labor hour contrasted against industry norms, to determine the effectiveness of a safety program. Project-controls (cost and scheduling) sampling procedures should be used to compare actual and estimated costs.

14   Supporting Other Industrial and Process Businesses

Controlling Suppliers and Subcontractors

- Responsibility
- Material Requisitions
- Purchase Orders
- Supplier and Manufacturer Surveillance
- Receiving

Acceptance of Material That Conforms to Requirements

Receipt of Material That Does Not Conform to Requirements

The process of supporting other industrial and process businesses with an effective quality program varies a great deal depending on the customer, the country in which the facility is being erected, the type of contractual relationship, and the complexity of the project. Although many approaches can be used, depending on these factors, one standard is gaining popularity in the industrial and process industries: the ISO 9000 series, previously noted in our design of an overall program.

Chapters 6–11 of this text describe a suggested quality system with distinct elements. These quality elements blend various customer and industry standards into one system specific to the A/E&C community. Since the overriding standards in this quality system are the ISO 9000 series and the Baldrige Award, the system can be implemented for the industrial and process businesses with little modification.

A quality program to be used by the A/E&C community in support of these businesses should require the establishment of procedures to control submittal of technical documents and material for compliance to Contract AIA Document A111 (or international equivalent) requirements, and applicable construction and technical specifications.[1] In addition, the program should provide for the establishment of procedures to ensure that incoming shipments of equipment and materials have been fabricated and processed in compliance with the governing contract specifications and PO requirements.

One of the most important parts of the quality program for a project in other industrial and process businesses is procurement control. This chapter concentrates on suggested A/E&C mechanisms for controlling suppliers and subcontractors.

Controlling Suppliers and Subcontractors

The quality program for other industrial and process businesses should address the quality of procurement of services, permanent construction materials, and those nonpermanent materials that significantly affect the outcome of the facility. To meet these quality needs, the project manager should work with the engineering, quality, procurement, and accounts payable functions.

Responsibility

The project manager, supported by the quality practitioner, should notify subcontractors performing installation of incoming material shipments, maintain a file of outstanding POs, and document, control, and distribute reports of any item discrepancies. He or she should

- Establish and monitor a file of MRs to review the technical information provided against drawings and specifications. If discrepancies are noted, the project manager ensures that CA is taken.
- Establish a file of POs that aid in monitoring the project and communicating with suppliers or subcontractors to correct discrepancies in specifications.
- Control receiving of all shipments with a focus on quality to ensure compliance with specifications and PO requirements.
- Segregate or tag items identified as nonconforming if a disposition cannot be given immediately. Conforming items should be released to the field at once.
- Document the action taken on the PO and on a receiving report. The supplier should be contacted also if technical aspects of a purchase must be negotiated.
- Ensure the removal from site of material deemed unsuitable for construction purposes or otherwise unsatisfactory. Conduct supplier and manufacturer source surveillance when necessary.

Material Requisitions

The following is a standard job-site procedure for MRs. Actual site methods may vary but should meet requirements.

Upon receipt of MRs generated by the subcontractor, the project manager separates those for permanent construction materials (for example, piping, embedments) or nonpermanent materials (for example, aggregate, sand) needing quality acceptance from those for materials (for example, stagging materials, dunnage) requiring no action. The project manager and the quality practitioner reviews each MR for technical/quality accuracy.

The project manager meets with the subcontractor to correct inaccuracies as soon as they are detected. A summary of actions taken is forwarded with the MR to purchasing. The subcontractor works with the MR originator not to issue a request for proposal (RFP) until required corrections are made. The MR and accompanying documentation are filed for future reference. The MR file should be dynamic in nature. As the purchasing function issues POs for particular MRs, the MRs are then moved to the PO file.

Purchase Orders

POs awarded by the subcontractor's purchasing function are forwarded to the A/E&C organization's home office. Only those POs for permanent materials or nonpermanent materials requiring quality acceptance must be reviewed and evaluated. POs must be evaluated for conformance to the requirements of the MRs issued to date. One of two conditions will exist.

- The PO conforms to the MR.
- The PO does not conform to the MR.

A PO file is initiated and each PO filed by PO number. The corresponding MR file is incorporated into the new PO file, along with the PO and its supporting documentation. The PO file will be maintained until receipt and final acceptance of the materials, at which time it will be closed out but retained.

Supplier and Manufacturer Surveillance

In the case of construction management, the project manager or subcontractor should conduct supplier and manufacturer surveillance as necessary to evaluate their capability to produce and deliver quality material and to comply with PO or other requirements.

Receiving

The supplier should inform the project manager of all incoming shipments identifying them by PO number. Once a shipment has arrived, the project manager or his/her designatee should remove the appropriate PO from the file and proceed to the receiving area to review the material. This preliminary inspection serves to identify the contents of the shipment. Material should be checked for conformance to the standards and specifications set forth in the PO. This check should include, but should not be limited to, visual inspection of the material and review of the supporting documentation, such as

- Certificate of compliance
- Mill certificates
- Heat tags or imprinted heat numbers

Conforming test reports may be used in lieu of mill certificates for material acceptance. Tests should be performed by an approved independent testing laboratory.

Acceptance of Material That Conforms to Requirements

If the material received conforms to the requirements of the PO, including required documentation, the subcontractor, by signatory acceptance on a copy of the PO, will release the material to the field.

Receipt of Material That Does Not Conform to Requirements

If the material received does not conform to the requirements of the PO, the following steps should be taken.

- The project manager should record on the PO copy the reason for nonacceptance of the material. Copies of this nonacceptance PO should be forwarded to the operating officer of the A/E&C organization.
- Immediately upon nonacceptance of the material, the subcontractor should contact the supplier concerning the reason for nonacceptance in order to expedite disposition.
- Copies of the outgoing related correspondence should be forwarded to the A/E&C organization's home office.
- The supplier and the project manager should agree on a resolution to the nonconformance problem.
- The accounts payable department should withhold payment pending disposition acceptable to the project manager.
- Nonacceptable material should be stored in a segregated location pending disposition with signs posted and the material flagged. A yellow flag indicates material being held pending receipt of one or all of the following: applicable PO, certificate of compliance or mill certificate from the supplier, or test report on samples taken. A white flag indicates material approved for temporary construction

only. A red flag indicates rejected material that is removed immediately from the site by the supplier or subcontractor.

Notes

1. For more information about Document A111, contact the American Institute of Architects at 800-365-2724 or 212-683-0023, 200 Lexington Avenue, New York, NY 10016.

15   Supporting the Transportation Industry

Supporting Conventional Railroad Design and Construction Activities

Supporting Other Construction in Transportation

Supporting the Transit Industry Quality System

- Organization Chart
- Position Description: SQE
- Position Description: Quality Engineer
- Project Submittal Procedure
- Testing Procedure
- Inspection Procedure
- Reporting Deficiencies Procedure
- CQC Daily Report Instructions
- Test Report Instructions
- Submittal Register Instructions

Supporting PMO of Transportation Projects

- Preparing a Summary of Major Observations and Recommendations
- Project Review Analyses and Observations
- Review Documents, Conduct Interviews, and Review Planning, Design, Specification, Schedules, and Estimates

Interaction Among the Transit Agency, the CM, and the Designer

Transit Design Criteria

- QA Specifications
- Vehicles
- Track Work and Ballast
- Stations and Guideways

Transit Contract Review, Design Management, Schedule, and Cost Control

- Contract Review
- Design Management Review

Transit Construction Management Review

- Construction Management Contract Review
- Evaluating the Adequacy of the CM's Organization
- Reviewing the CM's Inspection and QC

Responsible Architect or Engineer Review and Monitoring Transit Practices

- Examining the System Contracts and Procurement Standards and Procedures

A/E&C firms support the transportation industry through private customers and regulatory bodies. The regulatory bodies may be at the city, state, or federal level. In any case, related work activities that support this vast industry can be divided into the following business lines or opportunities for quality enhancement.

- Conventional railroad design and construction activities
- Other construction in transportation (for example, bridgework)
- Design and construction for the rapid transit industry
- Project management oversight (PMO) of transportation projects

The intent of this chapter is to define how the transportation industry fits into the quality system description and elements contained in chapters 6–11.

A/E&C firms tend to serve the transportation industry along certain business lines. The work breakdown and scope may be self-performed work, subcontract management, or PMO. In each role, certain elements of the quality system description become more important than others. For example, in the role of PMO, one is an agent or consultant to the owner or transit agency, advising on the present direction of the project. The project is being run by a project manager and numerous subcontractors. There should be elements of quality assessment to appraise the other parts of the overall quality system.

The four types of transportation projects listed previously are described in this chapter. Further, each type highlights the quality system elements most important to it.

Supporting Conventional Railroad Design and Construction Activities

This section describes the activities performed that affect the quality of installing railroad structures, systems, and components, including the supply and erection of such equipment as railroad trackage and signals.

The scope of work should include the activities of the prime contractor, rail subcontractor, and the earthwork subcontractor: submittal requirements, preparation of the subgrade, laying of the rail, and quality of ties, ballast, turnout construction, track circuits, warning devices, signal foundations, power supply and control system, distribution system, and field measurements.

The project manager should be responsible for ensuring that the design conforms to, and the subcontractor erects and supplies the railroad in conformance to, AIA/CSI specification section 02800 and for monitoring quality in accordance with the quality system description. The rail subcontractor should be responsible for directly affecting the quality of railroad work, excluding the preparation of the subgrade. The subcontractor for subgrade activities should be responsible for preparing the subgrade within tolerance, watered, and properly compacted.

The project manager, after notice to proceed (NTP), should transmit to the customer a materials parts list, manufacturer's data, and procedures. Prior to work activities, he or she should examine surface conditions for any problems. Construction of the subgrade should be performed within a set tolerance for design grade in accordance with specification requirements. All rock used for ballast should be sound-crushed or water-worn tested to American Society for Testing Materials (ASTM) C-127, C-136, C-117, and C-131. Foundations for railroad signals should be constructed according to contract drawings and should use standard methods for controlling the quality of concrete construction. All ties should be checked to conform with American Wood Products Association Standard AWPA, Standard P-4, and WCLA Rule 16. The project manager should verify that track installation meets the following requirements.

- Contact surfaces of all joint bars and rail are wire brushed and coated with dielectric black to the manufacturer's specifications.
- No rail is laid until subgrade has been completed, and rail is only cut mechanically in the field.
- Joints have proper gap for ambient temperature and are staggered.
- Any raising of rails does not bend or strain joints, and rails are not dropped.
- Rail bolts and washers are properly fitted and tightened.
- Rail bottom is cleaned prior to being laid and is gauged to specified standards.
- Alignment is to outside rail, maintained throughout a curve, and shimmied appropriately.
- All ties are checked to set centers, except for joints.
- When spiking, proper distance to the edge of ties is assured so the head just touches the rail base: for tangent track, n spikes per tie,

and for curved track, x spikes per tie, unless y degrees curvature is exceeded; then y spikes per tie.
- Two courses are used for ballasting: The first is a basecourse, while the second is tamped within a foot of the inside of the rail and to the end of the ties.
- Tie plates are used on all ties, and tie rods are placed every 6 feet.
- The turnouts correspond to the alignment drawings.

The project manager should verify that railroad signal installation proceeds according to the following guidelines.

- Two sources of independent power to signals, VAC 110 and direct current (DC)—(within the U.S.)—with 12 hours of standby, are present.
- The test of the automatic transfer of power supply from commercial to the DC backup supply is witnessed.
- The arrester ground configuration is in accordance with the Association of American Railroads (AAR) manual.
- Within an electrical enclosure, there is no single conductor wire smaller than No. 16 AWG.
- Grounding tests are performed using the three electrodes, alternating current (AC), or DC voltage drop method.
- All supplier tests are performed in accordance with standard supplier procedures.
- All cables are buried at least 30 inches, free of splicing, and in conduit when under track or paving.
- After installation of the railroad signals, all equipment and materials are adequately protected to prevent inadvertent damage.

Supporting Other Construction in Transportation

This section provides guidelines for transportation bridgework facility turnover. It applies to all activities and disciplines of the completed facility. It is the project manager's responsibility to ensure that bridgework activities conform to design specifications.

One should provide a systematic program of bridgework and systems turnover to the customer that verifies completeness and ensures satisfactory performance of the equipment. This system should include facility turnover by area with a series of standardized punch lists provided in the respective quality procedures (for example, quality of structural, architectural, and finish construction for bridgework). In addition, any required documentation (such as material test reports, certificates, reports, or warranties) should be supplied in a manner sorted by bridgework area.

For turnover of a bridgework area, one should ensure completeness of the following items to obtain usage approval.

- Interface of bridge to roadway, parking garage, or transportation facility
- Fire protection (sprinkler heads)
- Power to lighting and security surveillance equipment
- Lighting layout in accordance with drawings and revisions
- Proper temporary bridgework cutoff to ongoing construction areas
- Dimensional layout per contract drawings
- Heating, ventilating, and air conditioning (HVAC) system, when necessary, per contract drawings, including plumbing
- Stairways complete with proper handrails
- Finishing activities (when applicable): floor mats, wallboard, handrail and connections, cove caps, ceilings, and signage in accordance with contract design drawings

Systems operation and testing should be performed as a demonstration to the customer that the system will perform satisfactorily in service. Final acceptance testing and demonstration evaluation is as follows: A system testing plan should be developed to identify activities and items requiring final testing and evaluation as well as the testing methods to be used; this will require instructions for performing the tests (acceptance and rejection specifications) and forms to record results. Test results should be submitted to the customer as specified by the contract, and testing sheets should be added to the plan as developed. For the bridgework area, a punch list should be prepared to ensure completeness of electrical, plumbing, HVAC, sprinklers, fire safing, roofing interface, utilities, and finishing work. Other activities should conform in part to related electrical, mechanical, structural, and civil activities.

The respective quality procedures must include a comprehensive final acceptance test and an evaluation checklist to be used when performing this function. This completed record becomes part of the test packages in the quality records file available to the customer.

A set of O&M manuals and as-built drawings may be prepared from the manufacturer's standard information. A facilities overview can be prepared defining the mechanical systems installed.

Supporting the Transit Industry Quality System

A planned quality program for the rapid transit project should involve establishing a design office and on-site quality organization to ensure that all materials and workmanship addressed in the customer quality items comply with the contract plans and specifications. The project quality plan should consist of the plans, procedures, and organization necessary to provide materials, equipment, workmanship, fabrication, construction, and operations for all permanent structures, systems, and components that are to comply with the contract requirements.

The organization should be headed by a quality system manager (QSM) who will be responsible for overall management of the contractor quality control (CQC) system and who must have the authority to act for the contractor in CQC matters. He or she should take any steps necessary, including stop-work recommendations, to ensure that each item of the facilities and its installation meet with contractual requirements. This person normally reports directly to the project manager and to a central QA manager to resolve matters of quality beyond the project level. The quality system manager should be assisted by a staff of qualified quality engineering or inspection personnel to implement the project quality plan. The actual size of the quality staff will vary to reflect the needs of the project, but will be sufficient to implement the quality program.

The program should not preclude transit system design office audits and field inspections. The quality program normally places responsibility for compliance to contract requirements within the contractor's jurisdiction.

Contractually, it is normally required that subcontractors and suppliers maintain a quality system consistent with the one described in chapters 6–11, and with transit-agency contract requirements. Subcontractors and suppliers should be responsible for certification of materials and quality of services, including tests and results, and should maintain appropriate records as required by their programs.

Subsequently, subcontractors and suppliers should employ appropriate quality engineering or inspection personnel to augment the contractor's quality program. If any subcontractor site staff personnel has problems in performing his or her duties that affect, control, or ensure quality, the prime contractor's quality staff should temporarily assume direct responsibility until the subcontractor's quality program is operating effectively. In any case, the prime contractor's quality manager should continue to be responsible for controlling matters of quality to fully comply with contractual requirements.

A quality program may be updated at various times during contract duration. Each revision should be submitted in writing to the customer or proper authority and adopted subject to their approval. Interim modifications to the quality plan may be made as necessary on a case-by-case basis to allow design and fieldwork to continue uninterrupted. Interim modifications may be made by individual page substitution after the proposed modifications have been hand carried to and approved by authorized office or site review and approval personnel.

The following is a typical project quality program or plan outline for the rapid transit industry.

Organization Chart	QP-XXX-01
Position Description: QSM	QP-XXX-02
Position Description: Quality Engineer	QP-XXX-03
Sample Letter of Appointment	QP-XXX-04
Project Submittal Procedure	QP-XXX-05
Testing Procedure	QP-XXX-06
Inspection Procedure	QP-XXX-07
Reporting Deficiencies Procedure	QP-XXX-08
CQC Daily Report	QP-XXX-09
Test Report	QP-XXX-10
Submittal Register	QP-XXX-11
Inspection Plan[1]	QP-XXX-12
Testing Plan[1]	QP-XXX-13
Quality Control Procedure For[2]	QP-XXX-NN

Organization Chart

The prime contractor's quality manager (the supervising quality engineer or QSM) partially reports to the project manager and is a part of the project manager's staff, with a matrix link to corporate management for quality matters that cannot be resolved at the job level. There is a strong written and oral communications relationship with project engineering, particularly material specifications. There is a strong fieldwork relationship with the general superintendent, as he or she is the first to know about deficiencies and is responsible for corrections.

All support personnel in quality matters report to the QSM. Inspection and quality engineering personnel should be under the direct supervision of this manager. They should have responsibility and authority for all first-level QA not delegated to subcontractors. Quality personnel should maintain direct surveillance and control over the installation of all permanent structures, systems, and components.

Subcontractor quality personnel at the design office or at the site who are working on permanent structures, systems, and components report to the QSM on all matters of quality. Their quality force and organizational relationships are clearly established and defined in their respective quality plans. A typical subcontractor/QSM quality relationship has the following two elements.

- Testing laboratories or agencies working on design and installation of permanent structures, systems, and components receive their directions from the SQE on testing activities to be performed.
- Suppliers for permanent structures, systems, components, and materials work directly with the SQE on matters pertaining to quality.

In the event that any one of these subordinate quality personnel responsible to the QSM fails to adequately ensure the required quality of the in-place permanent structures, systems, and components, the QSM initiates immediate remedial action to comply fully with contractual requirements.

Position Description: QSM

Qualifications: Competent, experienced, full-time supervisor, and registered professional engineer licensed to practice in the state. If not currently licensed, license should be obtained not later than 90 days after the NTP date.

Purpose: To develop and execute a program of quality engineering, inspection, testing, and control of design process, documents and records of materials, equipment, workmanship, fabrication, construction, and operations. To assign the responsibility, authority, and organizational freedom to identify quality-related problems, initiate management action (including stop-work recommendations) that results in acceptable solutions, and verify satisfactory implementation of solutions.

Responsibilities:

- Manage quality-related activities within the quality department of the design office or project site. Maintain adequate quality and inspection coverage of the design process and construction facilities and activities, and coordinate these activities with project requirements.
- Maintain and submit quality documents and records. Arrange for and monitor any off-site testing and reports that relate to project quality.
- Develop and administer a CA program in accordance with project specifications.
- Develop general work schedules and duties of I&T to provide adequate inspection coverage.
- Coordinate testing activities with outside testing agencies.
- Coordinate and monitor I&T activities with subcontractors.
- Interface as necessary with the customer or customer's representative in matters involving quality activities and policies.

Position Description: Quality Engineer

Qualifications: Completion of associate degree in a related discipline plus two years of related experience in equivalent activities, or the successful completion of the American Society for Quality Control (ASQC) certified quality engineer (CQE) examination and three years of related experience in equivalent activities.

Purpose: Perform, as necessary, such activities as in-process and final surveillance of concrete preplacement; concrete placement; concrete curing; installation of reinforcing steel, soils, backfill, and utilities; structural steel erection; welding, waterproofing; architectural finishes; and testing of concrete and soils. (Refer to AIA specifications for a complete listing.)

Responsibilities:

- Monitor design and construction personnel during assigned operations to ensure quality workmanship and compliance with project specifications. Perform assigned surveillance and testing in compliance with the quality program and project specifications to ensure required quality of project.

- Document quality activities in accordance with the quality program. Report and document unsatisfactory conditions using appropriate quality program procedures. Interface with A/E&C and management personnel to resolve quality-related problems.
- Report to the QSM any condition or activity that warrants a work stoppage to prevent further occurrence of deficiencies.

Project Submittal Procedure

This guideline provides information on control over procurement, inspection, documentation, and review of materials, tests, and services required by contract specifications.

Date

Dear   :

You are hereby appointed to the position of QSM for the transit agency project (reference contract numbered XXXXXX) effective XXXXX 19XX. This appointment is contingent upon the agency authority's approval.

Your prime initial task will be to develop and maintain a quality program to conform to overall corporate quality policies and the transit agency authority's project specifications and related documents. You are authorized to communicate directly with my office in any matters pertaining to quality on items beyond project level. Further, you will be expected to provide periodic reports on the execution of the CQC system to my office for review.

Sincerely,

Manager, QA

Figure 15.1.   Sample letter of appointment.

Specifications

The procedure should fulfill contract general provisions, article and amendments, and the general requirements sections, article, amendments, and paragraphs.

Procedures

A submittal register should be developed to list all submissions of material certifications, services, test results, plans, and samples that are required by the contract specifications. Submittal of materials, services, tests, plans, drawings, and manuals that require approval by the field engineer should be reviewed by contractor personnel prior to submission to the engineer.

A review stamp should appear on all copies of the submittal to verify review. Only the first page or cover page needs to be stamped on multiple-page submittals. Submittals should be sent to the engineer via transmittal letter in the quantities and configurations set forth in the contract specifications.

The engineer should have a minimum of XX days to review, take appropriate action, and return the submittal or notifications of approval thereof. Submittal of material certifications, mill reports, test results, plans, drawings, samples, and the like that do not require approval by the engineer should be reviewed by the appropriate individual as indicated on the submittal register and submitted to the resident engineer.

Any item on a submittal that deviates from the contract specifications should be plainly marked and described. The review process should include the project manager, the project engineer (PE), the QSM, and the subcontractor's quality representative to ensure the following:

- Conformance to the plans and specifications
- Compatibility with other materials
- Availability of materials as required by design or construction sequence
- Completeness of test data and performance information
- Availability to the architect or engineer of facilities for surveillance or verification

Subcontractor Submittal

All subcontractors whose scope of work includes submittal of material certifications, samples, tests, plans, drawings, and the like should forward the submittal to the QSM for review and approval in the quantities and configurations required by contract design specifications. Personnel should review the submittal and transmit it to the architect or engineer in accordance with procedure.

Reference reports include the following:

- Submittal register
- Submittal review stamp
- Transmittal letter

Submittal Procedure
A submittal review verification stamp and the signature of the appropriate reviewer should appear on all submittals.

Testing Procedure
This procedure describes the testing plan, methods, and documentation required by the contract design specifications.

Specifications
This procedure fulfills contract general requirements and should be subject to applicable testing standards as referenced in the specifications.

Off-Site Surveillance
A testing plan should indicate which tests and surveillance are to be performed by subcontractors or suppliers at the place of production, manufacture, or assembly. Prior to employment of any independent testing agency, a review of the agency's capabilities should be made, and prior approval of the architect or engineer should be a condition of such employment. Review should include checks of activities, personnel, and a library of reference standards.

Procedures
A testing plan should be developed from the contract specifications to delineate all required testing and its frequency. Subcontractors should develop and submit for approval to the QSM a test procedure for on-site and off-site testing as required by the specifications, including

- Name of test
- Identification of the specification section and article where the test is specified
- Testing frequency
- Name of testing facility or agency responsible for each test
- Maintenance of a testing log to provide documentation of tests performed

Conducting Tests: Tests should be performed using current standards, methods, and equipment designed for such purposes and according to the requirements of the contract specifications. Tests may be performed by the QSM or his or her designee as indicated in the approved testing plan. Tests may be performed by an independent testing agency experienced in performing the tests, methods, and procedures subcontracted by the contractor and approved by the architect or engineer. Tests may be performed by the architect or engineer or his or her designee as required by the contract specifications at the testing laboratory.

Reporting Tests: All tests should be recorded on a testing log and the CQC daily report. Tests performed by contractor personnel listed in the approved testing plan should be recorded on a test report. Tests performed by an independent lab should be recorded on the laboratory's standard report forms and sent to the contractor's field office. All tests should be reviewed and approved by the QSM and transmitted to the architect or engineer for approval if required. Unsatisfactory test results are recorded as a deficiency on the deficiency log, and deficiency procedures are followed.

Referenced Reports
Quality-related reports should include
- Testing plan
- Testing log
- CQC daily report
- Standard test report
- Independent agency test reports

Inspection Procedure

This procedure provides guidelines for the necessary surveillance or inspection by the contractor's appointed quality control (QC) representative, the inspector, and the subcontractor's or supplier's representative in compliance with the contract specifications.

Specifications
This procedure should fulfill the contract general provisions article (inspection and acceptance) and general requirements sections, article amendments, and paragraphs.

Procedures
An inspection plan should be developed for each section of work and categorized into one of three types of inspection.

1. Preparatory inspections: The inspection or test required to prequalify an activity, document preconstruction conditions, or provide notification of pending activity.
2. In-process inspections: The ongoing inspection, testing and surveillance required to document work, activities, and materials during day-to-day construction activities.
3. Follow-up inspections: The inspection or test required on completed activities, items, or intermediate work. This may involve joint inspections with the architect or engineer to verify compliance and acceptance criteria for payment purposes of products, services, or activities.

Inspector's Responsibilities
Prior to the start of a work activity, the inspector should review the inspection plan for the activity and comply with the preparatory inspection directions. At the start, and during construction, of a transportation segment, the inspector should perform daily inspections, tests, and surveillance, and comply with the in-process inspection directions. At the completion of construction of a transportation segment or interim construction, the inspector should perform final inspections or tests in compliance with follow-up inspection directions. All preparatory, in-process, and follow-up inspections should be documented on the CQC daily report and the testing log, submittal log, or deficiency log, as applicable.

Inspections should be coordinated with either in-house or independent agency testing personnel, so that required tests are performed at the indicated frequencies and in a timely fashion. The SQE should also obtain test results as soon as they are tabulated, evaluate the results, document that the tests were performed according to accepted procedures, and submit the results as required.

Subcontractor or supplier inspection activities should be conducted per the subcontractor's CQC plan. It should be the SQE's responsibility to monitor or provide surveillance over the subcontractor's or supplier's QC representative to the degree specified in the inspection plan, to ensure compliance with the CQC plan and the contract specifications. The subcontractor's CQC representative should report work activities, inspections, and tests performed to the contractor's QSM for inclusion on the CQC daily report. All test results should be forwarded to the contractor's QSM for evaluation and submittal.

Provisions should be established to permit the authority's designated architect or engineer to have free access to all quality records, documents, and log books maintained for a project. Inspections of material received by the contractor should be conducted upon arrival of the material on-site or possession of it off-site. Damaged or defective material should be returned, rejected, or segregated from the acceptable items and recorded as a deficiency subject to deficiency procedures. When immediate action is taken to remove material from the site upon determination of acceptability during receiving inspection, a deficiency report (DR) is not required.

Referenced reports should include the following:

- Inspection plan
- CQC daily report
- Testing log
- Submittal register
- Deficiency log

Reporting Deficiencies Procedure

This procedure should be adopted to identify, document, and bring to a satisfactory conclusion all specification or drawing noncompliances found in permanent materials, products, installations, tests, or workmanship.

Specifications

This procedure should fulfill the contract general provisions article and amendments, and the general requirements sections, article amendments, and paragraphs.

Procedures

Reporting Deficiencies: All deficiencies found during construction activities should be recorded on the deficiency log and assigned a DR number. Subcontractors should submit their deficiencies on a daily basis to the QSM for recording and assignment of a sequential number in the deficiency log. The section and article to which the deficiency does not conform should be referenced. The date the deficiency is found, its location, and its description should be recorded. This information should be reported on the deficiency log and the CQC daily report. If an inspector finds a condition he or she believes warrants a work stoppage, he or she should immediately report it to the QSM for evaluation. The QSM should investigate and make recommendations to the project manager, who will then make the final work-stoppage decision.

Remedial Action: When remedial action is taken, a description of the action should be recorded—along with the date, section, article, and DR number—on the deficiency log and the CQC daily report. If remedial action is deferred, then a description of the action to be taken should be recorded on the CQC daily report. Outstanding deficiencies should be listed daily on the CQC daily report. Remedial action may be directed by the QSM or inspector for deficiencies that can be corrected with no adverse effects and that need not be referred to the engineer for approval. Remedial action for deficiencies that cannot be restored to plans and specifications without redesign, considerable rework, or considerable monetary expense may be submitted by the contractor to the architect or engineer for approval.

CA: To prevent recurrence of deficiencies, the inspector should use the deficiency log to concentrate on certain areas requiring closer inspection. To stop trends of recurring deficiencies, the QSM may require or recommend appropriate action to be taken, including, but not limited to training sessions, change of work techniques, and dismissal of chronic offenders.

For the purposes of this procedure, all references to *inspector* shall mean both the contractor's inspector and the subcontractor's inspector. Referenced reports should include the deficiency log and the CQC daily report.

CQC Daily Report Instructions

This procedure provides instructions for completing the CQC daily report. A report should be filed for each contract day, regardless of work performed or not performed, and two copies should be forwarded to the architect or engineer by the next workday.

Heading

Page numbers should appear on all pages. Additional pages and attachments should have page numbers in sequence. The contract day will be entered on page 1 of the report. The contract day is calculated from the NTP date and coincides with the actual contract calendar. The date (contract day) of the report should appear in the heading. For days with no construction activities (for example, weekends or holidays), the report may be predated or postdated and submitted the next workday following the nonactivity day.

The CQC daily report should begin with the following topics.

- Part I: Preparatory inspection
- Part II: In-process inspection
- Part III: Follow-up inspection

All inspections performed as required by the inspection plan should be described. Details should be enough to identify the activity or conditions. The activity under inspection should be listed.

Each inspection activity should be marked either *satisfactory* or *unsatisfactory*. *Not applicable* (*NA*) may be entered if the inspection description does not reflect a required satisfactory condition. All inspections by subcontractor inspectors should be identified on the subcontractor's daily report.

Part IV: Tests Performed. All required tests performed on the day of the report should be described. The activity under *testing* should be listed. Each inspection activity should be marked either *satisfactory, unsatisfactory,* or *pending*. Test reports and results received should be listed and marked either *satisfactory* or *unsatisfactory*. Copies of received reports should be attached to the daily report. A description of the test method used, type of test, and inspection instrument used should be included. All testing by sub-contractors should be reported on the subcontractor's daily report.

Part V: DR From Parts I, II, III, or IV. All unsatisfactory conditions reported under Parts I, II, III, or IV should be described in specific detail in Part V. The activity under which the deficiency is identified should be listed. The DR number (DR No.) recorded on the deficiency log should also be listed.

Part VI: Deficiency Remedial Action. Any remedial action taken on a deficiency should be described in detail, including action taken to correct any previously deferred remedial action as well as action taken on the day of occurrence. The activity section under which the deficiency is identified should be listed. The DR No. recorded in the deficiency log should be listed. Any remedial action deferred to a later date should be described.

Part VII: Outstanding Deficiencies. All outstanding deficiencies should be listed by brief description and DR No.

Part VIII: General Work Performed. This section should contain general descriptions of the work performed daily. This section is not intended for job tracking; it is intended to identify the areas of work as they relate to the responsibilities of QC. Any item listed by someone other than the QC signatory should be initialed by the contributor. A list of all attachments, including the subcontractor's daily reports, should be entered in this section of the daily report.

Part IX: Remarks. This section covers any remark or condition that is not provided for elsewhere but is deemed necessary to document the project. Any remark entered by someone other than the QC signatory should be initialed by the contributor.

Part X: Weather. The day's weather should be entered here, including high and low temperatures and any weather conditions that affect construction.

Signatures. The SQE or appointed designee should sign and date the report prior to management review, signifying his or her certification of the report and all referenced attachments. The SQE should forward two copies of the completed report to the architect or engineer by the next workday. The project manager should review the completed report, make any required entries in Parts VIII and IX, and sign and date the report. Copies of the cosigned reports should be kept on file.

Test Report Instructions

This procedure provides instructions for completing a test report (TR). The TR number should be entered as recorded on the test log. The date of the report should be entered. The item, system, or part of a system that has been tested should be identified and described, and the areas and station numbers tested should be listed. The type or name of the test as well as the results should be listed; if the results cannot be obtained immediately, *pending* should be entered. The name, title, and signature of the person conducting the test should be entered. The QSM or his or her appointed designee should certify by signing and dating that the test is *satisfactory* or *unsatisfactory*. Any remarks deemed necessary to document the report by further describing the test, test results, or conditions should be entered.

Submittal Register Instructions

This procedure explains the use of the submittal register and provides instructions for its completion.

Explanation for Usage

The submittals are listed by section for each article requiring a submittal or transmittal. The due date is calculated from the time schedule network analysis minus approval turnaround time. The individual responsible for review or approval places a check in the appropriate column: the PE column or the SQE column.

Instructions for Completion

The date the submittal is transmitted to the engineer is entered in the *sent date* column. When the submittal is forwarded to the engineer and is assigned a transmittal number (T No.), that number should be entered in the *number* column.

Concrete Quality

This procedure establishes methods, direction, and actions necessary to control the quality of concrete batched and delivered to the job site for incorporation into the project. The material supplier is responsible for first-level quality, ensuring that the mixes shipped are as stated in the specifications.

References

Contract specification American Concrete Institute (ACI), Manual of Concrete Practice, and ASTM C-94.

Application

The ASTM/ACI classes of concrete should be used for transit, approved mix design and mat, protective covering, guide wall, miscellaneous non-structural, and duct and utility encasement. General structural concrete should be used for cast-in-place (CIP) structures, slurry walls, precast structures, bag use, grout, general use, priming concrete, pump use, bonding agent, construction joints, and the like.

Supplier Quality

The supplier of concrete for this project is XYZ Concrete Batch Company, which is responsible to the contractor for quality and the following:

- Verifying concrete design of mixes by an approved design laboratory per ACI 613 and ASTM C-94
- Verifying concrete ingredients by certificates of material quality and testing to include aggregates, cement, water, and admixtures
- Verifying batch plant proportioning and loading by batch tickets and computer printout of proportioning
- Verifying transit mixing by revolution counters on the transit drum
- Ensuring that at no time will unauthorized unmetered water be added to the mix
- Ensuring that water added for slump adjustment is at the direction of the concrete superintendent
- Ensuring that the specified water-cement ratio is not exceeded

The QSM should provide direction for matters pertaining to quality through the supplier's quality manager who should be licensed as a professional engineer in the state and be knowledgeable in design, surveillance, and testing of concrete and related materials.

Documentation: The following forms should serve as documentation of delivered concrete from the batch plant to the project site: delivery batch ticket and computer printout of proportions.

Daily concrete operations should not begin unless the approved[3] plant is fully operational. The supplier should inspect the batch plant prior to beginning permanent placements and then on an as-needed basis. In the event of an emergency situation such as a plant breakdown during a pour, the recordation from the approved backup plant should be noted. All details of the breakdown should be described and the responsible operator should sign the form attesting to its accuracy and authenticity. The following personnel should be authorized to sign the form: listed responsible individuals and the contractor quality manager.

The contractor should be responsible for quality and the following:

- Verifying that testing of concrete characteristics are in accordance with the inspection plans for Parts I and II
- Ensuring that test results are forwarded to the jurisdictional authority if required by the contract specification
- Ensuring that on-site testing is under the direction of the QSM
- Verifying that if deficiencies are found in either the concrete or equipment, the general superintendent, QSM, or designated inspector has the authority to reject the delivery

Batch Plant: The concrete supplier should use a computerized batching system. The system requires that all mix designs have a unique number and that all materials incorporated in the mix have project numbers. Approved mix design numbers should be assigned to each project and only those mixes available within the system should be dispatched to that specific project. A copy of the computer printout indicating proportions should be included as an attachment to each pour package.

Placement and Workmanship: Indicated in inspection plan.

Documentation will be provided on approved forms as referenced in procedures or as approved by the resident architect or engineer of the transit agency.

Prepour Conference

A conference should be held with all parties concerned with concrete quality to define and allocate responsibilities applicable to the concrete delivered and poured on the project. A completed prepour conference questionnaire can be jointly discussed and prepared by conference attendees.

Supporting PMO of Transportation Projects

Key areas designated for review in a work order should be assigned a priority ranking by the transit agency. The observations, conclusions, and recommendations in the oversight are developed from on-site interviews with key project personnel and from reviews of project-related documents. Oversight refers to working in a quality consultant function directly for the transit agency. The function should be independent of operational line functions such as project management, construction management, or QC.

Issues assessed are project costs, schedule, design, construction management, organization and interfaces, policies and procedures, QA/QC, contract administration, procurement practices and procedures, and adequacy of selected project documents. The oversight function performs follow-up reviews relating to critical issues addressed in the report as authorized by the transit agency. In all cases, the oversight consultant should notify the transit agency staff of any deficiencies or concerns identified during the review for appropriate action by the transit agency. In addition, the oversight consultant should help the transit agency resolve quality issues.

Preparing a Summary of Major Observations and Recommendations

The team should review the documentation, budget, and schedule of contracts, including contracts for overhead contact systems, rail transit vehicles, automatic train control systems, stations and guideways, and track work and ballast.

Review of these contract documents should reveal significant problems. The interface between vehicle and control contracts should be managed extremely well. The vehicle specifications should be reviewed for detail and tightness. The final version of the contract (on, for example, stations and guideways) should be reviewed for improvement. This includes surveying the document review process.

Track-work documents should be reviewed, and obvious flaws should be corrected. The final documents should be reviewed in a timely manner to ensure that any observations are incorporated. (One may even deliberately not inform the designer of these observations in order to test the effectiveness of the document review process.)

The budget and commitment to preventive quality should be checked, as well as the architect's or engineer's estimate. The estimate should be reviewed at various stages and closely monitored against the transit agency budget. The budget should be based on past procurement, adjusted for various known factors. PMO consultants should assist in the architect's or engineer's estimate.

Project Review Analyses and Observations

The transit agency should authorize the consultant to perform systemwide PMO by issuing a letter of contract or NTP. The NTP should include a memorandum of agreement specifying the scope of work and identifying key areas for review by the team.

The team should review project documents and conduct interviews with key transit agency personnel: the designer, the design management consultant, the construction manager (CM), the construction management consultant, the vehicle design consultant, and all construction management. Two sets of interviews should be conducted with some personnel. The first set should gather initial information about the project and work experience of the persons interviewed; the second set should verify the employee's understanding of key project issues developed in the first set of interviews and from reviews of project documents.

The limited time frame for these reviews restricts their being exhaustive. However, the observations in a PMO report should be accurate and conclusive. The PMO consultant should perform follow-up reviews relating to critical issues addressed in the report as authorized by the transit agency. In all cases, the PMO consultant should notify the transit agency staff of any deficiencies or concerns identified during the review for appropriate action by the transit agency.

During this initial review effort, the PMO consultant may be requested to perform several project-management-assistance tasks relating to specific items requiring immediate resolution or action. Such additional tasks should be performed when requested and authorized by the transit agency, to support the project management team in the execution of other critical tasks. These additional tasks may include the following:

- Reviewing the contracts and making recommendations on schedule, interface, and technical requirements; reviewing the completeness and stringency of contract requirements; and scheduling evaluations regarding manufacturer's capabilities, the procurement process, and potential problems.

- Reviewing and making recommendations on the scope of work for the designer and design services in construction and helping the transit agency staff categorize services, define the acceptable level of effort, and accelerate any contract negotiations.
- Reviewing and making recommendations on the scope of work for other design services and helping the transit agency staff categorize services, define the acceptable level of effort, and accelerate negotiations.
- Focusing on roles and responsibilities between the transit agency, designer, CM and others; providing team-building alignment workshops, including preparation, interviews, documentation, and facilitation of meetings; and determining critical issues needing clarification and definition.
- Reviewing agency documents; conducting interviews; and reviewing planning, design, specification, schedules, and estimates.

Technical specifications contain the functional requirements for the system and reasonably specific requirements for hardware to perform the functions. They also contain requirements for management controls, quality, and technical submittal. A budget and current forecast should be available with the design estimate. Technical specifications establish the requirement for a software nondisclosure agreement and technical criteria.

The state public utilities commission should be brought into the program early. It should hire an architect or engineer to review the contract documents since it must approve the system for service. The bid form, the proposal requirements, and the technical specifications should each provide requirements for the technical descriptions to be included in a proposal. These three documents may not be in agreement. The contractor may be required to submit a computer-generated critical-path-method (CPM) network schedule at some future time.

The interface definition and the procedure for managing the interface with the vehicle should be reviewed for adequacy. Interfaces with the cable transmission system, supervisory control and data acquisition system, rear projection display, radio, wayside, and traction power should be clearly defined in the specifications.

The contractor's schedule should provide an acceptable control over the project, providing it is prepared at an appropriate time and is accurate. The contract schedule turns over most of the train control to the contractor for preparation and equipment installation within a short time period. The contract schedule should encourage the contractor to manufacture and install most of their equipment in parallel.

All train control interfaces should be clearly defined but the contractor should be required to provide an interface control and definition if necessary. It should be clear which contractor is responsible for supplying and installing the train control cable through the duct bank along a right of way.

Review Documents, Conduct Interviews, and Review Planning, Design, Specification, Schedules, and Estimates

Adequacy of interfacing among the transit agency, the CM, and the designer must be ensured. As a priority activity, the transit agency should prepare a project execution plan for dissemination to all project participants, covering all functional areas within the project and all key organizations (the transit agency, the CM, and the designer). Emphasis is needed on communicating with all key project team members about the work plan and the schedule for updating the policies and procedures manual. All key project team members should also be given an opportunity to comment on the policies and procedures that are to be developed and to indicate which ones they want to assist in preparing.

After the policies and procedures are developed, a training program should be implemented to ensure that all project personnel are adequately instructed in the use and application of the policies and procedures. Key managers of the transit agency and the consultants need to be focused on using such tools as a team-building workshop and then periodic status meetings to review progress of action items that flow out of the initial workshops.

The CM should make a concentrated effort to ensure that a construction management plan (CMP)—including project policies, organization chart, action plan, procedures, staffing of field office, and the like—is implemented. The transit agency may direct the PMO consultant to assist the CM in this effort. The manuals produced by the CM must conform to the transit agency manuals being developed in the areas of QA, safety, and architectural/engineering (A/E) requirements and responsibilities.

A simplified and responsive change-order processing system should be developed and used. Processing the changes quickly will ensure continuity of the contractor's work. The change-order process should provide for an equitable adjustment in cost or schedule when warranted by changed conditions. The transit agency and CM should consider including a straightforward policy statement in their management plans regarding claims mitigation and control in an effort to avoid claims and disputes. This should be done by assigning contractual responsibility to the contractor so that he or she is in a position to control and provide prompt, equitable redress when changed conditions or design modifications result in additional costs or delays through no fault of the contractor.

The construction management organization should require appropriate staffing in order to perform the subcontract function in a satisfactory manner with a full-time supervisor. During review of the contract constructibility documents, a CM should concentrate on the constructibility issues and avoid involvement in items that the designer should correct during the normal design cycle.

The transit agency task force should include the responsible architects or engineers. In addition, these architects or engineers should be included in the task force's weekly meetings. The transit agency should include the CM in all steps of selecting the construction contractor.

A detailed basis and assumption should be developed for the project schedule. The CM should approve and present the project schedule and develop a team-building program to focus not only on the objectives of the project, but on the interaction among and responsibilities of the team members. This effort should begin immediately.

Line Design Criteria

A line design criteria manual should be prepared by the designer. Time should be allotted for the production of a responsible architect or engineer manual, with an understanding that the change-order procedures be the subject of further review and simplification. In the area of quality, a provision should be included for an inspection plan for each contract. The plan should be prepared by the responsible architect or engineer and approved by the CM, quality manager, and designer.

QA Specifications

The transit agency should give priority to the ongoing development of a clear and concise umbrella QA program plan and QA policies and procedures from which individual organizations can address their specific quality procedures and instructions. These additional specifics should be clearly understood by the QA manager.

The CM, the designer, and the QA manager should work together to clarify the assignment of tasks, responsibility, and authority for quality at the working level. The project QA team members should set procedures for communicating field reports of nonconformance and requirements for design modifications to the design office. The procedures should provide for proper authorization and control of the design effort.

When the project master schedule has been completed, the QA organization should work with the CM and the designer to plan and schedule quality activities and to perform constructibility, inspectibility, and readiness reviews of contract documents. The designer QA organization should revise its QA procedures manual to reflect any missing quality elements. Other non-QA activities should be covered in other project design management documents.

The transit system should be monitored to ensure that

- The designer incorporates reviewer comments
- The CM and the transit agency review project schedules for timely access, completion dates, and common work areas
- The transit agency and the design estimators review schedules and projections for compatibility
- The CM develops an access contingency plan
- The CM provides a special effort in the field with the transit agency regarding proper placement of foundations
- The transit agency develops goals and a strategy to be used during negotiations
- A contingency plan is developed for implementation if any negotiating strategy fails to achieve the goals
- The extent of the powers of the architect or engineer during contract negotiations is satisfactory
- The interdependence of the various contracting parties (for example, the transit agency, and the designer) are recognized and understood

Interaction Among the Transit Agency, the CM, and the Designer

The PMO consultant can recommend the following organizational changes, if they have not already taken place.

- A financial and administrative services team should be charged with updating the transit agency's policies and procedures. The transit agency should hire a full-time person responsible for managing changes to manuals and following up on training of transit agency staff in the use of procedures.
- Policies and procedures should be prepared so that they are in compliance with the U.S. Department of Transportation (DOT) and Federal Transit Administration (FTA) procurement and quality regulations applicable to federally funded projects. Revised policies and procedures should reflect any major reorganizations that occur (for example, the combining of the transit agency and a rail development organization in a new entity).
- The transit agency should have policies and procedures. If an increasing number of individual policies and procedures are adopted, the current plan should disseminate the new policies and procedures in separate manuals.
- During interviews with project personnel, any lack of understanding about the development of revised policies and procedures should be noted. The majority of those interviewed should express a clear and understandable knowledge of policies and procedures.
- Any tensions on the project among the transit agency and the major contractors should not be allowed to grow to a point where detrimental effects to schedule, quality, or cost effectiveness may occur.

Conclusions

Policies and procedures should be continually updated, and proper training provided in their use. Individual roles and responsibilities and proper procedures for executing tasks should be clearly defined and communicated. Leadership at various levels must be encouraged and exercised. Problems should be solved quickly to minimize the pressure—such as from schedule—that may drive the process.

Recommendations

All key project team members should be given an opportunity to comment on the policies and procedures that are to be developed and to indicate the ones they want to assist in preparing. The policies and procedures should be functionally organized and distributed.

Observations

The CM's contract should require that a CMP be written and followed and that project construction policies and procedures be established. The CM should have formal project operating policies and procedures to guide the contract administrator in the performance of his or her duties. The CM should have developed a QA manual and inspector's handbook, a safety manual, and a resident engineer's manual. The CM should be managing early contracts and adding staff to handle additional contracts.

The contract requirements may be different from the requirements in subsequent solicitation documents. Recently enacted state legislation requirements may prevent this problem. The responsible architect or engineer manual should include either of these documents—not both. The CM's contracts administration department needs to be thorough in qualifying potential employees. The CM's contract normally calls for constructibility reviews of designer and design packages, but these reviews sometimes go beyond constructibility into detailed critiques of the drawings.

The CM's contract sometimes may call for monitoring transit agency work on other related projects that affect the current project. The CM should participate in the transit agency construction contractor selection process, but may not be aware of what might have transpired during negotiations leading up to the award (for example, any adjustments or agreements between the transit agency and the contractor).

The basis and assumptions for the project master schedule should be documented. If not, the designer and the transit agency may have difficulty understanding the schedule. The team may need evidence that the CM and responsible architect or engineer understand and can effectively use the schedule. The CM may need control over the schedule, that is, the authority to accept input on major schedule elements from the designer and to question the validity of the input. The PMO team should recommend to change this process so that the CM has the authority to validate the content of schedule elements.

A change control board may be assembled for the project, but unless it observes certain rules, it may not always be effective. Different contract documents and the CM's responsible architect or engineer manual may contain differing language regarding the process of resolving contract disputes. Part of the reason is that a large percentage of the CM's staff assigned to a project may be from organizations other than those of the CM and his or her consultants.

Transit Design Criteria

Observations

At the beginning of a project, the transit agency may decide to forgo having a consultant prepare a project-specific design-criteria document, in which case the designer and his or her consultants should apply existing design criteria to the project. This would occur when the design team worked on a related transit project, and would therefore be knowledgeable and capable of producing a complete and reliable final design without the need for a specific design-criteria document. The transit agency's decision should be based on the fact that both projects are similar and that the designer's team is essentially the same team that designed a related project.

Design changes should occur early in the project, if at all. For example, a change from an overhead contact system to a third-rail system and then to an automatic train control with overhead contact system may result from the design being performed without adequate predeveloped design criteria.

Conclusions

The lack of a project-specific design-criteria document may result in ambiguity regarding direction on design and on other project elements. Numerous design changes may indicate the need for at least a partial design-criteria manual that addresses unique project elements and characteristics.

QA Specifications

Observations

The transit agency QA manager's position should be filled in a timely manner. The agency QA program manual should be completed and provide guidelines with additional agency-specific details. Engineering QA responsibilities may be defined, but not to the degree required for an effective QA program. The quality organizational relationships may appear to be reasonable; however, at the working level, both internal and external to the agency, they may need improvement. There may be an inconsistent and, in some cases, conflicting assignment of quality tasks in the organizations of the project team members, transit agency, designer, CM, and construction contractors.

The information from the master schedule may need to be translated into short- and long-term planning and scheduling of quality activities. The procurement process should include QA participation. However, the process requires additional QA involvement during the early planning stages to prevent problems rather than having to correct the plans after they are complete. The designer may have a QA procedures manual, but some elements, such as CA, may be missing. The manual may also include elements not pertaining to QA activities, such as engineering design approvals (signing and sealing).

Conclusions

The transit agency quality effort may need improving. The quality organizations may be working together to improve the overall quality program. Quality relationships, both internal and external to the agency, may need improvement in terms of integration and responsibilities. When the project master schedule revision is complete, the QA activity planning could be revised to reflect the content of the new schedule.

Early QA involvement in project planning allows preventive measures to be used so that all parties are committed to building quality into the product. A poor alternative is to have excessive dependence on appraisal activities such as inspection. Preventive QA produces timely identification of potential problems before they become real problems.

The designer QA manual may need revision to include all applicable QA elements, relocate non-QA elements, and conform to the latest transit agency quality program.

Recommendations

The transit agency should give priority to the ongoing development of a clear and concise umbrella QA program plan, policies, and procedures from which individual organizations can address their specific quality procedures and instructions. Separate transmittal details may be provided to the agency QA manager. The CM, the designer, and the QA manager should work together to clarify the assignment of tasks, responsibility, and authority for quality at the working level.

The project QA team members should set procedures for communicating field nonconformance reports and requirements for design modifications to the design office. The procedures should provide for proper authorization and control of the design effort. When a project master schedule revision is complete, the QA organization should work with the CM and the designer to plan a schedule for performing constructibility, inspectibility, and readiness reviews of contract documents. The designer's QA organization should revise its procedures to reflect missing quality elements. Other non-QA activities should be covered in other project design management documents.

Vehicles

Observations
This should be a well-prepared contract with equitable terms. The technical specifications should contain precise requirements for the design and construction of the car and for management control, quality, and technical submittal. However, the basic specification for car length and allowable weight should be specified.

The car builder may have to make a substantial commitment of its engineering and management resources to both the potentially lengthy negotiations and then to the risky work of designing a complex new car, to provide work for only a small part of its manufacturing facilities. The architect/engineer's estimate may need to be completed at the time of this PMO review.

The schedule period available may be adequate for the design and construction of a light rail car, but automatic operation, front mock-up, and AC propulsion systems could complicate the design. Some car builders may require more time to complete the design and manufacture of a car with such features.

Conclusions
A transit vehicle contract should be extremely comprehensive with well-defined requirements so that the agency can expect a well-controlled and precisely managed procurement. However, potential bidders may be concerned by the size of the contract documents, the lack of latitude to supply

subsystems that the builder may have provided in the past, or the precise controls that the architect or engineer will be required to exercise over the project. Bidders may think that the job is not attractive for the supply industry because of the high development risk and low production potential. It is not unusual under these conditions for car builders who bid on this work to offer high prices and longer schedules in their initial proposals.

Each proposed car design should be tested by computer analysis to determine if the weight and length provide an acceptable loading on transit-agency bridges. The load capacity of some transit may need to be confirmed. The penalty for proposing a car that does not meet bridge design load may need to be specified.

The full-scale mock-up of the front interior and exterior details, including the first set of seats, wheelchair provisions, entrance doors, and lights, should be normally available for inspection one year from NTP and should be inspected and approved before the represented designs are released for production. If this requirement is not met, it could prevent the car builder from meeting the schedule.

Recommendations

A contingency plan should be developed in case negotiation strategies fail to achieve the vehicle fabrication goals. Criteria for evaluating the weight and length of a proposed vehicle should be developed before bids are received. In the event that a vehicle is overweight and not compatible with the infrastructure, a statement regarding acceptability of the car should be specified.

Additional schedule controls should be placed over the vehicle design process. The schedule for producing and approving the full-scale front-end mock-up should be evaluated during negotiation, and a decision made about whether a complex mock-up is cost and schedule effective.

Management of the vehicle-radio interface should be addressed in the specifications even if adequate design information is not yet available.

Track Work and Ballast

Observations

The construction schedule may depend on the transit agency contractors' access to the guideway. The track-work contract schedule may currently be under review as part of a total examination of the project master schedule. The preliminary review should be performed. When final contract documents are ready, they should be reviewed to ensure inclusion of information that may have been missing in the preliminary design package.

Conclusions

The transit agency contractors should be continually monitored. The project master schedule review should be completed in a timely manner. Good communication and coordination between the track-work contractor and other contractors may be essential to maintain budget and schedule. Information not included in the design package should be provided in the final version of the contract. Otherwise, the contractors may have difficulty bidding accurately on the track-work contract.

Recommendations

The CM and the transit agency should review the project master schedule, which may be going through revision. Access dates, completion dates, and common work should be thoroughly understood and managed. The transit agency and the design estimators should review the schedule to ensure that estimates and the current schedule are compatible. The CM should develop contingency plans in case access dates cannot be achieved.

Stations and Guideways

Observations

Control of the design development schedule should be reviewed for effectiveness. Complete and satisfactory milestone submittal may need to be achieved. Documents should be appropriately coordinated and should not be prematurely printed. The contract schedule may be dependent upon access from the contractor who may currently be behind schedule. A recovery plan should be developed in this case. The schedule may be going through revision as part of a total review of the project master schedule.

A review of the bid documents should show a marked improvement in completeness from the design package to the contract documents. The accumulated preliminary design review comments should be examined to uncover problems with grammar, legibility of the architect's or engineer's stamp, spelling, incorrect or missing match lines, or missing drawings related to utility information.

Recommendations

The CM and the transit agency should review and plan as denoted in the track work and Ballast example. The comments of design package reviewers should be restricted to significant issues or design deficiencies. Better management of the design by the designer may be required. Milestone review documents should not be released until they are coordinated internally and are at the appropriate level of completion. The transit agency should not accept incomplete or premature submittals. Procedures should be followed, including those of the designer's QA manual.

Transit Contract Review, Design Management, Schedule, and Cost Control

Contract Review

Observations

The contract may require the designer to act as the transit agency's general engineering and construction management support contractor, in which case the designer is entrusted with significant responsibility for program management. The transit agency should be properly staffed and look to the designer to work closely with it in achieving project goals and objectives. The initial scope of work should be reasonably complete and detailed; it should contain major categories and subsections, each with a description of services and deliverables, and a recommended approach.

The contract may refer to a baseline work scope for illustration and reference. The contract should be clear in its requirement that the designer coordinate, integrate, and manage the services to achieve an operational transit system within the schedule set and design budget allowed. Payment should be made for work performed when written authorization from transit agency has been given.

If the project did not achieve the initial goals of schedule and design budget, an adequate change process should exist that consists of an engineering change request (ECR) process and an associated proposed budget change request (PBCR) process required by the agency. Many changes from external sources to controllable internal sources, including the transit agency, and consultant organizations, may contribute to project schedule expansion and design cost increases. The designer's contract should require that the designer immediately notify the transit agency if a change in scope occurs, regardless of whether the change is constructive or directional in nature.

Any significant differences existing within the overall team, involving project criteria, schedule, design comments, and design quality, should be resolved in an efficient and well-coordinated manner. This may be indicative of the growing ability of the total management team—the transit agency, the designer, and the CM—to function together smoothly and effectively, but within their respective responsibilities.

The scope of the designer's contract should be limited to a simplified work-breakdown structure (WBS) of the anticipated design effort, with the designer's proposed response for each WBS element. The failure of the designer and the transit agency to follow the contractual requirements for change orders may introduce numerous engineering change requests that result in increased costs. The designer's contract should require the designer to correct errors and omissions. The designer's QA contract requirements should be reviewed for adequacy.

Conclusions

The initial contract, scope, project definition, goals and objectives, and the change process should normally be adequate for management and control of the project. Due to factors both external and under the control of the team, the project schedule may sometimes slip, the project and design budget may increase, and the cohesiveness of the overall project team may deteriorate.

The design budget should be controlled to minimize design cost and to stay within the transit agency's budget. Project controls should be given priority by management and may sometimes be too complex or poorly communicated for effective implementation by the design team. To effectively control the cost of work done under the designer's contract, a clear, concise, and definitive scope of work may be required. The scope should be in sufficient detail to allow the cost of the work to be estimated accurately. The same scope of work should then be used to manage the work. For large projects with complex designs, it may often be difficult to precisely define the scope of work; in these cases, the contract should be structured as a task-order contract and funded by task. Each design package should be prepared under a task order, and the designer should be required to prepare a project drawing list for the package with associated work hours and costs. The drawing list should be the basis for reporting status, control, and invoicing.

Recommendations

The transit agency should require the designer to provide written notice to the transit agency when work needing to be done differs from that spelled out in the scope. No work outside the existing scope should be undertaken by the designer until it is authorized in writing by the transit agency.

For design and construction design support efforts, the designer should strictly abide by contract change and authorization requirements. The transit agency should ensure that the engineering change process is managed in a timely and effective manner.

The transit agency should require the designer to present a scope of work for design support during construction that is in sufficient detail to allow costs to be estimated with a high degree of accuracy and work that can be effectively managed. This means that contract effort should be tied to work products and deliverables.

The transit agency should establish controls to see that work done by the designer is covered by scope descriptions in the designer's contract. The transit agency and the designer should agree on who pays for work needed to correct errors and omissions. In any event, to protect both parties—particularly the designer—the responsibilities of both parties should be clearly delineated.

QA measures to be taken by the designer and his or her consultants during performance of the design work should be clearly identified and agreed to in the designer's contract.

Design Management Review

Observations

During design, the project should receive substantial upper-management attention from the transit agency. The transit project must take priority, and the transit agency should be staffed to adequately manage the project during design. The designer's responsibilities include project management assistance to the transit agency as well as management of the design and any subcontractors.

The designer's organization should be structured along functional lines by design discipline. Departments should consist of systems, civil, structural, third-party, and technical services. These report to project management, which should be assisted by project control and project administration.

Initially there should be a focus on project engineering functions responsible for the technical coordination of contract packages and adherence to budget and schedule. Configuration management should be located with project administration.

Limited engineering staff may be added during the project, but it should be added into a functional structure and report to a level that will be sufficiently effective. The designer's QA procedures manual should be written and approved prior to initiation of services. The manual should require that no deliverable document be released by the designer or officially transmitted to the transit agency or to any third party before receiving a suitable quality review. This requirement should be enforced by the designer or subcontractor personnel. Design review documents should be released by the designer prior to their internal coordination, quality review, and necessary determination that the documents represent the intent of the project and are at the required level of completion. The transit agency in turn should not accept the documents without initial review to determine acceptability. If these procedures are not followed, many unnecessary comments may be made by all parties, requiring additional resources to resolve matters and lengthening the project schedule.

The designer's management should sufficiently control the design process of its operation and that of its subcontractors. There may be schedule slippage due to external factors. The credibility of the designer's schedule management should then be brought into question, during the CM's evaluation of the designs and scheduled completion date. The CM's recommendations may conflict with the designer's estimate of design completion.

Conclusions

The designer should provide the management structure needed for effective project control and engineering coordination. Organizational structure should be appropriate to effectively respond to the needs of the project and to adapt when so required by project needs and external changes.

The transit agency should devote sufficient management and administration resources to monitor and control the designer. Approved project procedures should be followed by the designer and transit agency. Control of project changes and the management of external impacts should be effective to avoid schedule slippage and cost increases.

Recommendations

The transit agency should prepare a project execution plan. The work scopes of the designer and CM should be defined clearly and sufficiently and should be consistent with the management plan for all remaining work. The organizations of the designer and CM should reflect the management, technical, and coordination needs of the project. Critical project procedures should be updated as quickly and concisely as possible, and adherence to the procedures should be required by all entities involved in the project. All staff should be indoctrinated to and concur with project objectives and procedures.

Transit Construction Management Review
Construction Management Contract Review

The transit agency should require the CM to produce a contractually required CMP. The CM should participate in the bid evaluation and selection processes for construction or systems contractors. The scope of services should be further defined to permit good management of the delivery of services. The scope of work should be coordinated with the designer's scope of services during construction.

Any inconsistencies in the CM's contract relating to his or her authority over the construction contractor should be resolved quickly. The transit agency should include the CM in all steps of the construction contractor selection and award processes.

Both the transit agency and the CM should ensure continuous contract coverage, and negotiation of amendments before the contract term expires. The transit agency should review

- The adequacy of the CM's organization
- The CM's inspection and QC
- The CM's cost and schedule tracking, monitoring, and control efforts
- The CM's contract

Observations

The original CM's contract may have several amendments, with others in progress. The scope of work for the CM may have been expanded or may currently be under review by the transit agency. The initial letter contract issued to the CM may have one basic requirement—that of preparing a CMP. The follow-up, definitive contract may include the same requirement. The CM may have difficulty in producing a plan for review.

The CM contract's scope of services and expected results should be sufficiently definitive to permit accurate estimates of the cost of the services. Otherwise, it may not be adequate to permit effective management of the CM's contract by the transit agency. The CMP, if prepared, should compensate for, but not substitute for, the lack of specificity in the scope of work.

The CM's scope of services should be coordinated with the proposed designer's scope of design support services during construction. The contract may need clarification regarding the authority of the CM with respect to construction contracts under its management. The CM's contract should require participation in the construction contractor bid selection, evaluation, and award process.

Amendments to the CM's contract should be issued in a timely fashion.

Conclusions

From the original CM's contract, the scope of work may have been expanded to include work outside the original scope. This additional work may be seriously diluting the planning and preconstruction effort required in the CM's original contract.

The lack of a clear and concise definition of the scope of work under the contract may make it difficult for the transit agency staff to estimate the cost of the services and of management of the CM's contract services. If the CM's services have not been coordinated with the designer's proposed design support services during construction, there may be duplication of effort.

Inconsistencies in a CM's contract relating to his or her authority may place unintended liability on the transit agency in a claims situation. Excluding the CM from the construction contractor bid evaluation and award processes puts the CM at a distinct disadvantage in his or her dealings with the construction contractor after the contract award.

Evaluating the Adequacy of the CM's Organization
Observations

There may be a written project or CM procedure. There should be project-specific policies and procedures, and the project staffing plan and schedule should be fixed. The CM's field office should be fully operational because the responsible architect's or engineer's support organization may currently be operating from the field construction office. Due to the diversity of the CM's employees, previous employers, and construction experience, team building within the CM's team may be needed.

The transit agency task force may need focus. The reporting relationships among the CM's field inspectors, the responsible architect or engineer, the safety manager, and the QA manager should be clear. The responsible architect or engineer manual should be distributed in a timely manner. It should be updated as required and marked *revision*. Position qualification statements may need to be prepared by the CM. Some of the personnel interviewed may have limited experience on major projects.

The CM and the designer should make every effort to work well together. A safety program may need to be developed and implemented. The safety requirements should address all current and anticipated construction activities.

Conclusions

The CM's organization could be fragmented due to a lack of total project teamwork. A CM procedure and operating procedures may be needed. The CM's staff may be working independently, operating on past experience and principles rather than following a CM procedure. The present organization may need to be focused on supporting the responsible architects or engineers who provide the key function of CM. The transit agency focus should consider quality, schedule, and cost requirements. This may have been recognized by the CM, but may need greater emphasis.

A less-than-positive attitude by the CM's staff toward the designer's work could have a negative impact on project progress. Some improvement may be needed. When individuals are being interviewed for construction jobs, a positive attitude should be an important criterion for hiring. Still, a lack of previous experience in working as part of a team and diverse project backgrounds may indicate a need for team-building efforts and close management support.

A project may require superior communication and coordination among all contractors and management groups. Significant safety management tasks may be required due to project size, numerous and various contractors, variety of construction techniques, and public exposure and impacts.

Recommendations

A team-building workshop within the CM's organization may need to be undertaken, clearly establishing goals and objectives for each team member. In addition, overall project objectives developed from the roles and missions should be conveyed to the team.

The change orders process should be continually streamlined. Present organizational responsibilities should be reviewed with a major focus directed at supporting the responsible architects or engineers. The majority of the CM's support staff should be at the field site.

To provide stronger direction, the CM may need to increase involvement in the preparation of bid documents, review, and award. The CM's task force could be expanded to include all responsible architects or engineers. Communication between the CM's team and the designer should be encouraged. Weekly meetings involving CM support staff (for example, responsible architects or engineers, the designer, and the transit agency) should be encouraged.

The CM's support staff may need more direct involvement with the field functions—particularly the managers of QA, safety, cost, scheduling, and the like. Typically, QA and safety managers many times have little control of their functions; they may be covered by inspectors working under the responsible architects or engineers. Locating the support staff to the field and focusing on teams usually improves cooperation and teamwork.

When the support staff is located in the field, the operations function should direct the construction effort and support the responsible architects or engineers and their teams. Progress and results of individual construction team members should be closely evaluated for adequacy of job performance. A quality audit schedule should be developed by the transit agency, the CM, and the transit insurance administrators to avoid duplication of effort and maximize contractor coverage.

Reviewing the CM's Inspection and QC

Observations

The CM may be issued a QA manual in advance of the transit agency's issuance of a quality policies and procedures manual. The CM may require significant revision to the subcontractor's QC plan and inspector's handbook subsequent to the contract award, but these revisions should incorporate or refer to a field checklist, inspection documentation, and the subcontractor QC system.

The field nonconformance reporting system should provide for CA to preclude the recurrence of nonconformances. Both the CM's QA program manual and the subcontractor's QC plan should provide for inspection of their activities. There should be integration of the two programs for overall assessment or evaluation other than the quality activities that may have impact on quality.

The CM's or subcontractor's quality program should address coverage of independence laboratory testing and results verifications. The CM and field quality programs should be oriented toward detection and correction activities rather than prevention.

Conclusions

Issuance of the responsible architect or engineer manual should be integrated with the overall construction quality program, particularly in clearly defining QC roles. The requirements for quality may be under review by the CM and the subcontractor. However, lower-tier subcontractors may have well-developed programs.

The CM may be following the terms of the construction contract and may be performing the quality function. He or she may be attempting to require the construction contractor to assume the quality role. In this case, the contractual obligation imposed on the CM for quality may need enforcement.

Individual inspectors working for the responsible architects or engineers may have responsibility for all field functions, including QC and safety. They may be hired by the responsible architects or engineers with little input from the responsible discipline managers. If individual inspectors are not at least interviewed/reviewed by safety and QA functional managers, then there may be a concern that the inspectors are not adequately qualified in all fields.

Although both the CM's QA program and the subcontractor's QC program provide for quality coverage, each may be independent of the other. Integration of the two programs to provide an overall quality approach will probably improve overall results. A CM and field quality program oriented toward prevention may be needed rather than one oriented toward detection and appraisal.

Recommendations

The transit agency's quality policies and procedures manual should be issued without delay and incorporated into all new and existing contracts. The requirements in that manual should also be incorporated into the CMP and the responsible architect or engineer manual.

The responsible architect or engineer manual should be reviewed and updated after the transit agency's quality policies and procedures manual has been issued. The QA manager should have a direct role in the selection process of the field inspectors. The QA manager should normally be located at the field office, where he or she can observe and assist the inspection efforts on a day-to-day basis. Thus, the QA manager's and the field quality roles should be defined.

Construction management and site quality programs should be reoriented toward prevention rather than solely toward detection and correction activities.

Architect or Engineer Responsible for Reviewing and Monitoring Transit Practices
Examining the System Contracts and Procurement Standards and Procedures
Observations

The transit agency's contracting policies and procedures, which may in turn be part of a larger program/manual, should be reviewed. There may be numerous duplications of information and procedures within the policies and procedures manual (for example, duplicated contractor progress payments, supplicated quality requirements for procurement or installation contracts, and duplicate change-order administration).

Change-order administration requires that several forms and different continuation sheets be completed before a change order can be authorized; some sheets may require the same information, thus duplicating much of the effort. CM field personnel may express concern that the forms are overly complex and require too much time to complete. In addition, these individuals may be concerned that the processing of change orders in accordance with the existing procedures results in delays to construction work.

Conclusions

Detailed examination of all policies and procedures may reveal additional duplications. Some of the duplication may be the result of dividing the procedures into several volumes and then distributing them to different organizational units. The ordering of the contract procedures should be in a logical sequence, and the procedures may be functionally organized. This may result in a large manual; this in itself creates a psychological barrier to reading the contracts.

The change-order procedure should be properly reviewed and coordinated by the transit agency contracts personnel and the CM's personnel responsible for contract administration in the field. The focus of the change-order procedure may be toward the processing of information rather than the expeditious processing of the change.

Recommendations

Consideration should be given to splitting procedures by function. Dissemination of the procedures should then be limited to those who participate actively in their execution. The procedures in the contracts portion of the manual may need to be arranged in a manner that follows the same sequence as the acquisition process.

- Policies
- Preparation and issue of solicitation documents
- Disadvantaged business and affirmative action requirements
- Receipt of bids, proposals, quotations, or evaluations
- Negotiations
- Protests
- Award
- Initiation of work
- Contract administration
- Change orders and engineering change requests
- Contract modifications
- Progress payments
- Back charges
- Contract close-out

This list is not intended to be complete, but is provided as a guide. Putting the procedures in this order should allow them to be used as a learning tool for new personnel. Once assigned the task of developing a contract, one could work his or her way through a manual in a logical fashion. Specific contracting procedures are the foundation of good contract control. For this reason, all contracting procedures should be reviewed and modified as appropriate by a task force composed of transit agency contracts personnel, the CM, and the designer.

Notes

1. An explanation of this portion of the project quality program has not been provided in the text. However, this is a simple matrix between all sub-functions and when they will be performed during the A/E&C process.

2. The subsequent balance of the project quality program would be a series of procedures that would follow the ones provided in chapter 16 and appendices F, G, and H.

3. Approved means that the plant is cerified A.C.I. by a level III certified concrete QC engineer with an approved procedure.

16 Supporting Medium-Sized Construction Projects

Control of Design and Design Changes

Project Testing Coordination Activities

- Soil and Rock Testing
- Aggregate Testing
- Asphalt Testing
- Concrete Testing
- Calibration of Measuring and Test Equipment (M&TE)
- Mechanical and Welding
- NDE
- Electrical

Site Material Plant Operations

- Aggregate Supply and Concrete Batching
- Aggregate Supply and Asphalt Batching

Precast and Block Plants

- Precast Structural and Architectural Concrete
- Precast Manholes

Spread Footings for Building and Structure Foundations

Piling Footings for Building and Structure Foundations

Concrete in Building Construction

Concrete Masonry Units (CMUs) Construction

Kitchen Installation and Casework

- Installation of Food Service Equipment
- Installation of Kitchen Units
- Installation of Kitchen and Vanity Cabinets
- Installation of Freezers

A/E&C Building Expansion

Electrical Installations

- Interior Electrical Work
- Lighting Equipment
- Automatic Transfer and Bypass Isolation Switches
- Diesel-Electric Generator Sets
- Life Safety, Fire Detection, and Alarm System
- Annunciators
- Intercom and Paging Systems
- Radio and Public Address Systems
- Wiring of Electric Motors and Controls for Mechanical Equipment

Tenant Electrical Renovation and Operation

- Lighting Equipment
- Intercom and Paging Systems

Mechanical Installations

- Inspection, Sampling, and Testing
- Shop Boiler Welding
- Ventilation and Exhaust Systems
- Air-Supply and Distribution Systems

- Sheet Metal Ductwork
- Water Treatment Equipment for Swimming Pools
- Pressure Vessels and Pipe
- Fire Pumps
- Seismic Protection for Mechanical Equipment
- Thermal Insulation for Mechanical Systems
- Gas Piping Systems
- Forced Hot Water Heating Systems, Oil, Gas, and Combination
- Central Refrigeration System for Air Conditioning
- Air Conditioning System

Mechanical Installations for Building Expansion
- Inspection, Sampling, and Testing

Turnover and Startup

A/E&C activities during medium-sized construction projects have many of the attributes described in chapters 14, 15, and 17, and contain the elements of a good quality system, described in chapters 6–11. This chapter offers a good background on programs to help build a sound, successful business and to enhance the quality of medium-sized projects.[1] The information in this chapter will also help effect significant cost and schedule savings.

The following additional topics related to medium-sized projects and common to light and residential projects are covered in various appendixes.

- Organization of project quality (see appendix E)
- Earthwork and other geotechnical activities (see appendix F)
- Subbase and base courses, bituminous pavements, port and cement concrete pavements, pavement marking, and curbing (see appendix G)
- Structural, architectural, and finish construction for buildings (see appendix H)

Control of Design and Design Changes

This section establishes guidelines to be used by A/E firms in support of construction, modification, and installation activities important to quality. These guidelines apply to all project management personnel working with A/E firms, and to the architect or engineer to the extent agreed.

Responsibility

A project manager should delegate responsibility to appropriate support personnel for monitoring and surveillance of A/E activities. This delegation includes assuming that communication channels are maintained to expedite design changes. The responsibility for incorporating these changes into the A/E and installation activities lies with the project A/E&C organization.

Procedure

Initially, the corporate office should provide the project manager with copies of the design or construction specifications and design drawings from the customer. The project manager should verify that the specifications have been certified by a registered professional engineer competent in fieldwork and qualified in accordance with requirements (for example, ANSI/ASME N626.3).[2] The project manager will review with the owner of the completed facility when and how program activities are accomplished.

The project manager should work with the architect or engineer to ensure an adequate program that correctly translates the design input and criteria to design output documents such as A/E&C specifications, drawings, procedures, instructions, and the like. These output documents should be readily available to the customer. (This design process should follow the one described in chapter 9.) The design translation should be periodically monitored through the use of design reviews, calculations, and tests to ensure the design process is properly operating.

Changes to design documents: Requests for changes to design documents should be detailed in a document change request and submitted to the customer for approval by the PE. Records of the document change request and subsequent actions should be maintained on a document change requests log. Modifications of any document used for A/E&C, including reports of final design reviews, are reconciled with the design report by the person or organization responsible for the original design unless the owner specifically designates another responsible organization. A prepared and certified revision or addendum to the design report is required to indicate the basis or reconciliation of the changes. Changes generally fall into either of two major categories.

- A change in the prime contract with the owner that affects the contract and one or more of the subcontractors working for the A/E&C organization.
- A change to one or more subcontractors working for the A/E&C organization, but within the context of the prime contract between the owner and A/E&C organization. To avoid deferring interim payments due the subcontractor for work performed, a change order should be written with the condition that the right is reserved to adjust the authorized amount if a review uncovers reason to do so.

Any changes to the final documents issued with the contract normally are approved by the owner. To control any type of contract change, the procedures listed here should be followed.

• A number should be assigned upon receipt of any drawing, sketch, written directive, or any other directive from the owner, architect, or internal personnel by engineering and construction personnel.

• The project manager should be responsible for determining whether a directive affects the owner or the subcontractor within the context of the prime contract.

• An architect or engineer should then follow up with the subcontractors to ensure agreement on any cost or schedule change according to the general conditions.

• Upon receipt of the changes from a subcontractor, the architect or engineer should review the change against the contract documents to ensure that (1) all credits as well as additions are included, (2) the work described is a true change and not a contract requirement, (3) pricing is according to the contract documents, and (4) quantities are correct.

• The architect or engineer should then prepare a rough draft of a change letter to be issued to the owner in accordance with accepted formats.

• The project manager should be responsible for ensuring that the change is complete with respect to all affected subcontractors, that all related costs (such as design fees and A/E&C organization overhead) have been included, and that any schedule impact is included.

• The major thrust of this procedure is that *time is of the essence,* whether the change affects the prime contract or a contract with a subcontractor. Any changes to the final documents must be properly approved.

Surveillance

A periodic evaluation of the architect or engineer's corporate office activities should be performed to ensure compliance to contract specifications, the quality program, and guideline practices. This evaluation should make use of prepared checklists, and a report should be issued suggesting actions to be taken to preclude repetition of any identified adverse conditions.

Project Testing Coordination Activities

This guideline establishes methods and direction for controlling the site field-testing activities performed by testing laboratories, including on-site field testing in the areas of soil and rock, aggregates, asphalt, concrete, calibration control, mechanical and welding, NDE, and electrical. The purpose of such testing is to certify that site A/E&C activities meet technical requirements. Operational testing of systems and components, are normally excluded from laboratory responsibility. This responsibility should be vested with the subcontractor, as required. The laboratories are responsible for the organization and management of all on-site field testing activities.

Procedure

All testing performed by laboratories should include reports that cite the specification requirements and reference guidelines. The reports should also list sampling methods, other test procedures used, and actual test results. All test reports should be signed by a designated laboratory representative.

Soil and Rock Testing

Preparatory Inspection. Examine the current schedules and plans for earthwork and excavation. Review testing requirements in the technical specifications. Ensure that all test methods and equipment are approved and in operating condition.

Initial Inspection. Ensure that samples are taken and processed in accordance with requirements. When a test does not comply with requirements, initiate CA.

Follow-Up Inspection. Provide periodic surveillance of ongoing activities, and provide retesting on subsequent lifts (layers of reapplied, compacted earth).

Aggregate Testing

Preparatory Inspection. Examine the current schedules and plans for quarry operation. Review testing requirements and directives. Ensure that all procedures and equipment are approved and in operating condition.

Initial Inspection. Ensure that samples are taken and processed in accordance with requirements. When a product does not comply with requirements, initiate CA.

Follow-Up Inspection. Supervise the activities of the laboratory technician to ensure that he or she is kept informed of changes in test requirements.

Asphalt Testing

Preparatory Inspection. Examine the current plans and schedules for asphalt plant operations. Review testing requirements and directives. Ensure that all equipment and procedures are approved and in operating condition.

Initial Inspection. Ensure that samples are taken and processed in accordance with requirements. When a product does not comply with requirements, initiate CA.

Follow-Up Inspection. Supervise the activities of the laboratory technician to ensure that he or she is kept informed of changes in test requirements.

Concrete Testing

Preparatory Inspection. Examine all operational schedules, delivery schedules, and plans for receipt or production of materials that require testing. Review requirements and directives pertinent to the testing to be conducted. Ensure that all procedures and equipment are in operating condition.

Initial Inspection. Ensure that required samples are taken and processed in accordance with requirements. When a product does not comply with requirements, initiate CA indicated.

Follow-Up Inspection. Supervise activities of laboratory technicians assigned to the testing laboratory and ensure that they are kept informed of changes in testing requirements.

Calibration of Measuring and Test Equipment (M&TE)

Provide suitable facilities to control appropriate M&TE used on site by all project and quality personnel. Calibration should follow a recognized guideline that includes recording of recalibration due dates. If uncalibrated M&TE was used to perform a quality verification activity, sufficient traceability must be employed to ensure the precision and accuracy of the work in question.

Mechanical and Welding

Qualification. Provide a program to certify site welders in accordance with appropriate codes and ensure that recertification is handled in a controlled manner.

Support. Provide appropriate support in the mechanical testing activities for various destructive tests (for example, hydrostatic examination, pneumatic examination, and so on).

NDE

- Visual testing (VT). Provide examination by certified personnel in accordance with the recommended practice, SNT-TC-1A.
- Magnetic-particle testing (MPT). Provide examination by certified personnel and equipment in accordance with the recommended practice, SNT-TC-1A.
- Liquid penetrant testing (PT). Provide examination by personnel and equipment in accordance with the recommended practice, SNT-TC-1A.
- Ultrasonic testing (UT). Provide examination by certified personnel and equipment in accordance with the recommended practice, SNT-TC-1A.

Electrical

Provide appropriate support in electrical testing activities for various tests in accordance with appropriate codes of the IEEE, NFPA, NEMA, or state codes (for example, ground resistance measurements, meggering, lightning protection and the like).

Site Material Plant Operations

This guideline establishes methods and direction for controlling the quality activities performed at batch plants in the manufacture and supply of concrete, asphalt, rock, and aggregate. This guideline applies to all activities of these plants. The testing laboratories are responsible for the organization and management of the QC of all plant operations.

Aggregate Supply and Concrete Batching

Preparatory Inspection. The concrete batch plant scales should be calibrated by a competent organization qualified to perform and certify this type of work. (The accuracy of the batch-weight recording should also be determined at this time.) Batching controls should be checked to ensure that interlocks are working properly to prevent a new batching cycle from starting before all batches at the plant are completely empty. Mixing time should be monitored to ensure that the material is mixed for at least the required minimum time.

Initial Inspection. The coarse aggregate passing through the aggregate washing unit should be sampled as necessary to aid in any unit adjustments needed to achieve specified cleanliness. Periodically, additional testing during normal operation should be performed to maintain specified aggregate cleanliness.

Follow-Up Inspection. Control tests on fresh concrete at the forms should be conducted by the technicians, under the supervision of the A/E&C organization. These tests should include, but not be limited to, air content, slump, and compressive strength and yield point. If control tests at the forms reveal unacceptably high fluctuations in the fresh concrete characteristics, the testing laboratory must conduct additional tests at the batch plant or in the field to identify and resolve the problem.

Aggregate Supply and Asphalt Batching

Preparatory Inspection. The asphalt batch plant scales should be calibrated by a competent organization qualified to perform and certify this type of work. The accuracy of the batch-weight recording should also be determined at this time. The admixture dispensing systems should be checked using a container of known volume. Samples should be taken at the point of delivery into the mixer. Batching controls should be checked to ensure that interlocks are working properly to prevent a new batching cycle from starting before all batches at the plant are completely empty. Mixing time should be monitored to ensure that the material is mixed for at least the required minimum time.

Initial Inspection. Ensure that aggregates proposed for use meet specifications and are properly stockpiled, that segregation is controlled, that asphalt proposed for use meets specifications, that proper storage facilities are available, that access for sampling is adequate, and that scales have been properly calibrated.

Follow-Up Inspection. Ensure that materials, equipment, operating procedures, and products continue to comply with specifications and good practice.

Precast and Block Plants

This guideline establishes methods and direction for controlling the quality activities of the manufacturing and material handling of precast products and masonry units. The purpose is to ensure that such materials are carefully inspected on site prior to use. This guideline applies to all products manufactured in precast concrete and block plants. The A/E&C organization and any assigned subcontractor should be responsible for ensuring that materials delivered to the plants are as specified by the PO and are delivered in good condition and properly stored.

Precast Structural and Architectural Concrete

Preparatory Inspection. During a subcontractor selection process, ensure that the subcontractor has the capability of providing the complete product. Examine the drawings and specifications to ascertain details of structural precast concrete products.

Follow-Up Inspection. Review the test results. The subcontractor should ensure that the cure is performed satisfactorily. After the removal of the forms, inspect the surfaces of the precast product for defects.

Precast Manholes

Preparatory Inspection. Examine the drawings and specifications to ascertain the details and layout of manholes.

Follow-Up Inspection. Review the test results. The subcontractor should inspect the formed surfaces for defects. Ensure that remedial action or CA is taken if necessary.

Spread Footings for Building and Structure Foundations

This section establishes methods and directions for controlling the quality of materials and workmanship for spread footing installation for buildings and structures. It applies to all project activities associated with this work. Responsibilities for the various activities described in this guideline should be as indicated therein. The overall responsibility for coordination and implementation belong to the A/E&C firm and their subcontractors.

Inspection and Approval of Equipment. Examine the drawings and specifications to determine dimensions, strength, testing, and the like, of spread footings. Inspect the equipment and ensure that it is in good working order and well maintained.

Soil Tests. Perform and record soil tests of the subgrade prior to placement as required by pertinent specifications.

Inspection of Material. As soon as materials (reinforcing steel, anchor bolts, embedments, concrete, and the like) arrive on site, inspect them to see that they comply with pertinent specifications. Ensure that the subcontractor is installing materials in accordance with the section entitled "Concrete in Building Construction" later in this chapter.

Inspection of Work. Inspect the placement of the footings. Maintain a field report that includes such factors as footings number, subgrade depth, reinforcing-steel configuration, ground-surface elevation, net length and width of footing configuration, and weather conditions. Ensure that the forms for the footings are in the correct location prior to placement.

Completion of Placement. Ensure that footings are completed in accordance with the grade specified in the design drawings.

Piling Footings for Building and Structure Foundations

This section establishes methods and direction for controlling the quality of materials and workmanship for piling installation for buildings and structures. This applies to all project activities associated with this work. Responsibilities for the various activities described in this guideline should be as indicated. Overall responsibility for coordination and implementation belongs to the testing agencies.

Inspection and Approval of Pile-Driving Rig and Equipment. Examine the drawings and specifications to determine the dimensions, strength, testing, and the like of piles. Inspect the pile-driving rig and equipment; ensure that they are in good working order and properly maintained. Ensure that the planned air and steam capacity is adequate for the purpose.

Inspection of Material. As soon as materials arrive on site, inspect them to see that they comply with specifications. Check all piles for straightness and freedom from defects.

Inspection of Work. Inspect the driving operation for each rig in use. Maintain a pile-driving report that includes such factors as pile-cap number; pile number; ground-surface elevation; cutoff elevation; net length, diameter, speed, and type of pile; and weather conditions. Ensure that the piles are in the correct location.

Cut-Offs. Ensure that piles are cut off in accordance with the grade specified in the shop drawings.

Load Bearing Tests. Ensure that load bearing tests have been performed and that the piles meet load-bearing specifications and jurisdictional codes.

Concrete in Building Construction

This section establishes methods and direction for controlling the quality of materials and workmanship for concrete construction for buildings and other concrete structures. The purpose is to ensure that other embedded items are properly inspected prior to embedment. This section applies to all activities relating to the site erection of concrete buildings and other concrete structures. Responsibilities for the various activities described in this section should be as indicated here and by the project superintendent. Overall responsibility for coordination and implementation belongs to the appropriate inspectors.

Preparatory Inspection of Concrete Plant. This function ensures that the concrete batch plant is in good working order. This inspection should be done in accordance with the section titled "Site Material Plant Operations" earlier in this chapter.

Preliminary Sampling and Testing of Concrete Materials. Preliminary samples of the concrete materials should be taken for testing. This should be done in accordance with testing guidelines of ACI, ASTM, and the like.

Concrete Mix Design. Examine the job-mix formula and ensure that it is as specified. Review the quality reports from the concrete batch plant for conformance to specifications. Ensure that the design mix contains materials representative of those approved for use and conforms to the requirements of ACI standard ACI 301.

Reinforcing Steel Inspection and Records. Inspect the reinforcing steel lattice structure. Ensure that the rebar is firmly in place and in accordance with A/E&C drawings and specifications.

Inspection of Foundations. Inspect the foundations in accordance with the applicable guidelines in this chapter.

Preliminary Inspection of Concrete Forms. Inspect the concrete forms; ensure that tolerances are as specified in ACI 301. For the installed concrete forms, ensure that

- The forms are sufficiently tight to prevent leakage of grout and cement paste during placement
- The bottoms are accurately fitted and secured to the preceding lift
- The joints are arranged vertically and horizontally to match architectural lines
- The forms can be readily removed without damage to the concrete
- Retained-in-place metal forms conform to specifications
- The proper form ties are used to avoid deflection and concrete spalling upon removal

Inspection of Waterstop. Inspect the waterstop if one is used. Ensure that installation is a continuous, watertight diaphragm. For the installed waterstop material, ensure that

- Adequate provision is made to support the material during placement
- Splice tests are performed prior to placement in strict accordance with the waterstop manufacturer's recommended method

Inspection of Miscellaneous Metals, Conduit, Piping, and Other Embedded Items. Visually inspect various embedments; ensure that the items are properly set, true to proper grade and line, and firmly in place. Examine the drawings, specifications, and survey reports. Ascertain location dimensions and requirements. Verify actual results.

Checkout of Placement, Line and Grade, and Cleanup. During preplacement activities, maintain a checklist of open items. Ensure that the list is closed prior to placement. This task should include a final walk-through inspection for acceptable cleanup.

Inspection of Placement. Inspect the concrete placement activities. Ensure that vibrators are used as prescribed. Ensure that there is no shifting of dowels, tie bars, rebar, or forms. Ensure that the required field test samples are taken and processed; that surface finishing is performed while the concrete is in the plastic state; and that the surface of the concrete is not manipulated to the point where excess water and mortar rise to the surface.

Site Sampling and Testing of Concrete. Test the aggregate used as prescribed in ASTM C33 at least once every other day. Make tests for slump and air content of fresh concrete on samples taken at the forms.

The frequency of these tests should be the same as for strength testing. Obtain strength test cylinders (cubes) samples to the amount of prescribed yards of concrete or fraction thereof.

Sampling, Curing, and Testing of Cylinders (Cubes). Sampling, curing, and testing of cylinders (cubes) should be done in accordance with testing guidelines.

Curing and Protection. In the case of hot-weather concreting, ensure that the proper requirements of ACI 305R are maintained during the curing process.

Horizontal Joint Preparation. Prior to placing any concrete on a subsequent lift, check horizontal construction joints to ensure that the old surface has been roughened in an approved manner and is moist but without free water.

Stripping of Forms and Protection. Ensure that forms are removed in a manner that does not injure the structure. Forms should not be removed until sufficient strength has been obtained in the concrete to safely support its own weight and any loads placed on it. This strength can be verified by job-cured test specimens as well as by other methods.

Wall and Surface Finishes. Check drawings so that concrete surfaces not exposed to view can be formed with sound, tight lumber or other material producing equivalent finish.

Slab Finishes. Inspect slab finishes. For surface finish, ensure that

- Surfaces are finished to elevations shown on the drawings.
- Finished surfaces are placed with no deviations greater than $\frac{1}{4}$ inch for a 10-foot straightedge unless otherwise specified.
- Rough slabs are finished immediately after consolidation with no coarse aggregate visible. This should be sufficient for fill and mortar-setting beds.
- Wood floats are used for finishing by darbying or bull floating to bring surface to true, even place. This finishing step should be sufficient for carpentry, floor tile, resinous flooring, roof slabs, wood flooring, and the backs of precast panels.
- Steel trowels are used for finishing resilient flooring and exposed concrete slabs.

Remedial Action. Any concrete defects or imperfections should be repaired only with approved procedures by a competent authority.

Slab Hardness and Treatment. Ensure that hardeners are applied to all interior concrete floors that do not receive floor covering. Ensure that the procedure outlined in the specifications is followed.

Slab Toppings. Ensure that the method of floor topping is as delineated in the A/E&C drawings.

Final Inspection and Reporting. Ensure that all inspections—before, during, and after placement—are reviewed for adequacy and that results are available for the owner's review upon request.

Concrete Masonry Unit (CMU) Construction

This section establishes methods and direction for controlling the quality of materials and workmanship for CMUs as well as other precast architectural concrete units for building construction. This section applies to all vertical masonry installation activities, from sampling and inspecting incoming materials to final surface sealing.

The CMU subcontractor should be responsible for the organization and management of quality for CMU construction. The superintendent should be responsible for ensuring that the quality of materials is as specified by the PO and that materials are delivered in good condition and properly stored. The CMU subcontractor should be responsible for ensuring the integrity of mix ratios and the grade quality of quarry products.

Inspection Sampling and Testing of Materials. Inspect incoming CMU materials to ASTM C140 or ASTM C780. Ensure that an appropriate certificate of conformance is obtained from the previously approved manufacturer. (Refer to the previous section, "Concrete in Building Construction.")

Storage and Handling of Materials. Check the CMUs in storage at the site to prevent excessive buildup. Check to see that they are protected from weather and free of handling damage.

Preparatory Inspection. Examine the drawings and specifications to determine the details of the structure to be built. Ascertain the locations and types of joints, sills, partitions, corners, beams, reinforcements, and the like, as indicated in the contract documents.

Inspection of Workmanship. Inspect the mock-ups and courses for conformance to drawings and specifications. Inspect the walls. Ensure that they are plumb, level, and square. Ensure that the masonry units are properly prepared prior to being placed. Ensure that the mortar is of the type specified. Inspect the recesses for partition walls, and ensure that their location, size, and configuration are correct. Inspect the installation of anchors and tie bars. Ensure that the joints are filled flush with concrete or mortar. Inspect the anchorage of the CMUs to abutting walls and columns. Ensure that the anchors are placed as indicated in the contract documents. Inspect the control joints for location and construction, and ensure their compliance with drawings and specifications. Ensure that the bond beam blocks are properly reinforced or filled with mortar and that the filler strips are installed as required. Inspect the corner bonding for compliance to the technical specification.

Sampling and Testing of Mortar and Grout. Randomly select three samples per day to be tested by the methods described in the AIA/CSI Specification 04200, Masonry Preconstruction Test.

Precast Lintels, Jambs, and Sills. During the erection process, check the CMU to ensure tightness of joints, fit, alignment, cleanliness, and damage prior to plastering. Cooperate with on-site trades to inspect.

Anchors, Sleeves, Flashing, Grounds, and Other Embedments. Examine the drawings and specifications to determine proper installation of anchors, sleeves, flashing, grounds, and other embedments. Cooperate with other trades to inspect.

Chases, Pockets, and Block-Outs for Pipe, Conduit, and Ducts. Examine the drawings and specifications to determine proper installation of chases, pockets, and block-outs for pipe, conduit, and ducts. Cooperate with on-site trades to inspect.

Temporary Support for Doorways, Windows, and Large Openings. Ensure that the temporary support for doorways, windows, and large openings are safe and adequate for finished use.

Bond Beams. Ensure that bond beams are reinforced by no less than No. 4 bars and filled with grout. Examine the drawings and specifications to determine proper installation of bond beams.

Tie Bars and Wall Reinforcement. Ensure that vertical tie bars are located accurately at the centerline of the wall; minimum clearance between the bars and the CMUs should be $\frac{1}{2}$ inch unless otherwise specified. Check that the bars are secured properly and positioned in accordance with drawings.

Concrete-Filled Hollow Block. Ensure that hollow CMUs are of the ASTM C90, Type I, Grade N-I, having an oven-dry density of more than 125 pounds per cubic foot (pcf), unless otherwise indicated as non-load-bearing CMU walls.

Expansion Joints. Ensure that the joint material is of the ASTM D1056, grade number RE-41 E1 or RE-42 E1, or closed-cell vinyl or polyvinyl chloride conforming to ASTM D1667, grade number VE, VE42, or equivalent. Check that the installed joints are flush, tooled, and raked, with appropriate widths.

Field Testing. Provide coordination with the independent testing laboratory to perform compression testing for each type of wall construction at 7- and 28-day breaks for each 5000 square feet of wall.

Final Inspection and Reporting. As a final inspection, ensure that certification reports are in order, that test reports for air-dry condition have been performed, and that a final walk-through for damage has been made. These reports should be available for owner review.

Kitchen Installation and Casework

This section establishes methods and direction for controlling the quality of materials and workmanship for the installation of kitchen and casework. These methods include installing to the guidelines of the products, ensuring the accuracy of identification, ensuring that drawings are properly controlled and that O&M manuals are prepared, and ensuring the execution of installation inspections and appropriate operating and performance tests. This section applies to all subcontractor activities that relate to this work. The subcontractor should be responsible for the organization and management of the quality functions for kitchen, equipment, and casework installation.

Shop Drawings and Supplier Specifications. An in-depth review of the documents should be performed to ascertain constructibility and determine any potential areas of concern. Shop drawings describing the installations should be submitted to the controlling A/E&C organization for approval according to the methods and guidelines provided. The drawings submitted should consist of the following:

- Equipment and materials list
- Descriptive and technical data
- Catalog cuts and O&M manuals
- Installation diagrams and special inspections
- Equipment layout and anchorage
- Mechanical and electrical connections

Installation of Food Service Equipment

Preparatory Inspection. Examine the drawings and specifications to determine the National Sanitation Foundation (NSF), American Gas Association Laboratories (AGAL), and UL guidelines to be complied with. Inspect dimensions and equipment nameplates and also the performance tests that need to be performed.

Initial Inspection. Inspect welding or other fusion operations to the previous paragraph. Inspect any soldering or brazing for compliance with the federal guidelines listed in the technical specifications. Inspect any exposed welds or otherwise-fused joints to ensure that they are ground smooth, polished, and finished. Ensure that no overheating has occurred during fusion of the welds.

Ensure that fastening devices are properly used and of the same material as the metal being joined. Ensure that counters, sinks, utility distribution systems, hoods, walk-in refrigerators, gas burning equipment, and backflow preventers are properly installed. Inspect electrical connections for compliance with electrical quality guidelines (refer to the section titled "Electrical Installations"). Check plumbing connections for compliance with mechanical quality guidelines (refer to the section titled "Mechanical Installations").

Performance tests should be completed on selected items as follows:

- The refrigeration system should be tested for compliance with the quality guideline pertaining to mechanical (refer to the section titled "Mechanical Installations"). An operating test should be performed on refrigerators for sufficient duration to ensure a complete cycle of the control system and stabilization of temperature.

- The electrical system should be tested for compliance with the quality guideline pertaining to electrical (refer to the section titled "Electrical Installations").

Installation of Kitchens Units

Preparatory Inspection. Ensure that proper UL labels (or international equivalent) are affixed.

Initial Inspection. Ensure that top and sink, accessories, refrigerator, range and oven, cabinets, and hardware are properly installed, adjusted, and cleaned.

Installation of Kitchen and Vanity Cabinets

Preparatory Inspection. Review the certified test reports, drawings, catalog data, and samples to determine installation and layout details. Perform a first-article inspection and make the results available to the owner.

Initial Inspection. Inspect the installation of the cabinets and countertops for level, plumb, line trueness, and tightness against adjacent walls. Ensure that these items are secure and that the joints have been properly prepared.

Installation of Freezers

Preparatory Inspection. Examine the drawings and specifications to determine the details of A/E&C activities, including metal gages, fittings and mounting, size and spacing of anchors, and interconnection to other work.

Initial Inspection. Inspect the installation of the wall and ceiling panels, hardware, and mechanical refrigeration in accordance with the manufacturer's recommendations. Ensure that care is exercised to ensure plumbness, level, and line trueness.

Follow-Up Inspection. Execute a test of operational readiness in accordance with the guidelines for quality related to testing in chapter 9.

A/E&C Building Expansion

This section establishes methods and direction for controlling materials and workmanship used for A/E&C buildings during vertical erection, including architectural and finishwork.

Preliminary Inspections and Review of Specifications. An in-depth review of the specifications and A/E&C drawings should be performed to ascertain constructibility and determine any potential areas of concern. Any such areas identified should be handled according to the specifications.

Shop Drawings and Supplier Specifications. An in-depth review of the subject documents should be performed to ascertain constructibility and determine any potential areas of concern. Particular review areas of interest include the following:

- Precast architectural concrete. Check for indication of identification marks, location of units, elevations, fabrication details, welding details, reinforcement, connections, dimensions, interface of members, and any special handling recommended by the manufacturer.
- Elastomeric-membrane waterproofing. Look at the size and position of sheets, splicing, flashing, terminating, and expansion joint detailing.
- Bituminous-membrane waterproofing. Check for the certificate of compliance and manufacturer's instructions.
- Exterior insulation and finish. Examine the certificate of compliance, instructions, samples, and test data.
- Caulking and sealants. Check for samples and manufacturer's descriptive data.

Inspection, Sampling, and Testing of Materials. Architectural, structural, and finished systems and components identified in the previous paragraph should be inspected immediately upon receipt. Appropriate certified test results should be obtained, reviewed, and approved as defined in the specifications.

Storing and Handling of Materials. The materials identified in the previous paragraph should be stored and handled in strict compliance with the manufacturer's recommended practices. Storage should be such that there is no degrading of the received materials, including their material handling stages, through installations. Additional requirements include the following:

- Excessive handling should be avoided, and ground and weather protection should be provided when required.
- The alignment, grade, and plumbness of the installed materials should be checked using the manufacturer's recommended practices.

Measuring devices should be appropriately calibrated and should be of the precision and accuracy specified in the technical specifications. Additional requirements include the following:

- For precast architectural concrete and exterior insulation, tightness of joints should be monitored.
- For structural connections, American Institute Steel Connections (AISC) or international equivalent requirements should be used.
- For welded connections, AWS or international equivalent requirements should be used (see the section "Mechanical Installations").

Manufacturer's Specifications. When structures, systems, and components as detailed in the previous paragraph are being manufactured, conformance to requirements should be in the following order of precedence.

- Technical specifications and drawings
- Specified codes and guidelines
- The manufacturer's specifications

In a case of conflicting requirements, the document taking higher precedence should be that of the jurisdictional authority. The manufacturer's specifications should adequately provide descriptive data, erection, and installation A/E&C details, and sufficient O&M instructions for turnover to the owner.

Protection of Finished Work. Adequate protection should be provided to ensure prevention of inadvertent deterioration of the finished work.

In-Process Inspection. An in-process check should be performed according to a prepared checklist.

As-Built Drawings. In many cases, as-built drawings should be specified for submittal to the owner for items. These drawings should be in sufficient detail to permit O&M activities to be properly executed after installation. These drawings are developed after completion of the project, including a complete set of reproducible drawings to be submitted to the owner. These drawings should include the following:

- Location and dimensions of any changes within the building
- Revised grades and alignment structures
- Revised elevations
- Changes in detail of design or additional information

Other Inspection Activities. Other inspection activities may include the following:

• Elastomeric-membrane waterproofing. Check to ensure the proper preparation, installation, and application of waterproofing, primer, and insulation board, including types of membrane; ambient temperature is as specified; requirements for reinforcing strips are met; flashing, waterstops, lapping, wrinkles, and buckles are proper; flammable material is away from open flames; adhesion, additional mopping coats, and protective layers for insulation board are applied properly; there is no damage, defects, and protection; there is proper temperature and poundage of pitch.

• Bituminous-membrane waterproofing. Check to ensure the proper preparation, installation, and application of waterproofing membrane; ambient temperature is as specified; requirements for reinforcing strips; flashing, waterstops, lapping, wrinkles, and buckles are proper; flammable material is away from open flames; there are no defects or damage, and protection is provided.

• Cement-base waterproofing. Check to ensure the proper preparation of surfaces; proper application of materials and surfaces are clean and protected and free of damage.

• Exterior insulation and finish. Check to ensure the proper attachment of suspension system; proper attachment of accessories; fitness and alignment of finished soffit; tightness of joints, cleanliness of soffit finish; damage.

• Caulking and sealants. Check to ensure the proper condition of joints prior to application of compound; correct type of primer, back-up material, sealer, and caulking compound; weather conditions; application of compound including correct size and type of gun, installation of back-up material, neatness of finished joints and proper application of sealant; damage.

Final Inspection and Reporting. Check to ensure a final inspection and walk-through should be performed prior to turnover of the building to the customer. A/E&C maintenance instructions and warranties should be transferred at this time. Maintenance instructions for the items described should be prepared and furnished to the customer from supplier data, including the supplier's commercial warranties.

Electrical Installations

This guideline establishes methods and direction for controlling the quality of materials and workmanship used in interior and exterior electrical construction, including distribution and emergency power generation. This guideline defines the control of drawings, manufacturer's data, testing data, certification, inspections, and installations. It applies to all project activities associated with electrical work and other activities that interact with electrical work.

Code inspectors and local or municipal officials should be responsible for organization and management of the quality assessment on all electrical systems. The electrical-systems subcontractor should be responsible for the quality of electrical design and installations.

General Specifications and Shop Drawings. All work described in this procedure should comply with the following reference guidelines, as applicable.

- Federal specifications
- Standards such as those issued by ANSI, ASTM, OSHA, and IEEE
- Guidelines such as those issued by NEMA
- Publications such as those put out by the NFPA and UL
- Others as specified and mutually agreed upon between the customer and the A/E&C organization in the design specifications

Shop drawings describing electrical installations should be submitted to the customer for approval by the methods and guidelines provided in the specifications. The drawings submitted should consist of the following:

- Equipment and materials list
- Descriptive and technical data
- Catalog cuts
- Wiring diagrams and special inspections
- Equipment layout and anchorage
- Conduit and cable tray runs

Interior Electrical Work

Preparatory Inspection. Examine the drawings and specifications to determine the nature and extent of the installation. Prior to placement of the foundations, inspect the ground rods and ground potential equalization bar for proper size, material, configuration, and installation.

Prior to placement of the walls, ceilings, and floors, check the cable sleeves, conduit, and other devices that are embedded in or penetrate the structure. Check their size, material, location, and alignment.

Initial Inspection. Inspect the raceways, conduit, and cable trays for size, type, supports, routing, and alignment. Inspect the conductors for type, size, number, insulation, splicing, terminations, and connectors. Inspect the boxes and supports for size, type, and location. Inspect the device plates, receptacles, and wall switches for location, type, and workmanship. Inspect the panel boards for size, type, location, number, and type of devices installed, grounding, access, and enclosure cabinet. Inspect the motors for size (horsepower [h.p.] rating), type, alignment, anchoring, disconnect devices, power cables, controls, overload protection, and ambient operating conditions. Inspect the power supply and battery chargers; the lamps and lighting fixtures for type, size, and mounting; and special features (ballast, starters, and the like) for type and rating.

Prior to placement of the foundations, inspect the ground rods and ground potential equalization bar for proper size, material, configuration, and installation.

Prior to placement of the walls, ceilings, and floors, inspect the cable sleeves, conduit, and other devices that are embedded in or penetrate the structure. Inspect their size, material, location, and alignment.

Follow-Up Inspection. Witness all initial power-up tests and operational capability demonstrations.

Lighting Equipment

Preparatory Inspection. Examine the drawings and specifications to determine the location of cable trenches, manholes, and buildings. Determine the type and rating of lights, type of masts, and mounting details. Determine the number and types of control panels, their locations, and installation details.

Initial Inspection. Inspect the underground electrical work. Inspect the lights, masts, and foundations for compliance with specifications.

Follow-Up Inspection. Witness all initial power-up exercises and tests. If any test results indicate performance capability below specifications, initiate remedial action. Inspect all lighting adjustments, alignment, and aiming.

Automatic Transfer and Bypass Isolation Switches

Preparatory Inspection. Examine the drawings and specifications to determine the type, size, capability, and location of switches. Ascertain requirements for input power and ambient operating conditions. Inspect the manufacturer's test results.

Initial Inspection. Inspect the installation for ambient conditions, accessibility, anchoring, and cable connections. Inspect the input power voltage, current capability, and symmetry of phases; nameplate data for compliance with specified requirements; and the bypass isolation switches for functional operation in both the test and open positions.

Follow-Up Inspection. Witness initial power-up tests on the switches. Compare the results with the manufacturer's factory test results. Witness the functional tests of the automatic transfer switches and the bypass isolation switch. Witness the functional capability of all components. Witness any other tests that may be required by specification or the manufacturer's published data. If the results of any test indicate operational capability below specifications, take remedial action.

Diesel-Electric Generator Sets

Preparatory Inspection. Examine the drawings and specifications to determine the type, size, capability, location, and fuel-storage requirements for each generator unit.

Initial Inspection. Inspect the duct work for proper size, length, and location. Inspect the cables for size, insulation, marking, splices, and bends. Ensure that the cable markers are installed in their proper locations.

Follow-Up Inspection. Witness all operational capability tests. If the results of any test indicate operational capability below specifications, initiate remedial action.

Life Safety, Fire Detection, and Alarm Systems

Preparatory Inspection. Examine the A/E&C plans and drawings to determine system requirements. Examine the shop drawings and manufacturer's technical data to determine installation details.

Initial Inspection. Ensure that the wiring and installation of devices is in accordance with the previous section, "Interior Electrical Work." Check the primary and standby power supply installations.

Follow-Up Inspection. Witness all performance tests. Initiate remedial action when any test results indicate performance capability below specifications.

Annunciators

Preparatory Inspection. Examine the shop drawings and inspection manuals to determine system requirements and installation details.

Initial Inspection. Inspect the wiring and installation of the annunciators in accordance with the previous section, "Interior Electrical Work."

Follow-Up Inspection. Witness all performance tests. Initiate remedial action when any test results indicate performance capability below specifications.

Intercom and Paging Systems

Preparatory Inspection. Examine the shop drawings and operations manuals to determine system requirements and installation details.

Initial Inspection. Inspect the wiring and installation of the intercom and paging system in accordance with the previous section, "Interior Electrical Work."

Follow-Up Inspection. Witness all performance tests. Initiate remedial action when any test results indicate performance capability below specifications.

Radio and Public Address Systems

Preparatory Inspection. Examine the drawings and specifications to determine location, size, route, and extent of duct work, terminal boxes, wiring, and conduit; and layout of equipment and appurtenances.

Initial Inspection. Inspect the installation of pipes, conduit, cabinets, and junction boxes for size, type, location, and alignment. Ensure that the connection board and cables are identified and marked. Ensure that all components are connected to a ground. Ensure that the completed work does not interrupt other systems' alarms and emergency missions (unless approved by the customer).

Follow-Up Inspection. Witness all tests required by the contract, including continuity tests of all circuits, operating tests of all equipment, and system intelligibility tests.

Wiring of Electric Motors and Controls for Mechanical Equipment

Preparatory Inspection. Examine the drawings and schematics, specifications, and manufacturer's data to determine the wiring and controls to be installed. Work with the mechanical subcontractor to ensure the equipment is comprehensively inspected.

Initial Inspection. Ensure that all wiring is installed in accordance with the appropriate NFPA guideline (or international equivalent), and ensure that the wiring is neatly bound and parallel with or at right angles to equipment surfaces whenever possible. Ensure that all terminal boxes and conductors are properly identified. Inspect control panels for proper location and elevation. Ensure that controls within the panels have previously been inspected by the manufacturer.

Follow-Up Inspection. Witness or perform an inspection of the wiring and controls. Ensure that systems checkouts have been performed. Ensure that the wiring has been inspected for continuity and proper grounding. Initiate remedial action when necessary.

O&M Manuals and Warranties. A complete set of O&M manuals should be prepared from the manufacturer's commercial information. An equipment and manufacturer list should also be included, as well as manufacturers' warranties on the systems and components.

As-Built Drawings. When requested, ensure that as-built drawings are prepared to the normal commercial level of detail and are furnished to the customer.

Final Acceptance Testing and Demonstration Evaluation. A testing program should be developed to identify activities and items requiring final testing and evaluation, including methods to be used, instructions for performing tests with acceptance and rejection specifications, and forms to be used for recording results. Test results should be submitted to the customer as required by the contract. Testing data sheets should be added to the plan as developed.

Tenant Electrical Renovation and Operation

This section establishes methods and direction for controlling the quality of materials and workmanship used in interior electrical construction in existing buildings, including distribution. This guideline covers the control of drawings, manufacturer's data, testing data, certification, inspections, and installations. It applies to all activities of the electrical subcontractor and others who interact directly with the electrical work.

Local inspectors or officials should be responsible for organization and management of quality on all electrical systems. The electrical-systems subcontractor should be responsible for effecting quality of the electrical design and installations.

Procedure

All work described in this guideline should comply with the applicable reference guidelines specified in the "Electrical Installations" section of this chapter.

Shop drawings describing electrical installations for the tenant should be submitted to the customer for approval by the methods and guidelines provided in the specifications. Ensure that the drawings consist of the items listed in the "Electrical Installations" section of this chapter.

Examine the drawings and specifications to determine the nature and extent of the installation. Check the ground rods and ground-potential equalization bar for proper size, material, configuration, and installation. Rough and finished wiring activities should be as specified in the "Electrical Installations" section of this chapter.

Lighting Equipment

Examine the drawings and specifications to determine the location of cable trenches, manholes, and buildings. Determine the type and rating of lights, type of masts, and mounting details. Determine the number and types of control panels, their locations, and the installation details. Inspection should be performed in accordance with the "Electrical Installations" section of this chapter. Particular attention should be directed to planning to minimize rework caused by tenant changes.

Examine the drawings and specifications to determine the nature and extent of the installation. Inspection should be performed in accordance with the "Electrical Installations" section of this chapter. Particular attention should be directed to planning to minimize rework caused by tenant changes.

Intercom and Paging Systems

Examine the shop drawings and operations manuals to determine system requirements and installation details. Inspection should be performed in accordance with the "Electrical Installations" section of this chapter. Particular attention should be directed to planning to minimize rework caused by tenant changes.

Mechanical Installations

This guideline establishes methods and direction for controlling the quality of materials, equipment, and workmanship for interior and exterior mechanical A/E&C activities. It includes plumbing, HVAC, and special systems. This guideline applies to all project activities associated with mechanical installations, from review of shop drawings through inspections and testing to final acceptance and demonstration. The mechanical subcontractor should be responsible for the direct implementation of procedures for mechanical installations.

Procedure

General and Specifications. Ensure that the materials and equipment at least meet guideline products of a manufacturer and specifications regularly engaged for a period of time prior to the start of work. Inspect each major item for the proper information on the nameplate and verify the dimensions.

Shop Drawings and Supplier Specifications. Shop drawings of the subject mechanical installations should be submitted to the customer for approval by the methods and guidelines stated in the specifications. Ensure that the fire-system drawings conform to established work plans, are signed by a registered architect or engineer, and are detailed as defined in the specifications. Ensure that supplier specifications, data sheets, catalog cuts or guidelines, and the like are submitted as required by the specifications.

Inspection, Sampling, and Testing

Inspection. The general inspection and test practices defined in chapter 9 directly apply and should be incorporated herein.

Sampling and Testing of Mechanical Equipment. Ensure that all equipment to be installed has the appropriate manufacturer's certified test reports and meets specification requirements. If any such equipment requires routine monitoring (including environmental condition), routine maintenance check, gas purges, or contamination, ensure that these tests are performed.

Shop Boiler Welding

Welding Procedures. A welding procedure qualification record (PQR) and a welding procedure specification (WPS) should be completed for every shop weld, as required by the appropriate sections of the ASME Boiler and Pressure Vessel (BPV) code (or international equivalent). The WPS data sheets should be added to the welding procedure prior to performing any welding work.

In preparing PQRs and WPSs, the manufacturer or subcontractor should report the specific values for the *essential variables* that are specified in the society code (ASME or ANSI code for vessels and piping and AWS—for structural welding—or international equivalent. If there are any essential changes in a welding process used from a previously approved WPS/PQR, then a new procedure should be qualified. The basic welding processes included under this jurisdiction are the following:

- Shielded-metal arc welding
- Submerged arc welding
- Gas-metal arc welding
- Flux-cored arc welding
- Electroslag and electrogas welding

Welder Certification. The qualification tests used should be especially devised to determine the welder's ability to produce sound, flawless welds. The following criteria apply for welder qualification.

- The welder's qualification should be specifically established.
- The welder should be qualified by test or other suitable means.
- A welder qualified for one process may be qualified for others as defined by the society code.
- A change in welder position should also require requalification.
- In the vertical position, a change in direction should also require requalification. The welder's requalification should remain with the

A/E&C organization certified to the society code in effect unless (1) the welder is engaged in a given process for less than six months, or (2) there is a specific reason to question the welder's ability. In either case, requalification is required in accordance with ASME BPV Code, Section IX (or international equivalent). The welder's qualification from another contractor may be used in lieu of certification by the A/E&C organization. In such a case, the qualification may also meet the requirements of ANSI B31.1 (or international equivalent).

Ventilation and Exhaust Systems

Preparatory Inspection. Examine the drawings and specification to determine the location, size, construction details, and installation of the ventilators in accordance with approved shop drawings.

Initial Inspection. Inspect the ventilators prior to installation to ensure compliance with the shop drawings and A/E&C details. Inspect installations for anchoring, bracing, and fitting for roof slope. Ensure the vertical alignment of the ventilator and installation of screens. Inspect the connection to ducting (if required), and ensure that the connection is properly aligned and mechanically strong.

Follow-Up Inspection. Ensure that the rotor (turbine), if installed, rotates freely, is well balanced, and does not vibrate excessively when in motion. Ensure that vent controls are accessible, operate freely, close and open the vent completely, and remain in the position set.

Air-supply and Distribution Systems

Preparatory Inspection. Examine the drawings, plans, and specifications to determine the requirements of the system.

Initial Inspection. Inspect the duct work and air moving devices according to the previous paragraph. Inspect the manufacturer's data on filters. Ensure that installation is in accordance with the specifications and manufacturer's instructions.

Follow-Up Inspection. Witness all tests required by the specifications or the manufacturer. Inspect the paint for preparation of surfaces, type of paint, color, and application. Ensure that the following testing program is provided for the air-supply and distribution systems.

- Control devices: Certified performance tests should be conducted on the pressure-sensing components of each control device.
- Field testing: Hydrostatically test piping (for example, 150 percent for at least two hours); perform leak tests of low pressure duct work (for example, a maximum of 5 percent); and perform leak tests on high-pressure duct work (for example, a maximum of 0.8 percent), or as required by the specifications.
- Performance testing: Operationally test the entire system at normal and possible abnormal conditions for at least five days and certify and record results on forms, as required by the Associated Air Balance Council (AABC) or the American Society of Heating, Refrigerating, and Air Conditioning Engineers (ASHRAE) standards.

Sheet Metal Ductwork

Preparatory Inspection. Examine the shop drawings, plans, and specifications to determine the configuration, type, size, and extent of required ducts, plenums, and casings. Ascertain the requirements for air extractors, dampers, splitters, deflectors, diffusers, registers, louvers, hoods, grilles, access doors, supports, connections, and linings.

Initial Inspection. Inspect the ducts for material used in A/E&C, dimensions, configuration, and condition of joints, anchors, and hangers. Inspect the hoods for material used in construction, location, mounting, and compliance with NFPA Guideline No. 96 or international equivalent. Ensure that air deflectors are provided in accordance with specifications. Ensure that the test holes with covers are provided where indicated. Inspect the connection of dissimilar metals to ensure the connections are made with flexible connections according to the specifications. Inspect the duct passage through floors, walls, ceilings, and roofs to ensure required sleeves and frames are installed and that caulking and sealing are intact. Inspect the dampers for type, installation, and operational characteristics.

Follow-Up Inspection. Witness tests for air leakage and performance tests on operational items. Initiate remedial action when required.

Water Treatment Equipment for Swimming Pools

Preparatory Inspection. Examine the drawings and specifications for equipment, dimensions, and layout.

Initial Inspection. Provide surveillance over the manufacturer's representative installing the system.

Follow-Up Inspection. Ensure that an operational test is performed prior to turnover to the customer.

Pressure Vessels and Pipe

Ensure that welding and NDE procedures are in accordance with NDE specifications and that welders are certified in accordance with the section on "Shop Boiler Welding" in this chapter, and that welding inspection personnel are qualified according to SNT-TC-lA recommended practices and are certified according to AWS Welding Inspector Quality Control (WIQC) standards or international equivalent. Ensure that welding materials comply with Section II of the ASME BPV code or international equivalent, and that weld materials are properly environmentally controlled prior to use.

Fire Pumps

Preparatory Inspection. Examine the drawings and specifications for safety requirements, nameplates, wiring (if required), and governing requirements. Ensure that material test reports (MTRs) are obtained for the pumps.

Initial Inspection. Ensure that installation is performed in accordance with NFPA Guideline No. 20 (or international equivalent).

Follow-Up Inspection. Ensure that the following test plan is executed.

- Hydrodynamically test the pump to a head and capacity specified by the customer for a minimum of 2 hours or as required by the specifications
- Perform a test run of any engines at the rated speed for a minimum of 8 hours or as required by the specifications
- Perform a field-acceptance test through calibrated nozzles and flow meters as detailed in NFPA Guideline No. 20 or international equivalent

Seismic Protection for Mechanical Equipment

Preparatory Inspection. Examine the drawings and specifications for metal, dimensions, A/E&C details, and reinforcement anchorage and installation.

Follow-Up Inspection. Ensure that seismic protection is provided with the following:

- Sway braces for piping and duct that are not rigidly anchored
- Spreaders that are provided between adjacent piping runs for a surface distance of less than 4 inches apart
- Flexible couplings at joints that are provided for all $3\frac{1}{2}$-inch or larger pipe risers in the building and for all underground piping
- Emergency gas connections that are provided for actual gas distribution systems
- Anchor bolts conforming to ASTM A307 or as specified
- Resilient vibration-isolation devices as required
- Equipment sway braces for items supported from overhead
- Suspended acoustical ceiling assemblies
- Special smokestacks

Thermal Insulation for Mechanical Systems

Preparatory Inspection. Examine the manufacturer's insulation data and display sample cutaway sections for diagrams, proper installation, and correct materials.

Follow-Up Inspection. Inspect installation for cleanliness, freedom from moisture, and conformance to the manufacturer's recommended practices.

Gas Piping Systems

Preparatory Inspection. Examine the drawings and specifications in accordance with the previous part, "Pressure Vessels and Pipes."

Follow-Up Inspection. Ensure that the following test plan is executed.

- Perform system tightness tests prior to service.
- Perform leak tests of the system to ANSI Z222 (or international equivalent) prior to applying gas under pressure.

Plumbing, General Inspection. Inspect the piping, penetration, hangers, hot water heater, air lines, insulation, tanks, wash accessories, pumps, and oil skimmer. Pressure test the line to requirements when inspections are complete.

Sprinkler System Inspection. Inspect the installation against the guidelines prescribed in NFPA Guideline No. 13 (or international equivalent). Provide a performance test prior to customer acceptance.

Forced Hot Water Heating Systems, Oil, Gas, and Combination

Preparatory Inspection. Examine the drawings and specifications to determine the requirements of the subject system. Review the equipment and materials to verify the nameplates, equipment guards, dimensions, and welding according to the previous part, "Pressure Vessels and Pipe." Review the layout and anchorage of equipment and appurtenances.

Initial Inspection. Inspect the boiler according to preparatory inspection (or international equivalent). Inspect the fuel burning and combustion-control equipment in accordance with ASME CSD-1 Guideline. Inspect the circulating pumps. Inspect the stacks in accordance with NFPA Guideline No. 211. Inspect the fuel oil system in accordance with NFPA Guideline No. 31.

Follow-Up Inspection. Execute the following test plan.

- Hydrostatically test the system.
- Hydrostatically test the fuel oil system.
- Test the gas system to NFPA Guideline No. 54 (or international equivalent).

Central Refrigeration System for Air Conditioning

Preparatory Inspection. Examine the drawings and specifications to determine the requirements of the system. Review the equipment and materials to verify the nameplates, equipment guards, dimensions, and welding according to the guidelines noted in the previous part, "Pressure Vessels and Pipe." Review the layout and anchorage of equipment and appurtenances.

Initial Inspection. Inspect the hookup to ensure that it conforms to the manufacturer's recommended practices. Inspect the insulation. Inspect the field painting to be certain it meets Steel Structures Painting Council (SSPC) standard painting specifications. Inspect the field installation of piping according to the appropriate sections of either the ASME BPV Code or ANSI B31.1 (or international equivalent).

Follow-Up Inspection. Field pressure test with hermetic machines to a specified pressure. Provide an operational system test to expected normal and to abnormal conditions.

Air Conditioning System

Preparatory Inspection. Examine the drawings, plans, and specifications to determine the requirements of the system.

Initial Inspection. Ensure that the air conditioning unit's nameplate is dated. Ensure that the unit meets specified requirements. Ensure that mounting and anchoring are in accordance with shop drawings and the manufacturer's recommendations. Inspect the ductwork and filters in accordance with the shop drawings. Ensure that the ductwork connections are according to specifications. Inspect the chilled-water piping. Ensure that valves, fittings, and connections are of the type and size specified and that they are installed in accordance with specifications. Ensure that tubing is of the type indicated and is installed and secured as required and that caulking and sealants are installed as required. Inspect the pipe insulation. Inspect control and indicating devices.

Follow-Up Inspection. Witness all tests required by specifications, the manufacturer, or other competent authority. Initiate remedial action when required.

O&M Manuals, Warranties, and As-Built Drawings. A set of O&M manuals and as-built drawings should be prepared from the manufacturer's guideline information.

Final Acceptance Testing and Demonstration Evaluation. A final walk-through and operation test should be performed as part of the system's turnover to the customer.

Mechanical Installations for Building Expansion

This section establishes methods and direction for controlling the quality of materials, equipment, and workmanship for interior and exterior mechanical A/E&C activities for building expansion. This includes plumbing, HVAC, and special systems.

This section applies to all activities pertinent to the mechanical installations, including review of shop drawings, inspections and testing, and final acceptance and demonstration. The mechanical subcontractor should be responsible for direct implementation of procedures for mechanical and design installations.

Procedure

General and Specifications. See the "Mechanical Installations" section of this chapter.

Shop Drawings and Vendor Specifications. See the "Mechanical Installations" section of this chapter.

Inspection, Sampling, and Testing

Inspection. The general inspection and test practices defined in chapter 9 directly applies, and are incorporated herein.

Sampling and Testing of Mechanical Equipment. See the "Mechanical Installations" section of this chapter.

In addition, refer to the "Mechanical Installations" section of this chapter for details on the following:

- Inspection, sampling, and testing
- Shop boiler welding
- Welding procedures
- Welder certification
- Ventilation and exhaust systems
- Air supply and distribution systems
- Sheet-metal ductwork
- Water-treatment equipment for swimming pool
- Welding of pressure piping
- Fire pumps
- Thermal insulation for mechanical systems
- Gas piping systems
- General plumbing inspection
- Sprinkler system inspection

- Forced hot water heating systems, oil, gas and combination with the exception of hydrostatic testing of fuel oil system and testing of gas system
- Air conditioning systems

Operation and Maintenance Manuals, Warranties, and As-Built Drawings. A set of operation and maintenance manuals and as-built drawings (when requested) are prepared from manufacturer's information.

Final Acceptance Testing and Demonstration Evaluation. A final walk-through and operation test are performed as part of the system's turnover to the customer.

Turnover and Startup

This section establishes direction for building turnover to the customer and start-up activities of the facility. This section applies to all activities and disciplines of the completed facility.

The project manager is responsible for ensuring that turnover and start-up activities conform to this procedure, which provides a systematic program of building and systems turnover to the customer in a manner that verifies completeness and ensures satisfactory performance of the equipment. This program is as follows:

- Building turnover should be performed by the completed building area, using a series of guideline checklists for the respective quality procedures. In addition, any required documentation (such as MTRs, certificates, reports, and warranties) should be supplied in a manner sorted by these building areas.
- Systems operation and testing should be performed to demonstrate to the customer that the system operates satisfactorily. This test and demonstration should comply with the following procedure.

Final Acceptance Testing and Demonstration. System testing plans and programs should be developed to identify activities and items requiring final testing and evaluation, methods to be used, instructions for performing the test, including acceptance and rejection specifications, and forms to be used for recording results. Test results should be submitted to the customer as specified by the contract. Testing data sheets should be added to the plan as they are developed.

This final verification method may involve the use of special instrumentation or simulating test inputs to prove that specified requirements have been met. This method is employed when specified external stimuli (for example, hardware or software) or external devices are required to produce or measure (record) predictable results (such as verification of response times). It is also applicable when special environmental, interference, noise, or other conditions are involved.

A comprehensive final acceptance test and evaluation checklist to be used when performing this function should be contained in the quality procedures. This completed record should be added to the test packages in the quality-records file prior to turnover to the customer.

O&M Manuals, Warranties, and As-Built Drawings. A set of manuals and as-built drawings may (if specified) be prepared from the manufacturer's information. A facilities overview can be prepared defining the mechanical systems installed. This set of documents can be categorized by building, structure, system, or component. Equipment manufacturers' lists can also be included.

Notes

1. For more information about work execution, see *Mark's Standard Handbook for Mechanical Engineers,* 8th ed. New York: McGraw-Hill, 1978 and *Standard Handbook for Civil Engineers,* 2nd ed. New York: McGraw-Hill, 1976.

2. ANSI/ASME N626.3-1988 with Addendum B. "Qualifications and Duties of Specialized Professional Engineers," 1992.

17   Supporting Light and Residential Construction Projects

Procurement and Contracts: Controlling Quality for Light and Residential Construction Projects

Sample Questions

Trend-Analysis Program

Project Testing Coordination Activities

- Soil Testing
- Aggregate Testing
- Asphalt Testing
- Concrete Testing
- Calibration of Measuring and Test Equipment (M&TE)
- Mechanical and Welding Testing
- Nondestructive Examination Operations
- Electrical Testing
- Other Testing

Design and Design Changes

- Changes to Design Documents
- Design Surveillance
- Design Criteria
- Typical Design Specifications

Earthwork and Other Activities for Development Projects

- Clearing, Grubbing, and Stripping
- Embankment and Preparation of Subgrade for Driveway and Parking Areas

Earthwork Associated with Installing Water at Large-Project, Multiple-Residential Units

- Stripping
- Manhole Frames and Covers, Boxes, and Other Structures in Pavement

Subbase and Base Courses, Bituminous Pavements, Portland-Cement Concrete Pavements, Pavement Markings, and Curbing

- Subbase and Base Courses (Plant Material)

Nonwelded Pipe and Related Work in Exterior Utility and Drainage Systems

- Trenching
- Bedding, Filtering, and Selecting Backfill
- Drainage Systems
- Gravity Sanitary Sewer Systems
- Sanitary Sewers and Force Mains
- Water Lines

Spread Footings for Building and Structure Foundations

Concrete in Building Construction

Installation of CIP and CMU Materials

Framing

- Field Coordination (AIA #01050)
- General Engineering and Office Standards (AIA #01570)
- Housekeeping and Sanitary Facilities (AIA #01510)
- Temporary Office Facilities (AIA #01525)
- Personnel Training; O&M Manuals (AIA #01800)
- Site Preparation (AIA #02100)
- Wood Framing General (AIA Division 6)
- Erection of Wood Framing (AIA #6100)
- Miscellaneous Building Materials General (AIA Division 7)
- Erection of Wood Framing, Enclosures, and Windows or Doors (AIA #061000)

Installation of Structural and Miscellaneous Metals for Buildings

- Shop Drawings and Supplier Specifications
- Sheet Metalwork
- Metal Frame Hatch (for example, clerestory)
- Calibration of M&TE Operations
- Mechanical and Welding Testing
- NDE Operations
- Shop Welding

Control of Finish Construction for Buildings

Installation of Hardwood Floors for Residential Buildings

- Hardwood Strip Checklist

Architectural Construction of Buildings

Security Installations

Mechanical Installations

- Shop Drawings and Supplier Specifications
- Ventilation and Exhaust Systems
- Air Supply and Distribution Systems
- Sheetmetal Duct Work
- Gas Piping Systems
- Forced Hot-Water Heating Systems, Oil, Gas, and Combination
- Air-Conditioning System

Kitchen and Casework Installation

- Appliances
- General Kitchen Items
- Kitchen and Vanity Cabinets
- Freezer

Interim Turnover of a Portion of a Light Construction Project

A/E&C light and residential construction projects should have many of the attributes discussed in the previous chapters and should contain the elements of a good quality system described in chapters 6–11.

This chapter offers model programs for implementing a sound, practical quality system that will enhance the quality of light and residential constructed projects as well as effect significant cost and schedule savings.

Procurement and Contracts: Controlling Quality for Light and Residential Construction Projects

An important portion of this type of project is the contracting and the one-to-one personal communication between project management and each subcontractor. A substantial amount of the work for these projects is subcontracted by a firm that might also employ the developer and builder. In such a case, both the contractual and personal relationships are very important. An A/E&C organization has to work with small business subcontractors to ensure a quality project. Appendix I contains some sample contracts; they would require significant modification to fit the needs of a particular company or project and are therefore for illustration purposes only.

Sample Questions

Knowledge of required technical skills is an important quality consideration for light and residential construction projects. Many skills for this type of construction, particularly in finishwork, are important in an almost artistic way. Finish carpentry falls into this category. Such aspects as visual appearance (for example, how well all the joints are mitered) make all the difference in the world in terms of the quality of the project.

Since this type of construction may sometimes be technically less complex than larger projects and relies more on artistic elements, it is important to remember that personal knowledge rather than simple checklists is the basis for the quality system. This section contains sample questions that people in human resource management, education and training, and systems should ask potential subcontractors.

For this type of project, an A/E&C firm must be a licensed contractor in most states. A representative of the A/E&C firm must pass an examination based on the state building codes, which in turn are derived from such codes as the Uniform Building Code (UBC) or Building Officials Code Administration (BOCA). The following illustrative questions can help readers understand the content of this chapter and provide direction in hiring subcontractors.

1. When applying for a building permit, how many months must pass after filing before a project is deemed abandoned?

A. 2 months
B. 6 months
C. 1 year
D. Never

2. The definition of an *aisle* is the following:

A. A clear passageway with a minimum distance of 48 inches
B. Any clear and unobstructed passageway through a room
C. A clear passageway with a minimum distance of 36 inches
D. A clear passageway with a minimum distance of 42 inches

3. A type 2a motion picture theater has a height of 64 feet and a total of 21,280 square feet per floor. Does it meet code?

A. Yes
B. No
C. Partially
D. The square footage meets code

4. As far as hazards are concerned, dry cleaning establishments are considered:

A. Low hazard
B. High hazard
C. Not applicable
D. Hazardous only if the solvent's flash point is below 100 degrees Fahrenheit

5. What is the minimum ceiling height of habitable rooms, other than kitchens, for ventilation purposes?

A. 8 feet
B. There is no minimum height
C. 7 feet, 3 inches
D. 7 feet, 6 inches

6. What is the maximum length of exit-way access travel for a shopping mall in unlimited area buildings?

A. There is no maximum length
B. 100 feet
C. 150 feet
D. 400 feet

7. A hotel is being built in a downtown location. The architect has designed a ballroom with a floor span that will accept a live load of 90 pounds per square feet minimum. Does this meet code?

A. Yes
B. No
C. Partially
D. The drawings have to be reviewed to determine the answer

8. A foundation with timber piles is being constructed. A new order of piles has been delivered to the site. During unloading, the inspector notices that the diameter of the piles at the cutoff is 10 inches over the bark. Does this meet code?

A. Yes
B. No
C. Partially
D. The drawings have to be reviewed to determine the answer

9. The term *slump* refers to which of the following:

A. The flex point on the span of a hotel main floor
B. The movement of fill after compacting
C. A type of LVL material
D. A test used to measure concrete

10. CMU refers to which of the following:

A. Cubic meter units
B. Cast manufactured units
C. Concrete masonry units
D. A type of concrete admixture

11. In a building of type 2B construction, the fire-resistance rating required for exterior bearing partitions that support only one floor is:

A. 0 hours
B. 1 hour
C. 1.5 hours
D. 2 hours

12. The term *rebar* refers to which of the following:

A. An electrical conductor
B. Steel grilles
C. Reinforcing steel
D. Reinforcing pipe

13. Roof-valley flashing should be provided of not less than No. 28 gauge galvanized sheet corrosion-resistant steel and should extend at least 8 inches from the centerline.

A. True
B. False
C. Depends on the type of roof
D. Should be as specified in the drawings

Answers: (1) Depends on the location in which you are building, normally C. (2) C (3) A (4) B (5) A (6) C (7) A (8) B (9) B (10) C (11) B (12) C (13) B

Please note these answers are provided based on most state codes. Please check your state code.

Trend-Analysis Program

This section identifies the responsibilities of personnel who perform trend analysis, investigate the causes of adverse trends, and direct, and subsequently evaluate, the effectiveness of CA.

This section also reviews conditions affecting quality and describes the system that the senior executive of the A/E&C organization uses to analyze daily reports, the nonconforming condition log, problem action requests (PARs), and general conditions for possible trends. The project manager should be responsible for attending trend-analysis meetings and reporting on any adverse trends identified. The A/E&C organization's senior executive should be responsible for holding periodic trend-analysis meetings and ensuring that any adverse trends identified are promptly corrected and the quality loop is properly closed.

Procedure

Trend analysis is a technique that an A/E&C organization can use to examine accumulated nonconformance and other data and identify adverse trends or generic system problems. Individual reports may not necessarily identify potentially significant or generic problems; however, grouped or combined data should reveal conditions or causes that require further CA to preclude recurrence. Numbers or percentages of nonconformances within any one category should be evaluated and should serve as a guideline in determining the need for further investigation of possible adverse trends. Analysis of nonconformance data should be conducted using a current and compatible data base that includes the information and results of previous trend-analysis reports.

The senior executive should issue periodic trend-analysis reports and should document the results of the analysis and any investigations, including any recommended actions for correcting adverse trends. Significant deficiencies identified by any project manager should be reported to the senior executive, and management action should be taken immediately (for example, stop work, repair, rework, and so on).

The trend-analysis report should contain accumulated information from nonconforming items identified, daily reports, and the like. Each project manager should document and submit information, including his or her personal reports for a project, and forward it to the senior executive or delegated representative, who should then review and assimilate the information.

If any adverse trends are identified, a PAR should be issued in accordance with the A/E&C organization's procedure. The president or delegated representative may enlist the aid of outside consultants to provide a solution if the need arises.

The senior executive or delegated representative should document results of the analysis and investigations, including any recommended actions for correcting adverse trends. The completed trend-analysis report for construction activities should be distributed to all project managers and one copy should be filed. Each project manager should be responsible for investigating the causes of the unsatisfactory trends and for providing CA to preclude recurrence.

The project manager should document the results of his or her investigation, including the cause of the condition, the overall CA taken or scheduled, and the date all CA should be completed. The project manager should consider previous CA taken for recurring problems to determine the general effectiveness of that action. The project manager's response should be in the form of a memorandum to the senior executive so that it can be evaluated for adequacy and implementation.

The senior executive or delegated representative should document that objective evidence has been examined and evaluated for compliance to the project manager's original commitment. The evaluation should include a review of the procedures followed while the work was in process and should be verified by direct observation of the work being performed.

A description of an unsatisfactory project manager's response or any continuing adverse trends, along with any recommended actions, should include further action (such as disciplinary action) as the need arises. Satisfactory response and verification of closeout of the problem are considered resolution by the project manager of the senior executive's or delegated representative's trend-analysis report.

Project Testing Coordination Activities

This guideline establishes methods and direction with a purpose of such testing including operational testing similar to medium-sized projects (see chapter 16 on testing coordination activities.)

The laboratories should be responsible for the organization and management of all on-site field-testing activities. The A/E&C organization should be responsible for ensuring that proper and timely coordination is maintained between the work activities accomplished and the laboratories.

Procedure

All testing performed by laboratories should produce reports that cite the specification requirements and reference guidelines. The reports should also cover sampling methods, other test procedures used, and actual results. All test reports should be signed by a designated representative of the laboratory authorized to sign such reports.

Soil Testing

Preparatory Inspection. Examine the current schedules and plans for earthwork and excavation. Review the testing requirements contained in the technical specifications. Ensure that the laboratory is properly notified of test points.

Initial Inspection. The laboratory should ensure that required samples are taken and processed in accordance with current requirements. When any test does not comply with requirements, the laboratory should initiate the CA indicated.

Follow-Up Inspection. The laboratory should provide periodic surveillance of ongoing activities and provide retesting on subsequent lifts.

Aggregate Testing

Preparatory Inspection. The subcontractor should examine the current schedules and plans for quarry operation. Review testing requirements and directives. Ensure that all procedures and equipment to be used are approved and in acceptable operating condition. Ensure that the laboratory is properly notified of test points.

Initial Inspection. The laboratory should ensure that the required samples are taken and processed in accordance with current requirements. When any product does not comply with requirements, the laboratory should initiate the CA indicated.

Follow-Up Inspection. The laboratory should supervise the activities of the technician assigned to the quarry operations and ensure that he or she is kept informed of changes in test requirements.

Asphalt Testing

Preparatory Inspection. Examine the current plans and schedules for asphalt plant operations. Review the testing requirements and directives. Ensure that all equipment and procedures to be used are approved and in acceptable operating condition. Ensure that the laboratory is properly notified.

Initial Inspection. The laboratory should ensure that the required samples are taken and processed pursuant to current requirements. When any product does not comply with requirements, the laboratory should initiate remedial action.

Follow-Up Inspection. The laboratory should supervise the activities of the laboratory technician assigned to the asphalt plant operations and ensure that he or she is kept informed of changes in test requirements.

Concrete Testing

Preparatory Inspection. Examine all operational schedules, delivery schedules, and plans for receipt or production of materials that require testing. Review the requirements and directives pertinent to the testing to be conducted. Ensure that all procedures and equipment used are approved and in acceptable operating condition. Ensure that the laboratory is properly notified.

Initial Inspection. The laboratory should ensure that required samples are taken and processed in accordance with current requirements. When any product does not comply with requirements, the laboratory should initiate the CA indicated.

Follow-Up Inspection. The laboratory should supervise the activities of the laboratory technicians assigned and ensure that they are kept informed of changes in test requirements.

Calibration of Measuring and Test Equipment

Provide suitable facilities as requested, to control appropriate M&TE used on site by all project personnel. Calibration techniques should follow a recognized guideline, and equipment should be tagged with the next recalibration date. If uncalibrated M&TE was inadvertently used to perform a verification activity, sufficient traceability should be employed to ensure definition of the work in question.

Mechanical and Welding Testing

Qualification. Provide a program for ensuring that the certification of site welders is in accordance with the appropriate code and addenda. Ensure that recertification is handled in a controlled manner.

Support. Provide appropriate support in the mechanical testing activities for various destructive tests, such as hydrostatic examination, pneumatic examination, and the like.

Nondestructive Examination Operations

Visual Examination (VT). When specified, provide examination by certified personnel in accordance with recommended practice SNT-TC-1A (or international equivalent).

Magnetic-Particle Testing (MT). When specified, provide examination by certified personnel and equipment in accordance with the recommended practice SNT-TC-1A (or international equivalent).

Liquid-Penetrant Testing (PT). When specified, provide examination by personnel and equipment in accordance with the recommended practice SNT-TC-1A (or international equivalent).

Ultrasonic Testing (UT). When specified, provide examination by personnel and equipment in accordance with the recommended practice, SNT-TC-1A (or international equivalent).

Other NDE methods, such as impact hammer and sonoscope, can be used to test concrete, but cannot be the sole basis for acceptance or rejection.

Electrical Testing

The subcontractor should provide appropriate support of electrical testing, such as ground resistance measurements, meggering, and the like, in accordance with the manufacturer's recommendations.

Other Testing

Other testing, such as hydrostatic testing of piping and tests of fire/water facilities, recast, CMUs, sprayed-on fireproofing, and joint sealer adhesion, should be in accordance with the authorities having jurisdiction.

Design and Design Changes

This section establishes direction for A/E implementation of the design and design changes during the construction, modification, and installation activities designated as important quality items by construction personnel. This section applies to all project management personnel working with the architect or engineer to the extent agreed upon.

The senior executive should delegate to appropriate project managers the responsibility for monitoring the activities of the architect or engineer who performs according to chapter 9. This assumes that the interface is correctly maintained in order to expedite accurate design changes. The responsibility for incorporating these changes into the construction and installation activities lies with the project construction organization (the project manager or designated subcontractor).

Procedure

One should obtain a copy of the design or construction specifications and design drawings from the customer or designee and provide them to the project manager. The project manager should verify that the design or construction specifications have been certified by a registered professional engineer competent in the applicable field of design and any related construction requirements and qualified in accordance with the requirements (for example, with ANSI/ASME N626.3 or international equivalent).[1] The project manager should review with the customer program when and how activities are to be accomplished.

The project manager should work with the architect or engineer to ensure an adequate program that correctly translates the design input and criteria into design output documents, such as construction specifications, drawings, instructions, and the like. These output documents should be readily available to the client. The translation should be made using such methods as design reviews, calculations, and tests, and should be monitored periodically to ensure that the design program is operating properly.

Changes to Design Documents

Requests for changes to the design document should be detailed in a DCR, and submitted to the customer or designee for approval by the project engineer. Records of the DCRs and subsequent actions should be maintained on the DCR log. Modifications of any document used for construction, including reports of final design reviews, should be reconciled with the design report by the person or organization responsible for the original design, unless the customer specifically designates another responsible organization. A revision or addendum to the design report should be prepared and certified when required to indicate the basis or reconciliation of the changes.

Changes generally fall into two major categories: first, a change of significant impact on the project affecting marketability and the A/E&C organization's potential for selling or using the finished property, and second, a change to one or more subcontractors working for the A/E&C organization but within the context of the prime objective between the A/E&C organization and potential client. Any change to the final documents issued with the contract must be approved. To control any type of contract change, the following procedures should be observed.

- An identifying number should be assigned to any drawing, sketch, or written or other directive from the A/E&C organization or internally from an employee upon receipt of the document.
- The project manager should determine whether a directive has an impact on the A/E&C organization or on the subcontractors within the context of the prime objective.
- A construction employee should then follow up with the subcontractors to ensure receipt of information on any cost or schedule impact within the allocation per the general conditions.
- Upon receipt of the impact information from the subcontractors, the project manager should review the change against contract documents to ensure that (1) all credits as well as additions are included, (2) the work described is a true change and is not a contract requirement, (3) pricing is per the contract documents, and (4) quantities are correct.
- The project manager should then prepare a rough draft of a change letter to be issued in accordance with requirements.
- The project manager should be responsible for ensuring that the change is complete with respect to all subcontractors having submitted

impact information, and that all related costs (such as design fees and overhead) and any schedule impact information is included.

• The major thrust of this section is that *time is of the essence*. Should the subcontractor fail to meet the specified deadlines, the subcontractor should be required to pay for the change without reimbursement. This would be true whether the change affects one's contract or the contract with a subcontractor.

Design Surveillance
Surveillance of A/E activities should be performed. A periodic evaluation should be performed of the architect or engineer's corporate office activities to ensure compliance to contract specifications, the quality program, and guideline practices.

Design Criteria
An important factor of effective designs is the use of good design criteria. Typical design criteria for light and residential construction projects include such criterion as the following:

• Square feet of living space.
• Because of the unique construction methods used, and contrary to most new construction, all plans and specifications should not be subject to change at the discretion of the builder, should be considered final and complete, and should become a part of a fully executed purchase-and-sell (P&S) agreement.

At the time of a fully executed P&S agreement, all materials, structures, and components that have been fully contracted should not be subject to change. Other items desired by the buyer should be adjusted, and price differences should be fully itemized. Any changes by the buyer should be subject to the same design controls as the original design and mutually agreed to in writing.

Typical Design Specifications
Design specifications should be clear and concise. Typical design specifications for light and residential construction projects include

- Foundation: Walls XX"XX'X X/X" X000# pounds per square inch (psi) steel #X Bar reinforced cast-in-place (CIP) concrete. Waterproofing and insulation system is (for example, Owens Corning TUFF-N-DRI with XX-year guarantee waterfree, and X-inch insulation board R-10).
- Floor: X inches, X000# psi (CIP) concrete slab over 6-inch compacted gravel base, over 12-inch compacted fill with 2-inch insulation and waterproof membrane.

Earthwork and Other Activities for Development Projects

This section establishes methods and direction for controlling site earthwork activities, including earthwork for driveways, ditches, and structures, compacted fills, borrow, select materials, and fine grading. This applies to all earthwork and other geotechnical activities of project personnel. The contractor should be responsible for the organization and supervision of the control of earthwork and other geotechnical operations.

Clearing, Grubbing, and Stripping

Control. Control the clearing, grubbing, and stripping operations as necessary, including the removal of all stumps, stockpiling of existing loam on site, and stockpiling of natural stone walls on site in a designated area.

Preparatory Inspection. Examine the drawings, technical specifications, and project schedules to ascertain when, where, and how testing should be performed.

Follow-Up Inspection. Inspect and report the following:

- Unsatisfactory or unstable material is removed and replaced.
- Marking tapes are installed as indicated.
- Backfill is of satisfactory material and applied and compacted in courses as indicated.

Embankment and Preparation of Subgrade for Driveway and Parking Areas

Line and Grade. Monitor the shaping of the subgrade for line and grade. Excavation to final grade should be made to required surfaces. Inspect layout for conformance to drawings and specifications.

Initial Inspection. Inspect the surface of embankments and preparation of subgrade prior to sampling and testing. Inspect the area of the excavation; ensure that location, dimensions, and configuration are correct. Ensure that drainage structures are as specified. Ensure that unsatisfactory materials are removed from excavation and hauled away according to local regulations. Ensure that the use of satisfactory excavated material and borrow material is in accordance with current directives. Inspect the surface preparations for embankments. Ensure that foreign material and debris are removed. Ensure that the surface is properly prepared and that the moisture content is within specified limits. Ensure that embankment material is placed on and compacted in horizontal layers.

Ensure the Subgrade. Ensure that surfaces are prepared according to specifications and removed and replaced with properly compacted, satisfactory material. Ensure that shoulders are configured as indicated.

Follow-Up Inspection. Inspect and report the following:

• Straightedge requirements for finished grades are met.
• Excess or unsatisfactory material is disposed.
• Finished surfaces are smooth, compacted, in accordance with lines, grades, and cross sections or elevations indicated, and properly maintained during subsequent construction activities.

Earthwork Associated with Installing Water at Large-Project, Multiple-Residential Units

This section establishes methods and direction for controlling earthwork and other geotechnical quality activities; including earthwork and subsurface exploration; earth and rock excavation for roads, trenches, and ditches; backfill for trenches, compacted fills; borrow; grading; and binder reapplication in the disturbed areas.

This applies to all earthwork and other geotechnical activities associated with the installation of the water main, including I&T. This includes the installation of a X" waterline from an existing hydrant located (predetermine this location) through (specify layout), and terminating approximately XX feet beyond the building. Termination would be X" gate valve, box, and plug. A main gate valve should also be installed after the hydrant to isolate X" main from the hydrant. This also includes extending the existing X" water main in projects X, installing a hydrant, and terminating with X" gate valve, box, and plug as detailed in the site plan. Care should be taken to avoid the drainage line between any two projects.

The excavating contractor is responsible for the organization and management of the earthwork and other geotechnical operations.

Stripping
Control. Control stripping operations as necessary. Control excavation, trenching, and backfilling for utility and drainage systems.

Line and Grade. Monitor the preparation to receive fill in the excavated and trenched areas. Excavation should be performed to the lines and grades indicated. Check the layout for conformance to drawings and specifications.

Support and Protection. Monitor the dewatering and support of excavations, including the location and protection of existing utilities.

Control. Control the backfilling operation to be sampled and tested. Control the trenches for gas distribution lines. Ensure that the depth provides at least the specified cover over the top of the pipes, that the pipe bed is of specified material, that satisfactory excavated material is properly stockpiled, and that unsatisfactory excavated material is disposed of properly.

Control the Trenches for Water Lines. Ensure that the water lines are beyond the minimum required distance from sewer lines, that trench depth provides at least the specified cover over the top of the pipe, that the pipe bed is graded to avoid highs and lows, and that satisfactory excavated material is properly stockpiled and that unsatisfactory material is disposed of properly.

Inspect the Excavations for Appurtenances. Ensure that the dimensions and locations are as specified.

Manhole Frames and Covers, Boxes, and Other Structures in Pavement
Examine the drawings, specifications, and survey reports. Ascertain the location, dimensions, and requirements for these structures, and verify their placement.

Equipment Control. Control the spreaders, compactors, blowers, brooms, saws, drills, and hand tools to be used on the job. Ensure that all the equipment is of the approved type and in acceptable operating condition.

Control the transport equipment; ensure that the truck beds are clean, tight, smooth, and properly coated to prevent adhesion of the bituminous concrete. Control the edges of pavement; ensure that the edges are neatly trimmed to accommodate shoulders. Control the binder course; ensure that the thickness of the pavement is as specified.

Check Smoothness with a 10-Foot Straightedge. A surface variation of more than $\frac{1}{4}$ inch is unsatisfactory. Ensure that CA is taken if warranted.

Patch Test of Binder and Wearing Courses. Test the binder and wearing courses in accordance with the requirements of the specifications.

Field Testing. Hydrostatically test the piping at 100 percent of design pressure for at least 2 hours to check for leaks.

Subbase and Base Courses, Bituminous Pavements, Portland-Cement Concrete Pavements, Pavement Markings, and Curbing

This section should be used in conjunction with Appendix G which establishes methods and direction for controlling the construction of materials and workmanship for subbase and base courses; bituminous and portland-cement concrete pavements for road, street, sidewalk and parking areas; and pavement markings and curbing. This applies to all project activities associated with this work. The assigned subcontractor should be responsible for the organization and management of quality for all earthwork and paving efforts. Management should monitor compliance to site requirements.

Subbase and Base Courses (Plant Material)

Line and Grade. Monitor the subbase and base courses and check the layout for conformance to drawings and specifications.

Grade Sampling and Testing. Test the density of one random sample from the mat and one from the joint of each sublot.

Material Sampling and Testing. Asphalt content should be in accordance with ASTM D2172. Aggregate gradation should be in accordance with ASTM C136 and C117.

Initial Inspection. Inspect out the subbase and base course surfaces for adequate compacting and tolerances as specified. Unsatisfactory areas should be corrected.

Final Inspection and Recommendations. Inspect tolerance and protection of subbase and base courses.

The following should correspond to the requirements in Appendix G.

- Bituminous prime coat, including material sampling and testing, line and grade, checking, final checking, and reporting
- Bituminous tack coat, including material sampling and testing, line and grade, and checking
- Bituminous surface treatment (single or double) including line and grade, testing, sampling and testing materials, checking, second treatment when required, final checking, and reporting
- Bituminous binder and wearing course for streets, roads, and open areas, including line and grade, checking of grade, preliminary sampling and testing of materials, bituminous mix design, and leveling of shim courses
- Manhole frames and covers, boxes, and other structures in pavement, including checking the edges of pavement, patch tests of binder and wearing courses, core tests of binder and wearing courses, smoothness tests, final checking, and reporting
- Portland-cement concrete for other areas, including line and grade; checking and calibration of paving equipment; concrete mix design; checking and calibration of concrete; checking of forms or guide wires (for slip form); checking of grade; checking of keyways, dowels, tie bars, and pavement reinforcement; checking longitudinal construction joints and the transverse joints; checking of embedded items; daily sampling of concrete; sampling; curing; testing of beams; straightedging of plastic concrete; curing and protection; checking of saw joints; joint sealing; remedial action, concrete cores; final checking; and reporting
- Pavement marking, including checking of surface and layout, checking and calibration of equipment, sweeping and cleaning, checking of operations, final checking, and reporting.
- Concrete sidewalk and curbing, including checking of grade, checking of forms, line and grade, mix design, checking, curing and protection, final checking, and reporting

Nonwelded Pipe and Related Work in Exterior Utility and Drainage Systems

This section establishes methods and direction for controlling the quality of materials and workmanship in the construction of exterior or underground nonwelded-pipe utility systems, including the surface drainage, water lines, sanitary gravity sewers, sanitary sewer force mains, and siphons. This applies to all activities of the exterior construction areas, excluding hot-water lines (central heating), petroleum oil lubricant (POL) transfer lines, or gas lines.

The subcontractor should be responsible for the organization and management of the quality functions for the nonwelded pipe and related work. The project manager should ensure conformity to this section.

Trenching

Support and Protection. Support and protect the trenching excavations as detailed in the previous section.

Line and Grade. Check the line and grade as detailed in the previous section.

Overdepth in Rock Excavation. During rock removal and disposition defined in the technical specifications, unauthorized overexcavation should be backfilled equal to an unsupported vertical trench wall not exceeding usually 4 feet.

Bedding, Filtering, and Selecting Backfill

Sampling and Testing. Ensure that the bedding is of the type and thickness shown, including the maximum stone size. Ensure that the crushed-stone bedding is compacted with the minimum required passes of a hand-operated, plate-type vibratory compactor. Sample and test the final backfill in accordance with the previous section.

Inspecting and Reporting. Inspect and report the trenching operation in accordance with the guideline. In addition, ensure the location and protection of existing utilities and the layout and alignment of pipelines.

Drainage Systems

Inspecting, Sampling, and Testing of Materials. Inspect the drainage piping and structures, pipe trench widths, and pipe backfill. Watertight joints should be hydrostatically tested in accordance with recommended practice SNT-TC-1A. Compacted backfill should also be tested in accordance with the previous section.

Storage and Handling of Materials. Spot check as necessary to ensure that the pipe and other structures are delivered to the trench in good condition and are handled and lowered into the trench in an authorized manner.

Inspecting Workmanship. Inspect each section resting on the bed; ensure that installation of joints and fittings are assembled according to specifications. Finally, ensure that valves and their boxes are properly installed.

Concrete Drainage Structures. Unless otherwise specified, the structures should conform to requirements for concrete (for example, 3000 psi). During hydrostatic testing, only one joint sample of each type needs to be taken.

Miscellaneous Metals. Miscellaneous metals should conform to appropriate ASTM designations. The shapes, sizes, and layout should be as indicated by specifications and drawings.

Final Tests, Inspecting, and Reporting. Certified copies of the hydrostatic testing results should be retained.

Gravity Sanitary Sewer Systems

Inspecting, Sampling, and Testing of Materials. Examine the drawings and specifications to determine the size, location, and extent of sewers, including manholes. Cooperate with other personnel to check the excavation, trenching, and backfilling. Cooperate with the CMU and CIP subcontractors to check recast and CIP manholes.

Ensure that the distance of sewer lines to water lines is at least the minimum distance required. Ensure that the backfill is properly compacted where pipe crossroads are installed within, for example, 3 feet of the building foundations. Inspect pipe laying to ensure that bell-ended or tongue-and-groove pipes are laid with ends properly oriented. Inspect joints to ensure that they are made in accordance with approved guidelines. Inspect manholes for compliance with specifications for accessories, covers, frames, and pipe connections. Inspect the pump installations; ensure that the pumps are installed according to specification and the manufacturer's instructions. Witness all performance-capability tests. Ensure that the pump performance is in accordance with the manufacturer's performance curves, that pump motors turn in the correct direction, that the configuration of piping is in accordance with shop drawings, that the equipment is installed in accordance with the specifications and manufacturer's instructions, and that all valves, pipes, and controls are properly identified.

Inspect All Hoisting Equipment. Ensure that the travel in both horizontal and vertical planes is adequate and smooth. Ensure that all the equipment is installed in accordance with specification and manufacturer's instructions. Witness all performance-capability tests.

Inspect the Manholes. Ensure that required valves, fittings, and gauges are installed, that required tools (if any) are present, and that covers and other appurtenances are as specified.

Storage and Handling of Materials. Spot check incoming materials as necessary to ensure that pipes and other materials are delivered to the trench in good condition, protected from sunlight if required, and handled and lowered into the trench by approved methods.

Line and Grade. Verify the line and grade as detailed.

Inspecting Workmanship. Provide a complete inspection of the pipe joints and connections, and manhole construction, frames, and covers.

Concrete Manholes and Structures. Unless otherwise specified, the manholes and structures should conform to the requirements of ASTM C478 for portland-cement type II (ASTM C150) or international equivalent.

Miscellaneous Metals. Miscellaneous metals should conform to appropriate ASTM or other designations. The shapes, sizes, and layout should be as indicated by the specifications and drawings.

Building Connections. All connections should be visually inspected to ensure conformance to detail drawings. Unless otherwise indicated, all connections should be sealed with a flexible manhole seal assembly.

Final Tests, Inspecting, and Reporting. After the pipelines have been installed and the trench backfilled and compacted, the lines should be inspected by lamping for misalignment and displacement. Visually check for any defects. Infiltration tests should be made as required when ground water is normally at least 2 feet above the top of the sewer. Exfiltration tests should be substituted when normal groundwater levels are lower. In the case of polyvinyl chloride (PVC) pipe, deflection tests should also be performed.

Sanitary Sewers and Force Mains
Inspecting, Sampling, and Testing of Materials. Examine the drawings and specifications to determine the size, location, and extent of the piping. Review the location and sizes of valves and their boxes. Cooperate with other personnel to inspect excavation, trenching, and backfilling. Ensure that the minimum specified distances between utilities are maintained. Inspect the laying of pipe to ensure that the full length of each section rests on the pipe bed (except for redresses excavated to accommodate joints and fittings).

Storage and Handling of Materials. Spot check incoming materials as necessary to ensure that the pipe and other materials are delivered to the trench in good condition and are handled and lowered into the trench in a proper manner.

Line and Grade. Verify the line and grade as detailed.

Inspecting Workmanship. Inspect the installation of joints and fittings to ensure that the pipes are cut and joints are made according to specifications. Inspect the valves and their boxes to ensure proper installation.

Concrete Structures and Thrust Blocks. Unless otherwise specified, the structures should conform to the requirements of ASTM C478 for portland-cement type II (ASTM C150) or international equivalent.

Miscellaneous Metals. Miscellaneous metals should conform to appropriate ASTM or other designations. The shapes, sizes, and layout of the metals should be as indicated by specifications and drawings.

Final Tests, Inspection, and Reporting. After the system has been installed and trenches backfilled and compacted, pressure and leakage tests should be performed. Force mains should be subjected to a test pressure of 150 psig for at least 2 hours.

Water Lines

Inspecting, Sampling, and Testing of Materials. Examine the drawings and specifications to determine the type, size, and extent of water lines. Determine the types, sizes, and locations of valves, valve boxes, and fittings. Review the approved welding and weld testing guidelines. Cooperate with other personnel to inspect the excavation, trenching, and backfilling for water lines. Ensure that the proximity of water lines to sewer lines and nonferrous metal pipe is at least the minimum required distances, that the offset in alignment between adjacent pipe joints is within tolerance, that the fittings are of the type required for their particular application, and that the full length of each pipe, except for recesses excavated to accommodate fittings, rests on the pipe bed.

Storage and Handling of Materials. Spot check as necessary to ensure that pipes and other materials are delivered to the trench in good condition, handled in a manner that does not damage the coating or lining, and lowered into the trench by proper methods.

Line and Grade. Verify line and grade as detailed.

Inspecting Workmanship. Check the valve boxes and pits to ensure the proper location, size, depth, and cover. Inspect the welded joints to ensure the proper butting, welding, and testing in accordance with specifications and American Welding Society (AWS) (or international equivalent) requirements. Inspect the service stops to ensure proper connections. Inspect the field-applied mortar. Inspect the field-applied and repaired coatings for surface preparation and coating application. Provide a completed inspection report of the waterline system.

Concrete Structures and Thrust Blocks. Unless otherwise specified, the structures should conform to the requirements of ASTM C478 for portland-cement type II (ASTM C150).

Valves and Boxes. Ensure that all valves are of the type required for their applications and have proper working pressures.

Fire Hydrants. Ensure that the fire hydrants are located and installed as shown on the detail drawings. Each hydrant should be connected to the main with the specified branch line having at least as much cover as the distribution main. Inspect for plumbness, that the outlet is 18 inches above grade, and that the operating nut is 48 inches above grade. Ensure that the hydrant slab dimensions are as specified.

Building Connections. All connections should be visually inspected to ensure conformance to detail drawings.

Miscellaneous Metals. Miscellaneous metals should conform to appropriate ASTM designations. The shapes, sizes, and layout should be as indicated by specifications and drawings.

Final Tests, Inspecting, and Reporting. After the system has been installed and trenches backfilled and compacted, pressure and leakage tests should be performed. The waterline should be subjected to a test pressure of 150 psig for at least 2 hours. Final visual inspection should be performed for any defects. In addition, the water main should be subjected to bacteriological testing, with representative samples taken as specified. As-built drawings should be prepared by the subcontractor for vertical and horizontal piping runs, delineating the exact location of cleanouts.

Spread Footings for Building and Structure Foundations

For methods and direction for controlling the quality of materials and workmanship during installation of spread footings for buildings and structures, see the similarly titled section in chapter 16.

Concrete in Building Construction

For methods and direction for controlling the quality of materials and workmanship during installation of concrete (CIP) in light building construction, see the similarly titled section in chapter 16.

Installation of CMU Materials

This section details the installation of materials and workmanship for CMUs as well as other recast architectural concrete units for building construction. This section also establishes methods and guidelines for controlling the quality of materials and workmanship for CMUs as well as other recast architectural concrete units for building construction. It applies to all vertical masonry installation activities, from sampling and inspecting incoming materials to final surface sealing.

The CMU subcontractor should be responsible for the organization and management of control for CMU construction. He or she should be responsible for ensuring that the quality of materials is as specified by the PO and that the materials are delivered in good condition and properly stored. The CMU subcontractor should be responsible for ensuring the integrity of mix ratios and the grade quality of quarry products.

Procedure

Sampling and Testing of Materials. Check incoming CMU materials to ensure that they comply with ASTM C140 or ASTM C780 (or international equivalent). Ensure that an appropriate certificate of conformance is obtained from the manufacturer, who has previously been approved by a competent authority.

Storage and Handling of Materials. Inspect to prevent excessive buildup of the units in storage at the site. Ensure that they are protected from weather and handling damage.

Inspecting Workmanship. Inspect the mock-ups and courses for conformance to drawings and specifications. Inspect the walls; ensure that they are plumb, level, and square. Ensure that the CMUs are properly prepared prior to being placed. Ensure that the mortar is of the type specified. Inspect the recesses for partition walls. Ensure that the location, size, and configuration are correct. Inspect the installation of anchors and tie bars. Ensure that the joints are filled flush with concrete or mortar. Inspect the anchorage to abutting walls and columns. Ensure that the anchors are placed as indicated. Inspect the control joints for location and construction. Ensure compliance with drawings and specifications. Ensure that the bond-beam blocks are properly reinforced or filled with mortar. Ensure that the filler strips are installed as required. Inspect the corner bonding for compliance to the technical specifications.

Chases, Pockets, and Block-Outs for Pipe, Conduit, and Ducts. Examine drawings and specifications to determine proper installation of chases, pockets, and block-outs for pipe, conduit, and ducts. Cooperate with on-site trades.

Concrete-Filled Hollow Block. Ensure that the hollow CMUs are ASTM C90, type I, grade N-I and have an oven-dry weight of more than 125 pcf (unless otherwise indicated as non-load-bearing CMU walls). Ensure that the joint material is ASTM D1056, grade number RE-41 E1 or RE-42 E1 or closed-cell vinyl or PVC conforming to ASTM D1667, grade number VE or VE42 or equivalent. Ensure that the installed joints are flush, tooled, and raked, with widths as appropriate.

Preparatory Inspection. Examine the drawings and specifications to determine the details of the structure. Ascertain the locations and types of joints, sills, partitions, corners, beams, reinforcements, and the like as indicated in the contract documents.

Sampling and Testing of Mortar and Grout. Randomly select a number of samples each day (normally three) to be tested by the methods described in masonry preconstruction test specifications.

Precast Lintels, Jambs, and Sills. During the erection process, check the unit for tightness of joints, fitness, alignment, cleanliness, and damage prior to plastering. Cooperate with other on-site trades.

Anchors, Sleeves, Flashing, Grounds, and Other Embedments. Examine the drawings and specifications to determine proper installation of anchors, sleeves, flashing, grounds, and other embedments. Cooperate with other trades.

Temporary Support for Doorways, Windows, and Large Openings. Ensure that temporary support for doorways, windows, and large openings is adequate from a safety standpoint and for finished use.

Bond Beams. Ensure that the bond beams are reinforced by at least No. 4 rebar and filled with grout. Examine the drawings and specifications to determine proper installation of bond beams.

Tie Bars and Wall Reinforcement. Check that the vertical bars are accurately positioned at the centerline of the wall, that there is a minimum clearance between the rebar and the units of $\frac{1}{2}$ inch, and that the units are secured properly and positioned in accordance with drawings.

Field Testing. Coordinate with an independent testing laboratory to perform the Prism Test methods, which includes compression testing for each type of wall construction at 7- and 28-day intervals for each 5000 square feet of wall (when specified).

Final Inspection and Reporting. As a final inspection, ensure that proper certification reports are in order, that the report for air-dry conditions is completed; and that a final walk-through for damage has been made. These reports should be available for review by the customer.

Framing

Field Coordination (AIA #01050)[2]

The subcontractor should closely coordinate the work between his or her forces and any subtier contractors as well as other subcontractors and should become fully familiar with all work required under the contract.

The contract documents, drawings, and specifications are intended to describe and define a complete project ready for management's ability to sell the completed facility's intended use. The subcontractor should be responsible for producing a complete and acceptable project, as so described, for management.

The owner should obtain the necessary building and occupancy permits and any other permits necessary for obtaining the work; the subcontractors should obtain and pay for all other permits necessary for completing the work.

General Engineering and Office Standards (AIA #01070)

The subcontractor should verify all dimensions and conditions at the site and report in writing any discrepancy to management before ordering material and equipment or starting any construction activity.

All work should conform to the state building code's latest revision at the time of execution of the contract. All work should be inspected and tested. The owner should select inspection and testing (I&T) agencies approved by appropriate authorities. All sections, details, notes, methods, or materials shown or noted on any plan, section, or elevations should apply to all other similar locations unless otherwise noted.

All framing subcontractors should be insured and covered as follows:

- Workman's compensation and employer's liability, in accordance with the state laws
- Liability, including contractor's protective coverage, with the following limits:
  Comprehensive general liability personal injury
  $XXX,XXX each occurrence (completed operation)
  $XXX,XXX aggregate property damage
  $XXX,XXX each occurrence
  $XXX,XXX aggregate
  Comprehensive auto liability bodily injury
  $XXX,XXX each person property damage
  $XXX,XXX each occurrence
- Fire and extended coverage insurance provided by the contracting organization on the Builder's Risk Completed Value Form in the amount of the contract (covers the interests of management)

Housekeeping and Sanitary Facilities (AIA #01510)

Temporary toilet facilities for use by all personnel employed on the work should be provided and maintained by the contracting organization or a delegated subcontractor. It is the responsibility of each subcontractor to maintain cleanliness at the site during the use of the facilities.

It should be the responsibility of each subcontractor to notify the customer's site representative in a timely manner of the subcontractor's exact temporary water supply requirements during construction activities. Management should provide this service if and only if the organization's requirements are made known in writing at least 10 days prior to construction.

Each subcontractor should be responsible for timely cleanup, housekeeping, and general removal of rubbish as specified in the contract. If there is any discrepancy as to who is responsible during the progress of the work, it should be the contracting organization's sole authority to designate cleanup by the subcontractor. If the need dictates, each on-site subcontractor should be responsible for periodically designating a laborer to a cleanup crew to maintain job-site order. Such work should include, but not be limited to, the following:

- Complete removal of all rubbish, debris, and equipment from the site, and sweeping and dusting of all surfaces
- Removal of all temporary protection

Temporary Office Facilities (AIA #01525)

Each subcontractor should employ his or her own temporary field office in an area designated by the customer in order to supervise his or her forces and to keep plans, records, and documents pertaining to the work in his or her designated scope. It should be the responsibility of each subcontractor to ensure that he or she maintains close contact with the contracting organization's site representative in order to coordinate site activities.

Personnel Training; O&M Manuals (AIA #01800)

At least 45 days before completion of his or her work, each subcontractor should be required to submit in duplicate all O&M manuals (if applicable) and warranties applicable to his or her work. O&M manuals should consist of at least the following: catalog cuts with descriptive information; parts lists and descriptions; operating instructions; names, addresses, and telephone numbers where parts and service can quickly be obtained; and any other information needed to properly use, maintain, and service the structures, systems, and components.

Written guarantees and warranties should be submitted to the customer from each subcontractor performing work on the contract. The subcontractor should agree to correct all defects in materials and workmanship for three years following issuance of a Certificate for Substantial Completion (or for a longer period, if specified). Further, each subcontractor should warrant and guarantee that materials, equipment, and workmanship under the contract will remain free from defects, but that if defects appear, they will be corrected in a timely manner at the subcontractor's expense. The contracting organization has the right to correct defects at full reimbursement if the defects are not corrected to its satisfaction.

Site Preparation (AIA #02100)

Areas used for the subcontractor's convenience should be cleared and restored at no additional expense to the customer, including mulching, seeding, and planting. On-site vegetation should be protected as designated by the customer's site representative.

Wood Framing General (AIA Division 6)

All contract documents should complement the requirements in this section of the technical specifications. All other sections of the technical specifications and the contract drawings should be referred to in order to determine the scope of work of Division 6 whether or not the scope is specifically detailed in this division. The scope of work in this division includes the furnishing of labor, equipment, and materials listed in the contract as appended by the subcontractor's proposal and as shown on the contract and shop drawings.

Erection of Wood Framing (AIA #06100)

This section of the technical specifications specifies the wood frame construction. Dimensions, tolerances, and configurations of all wood framing should be in accordance with UBC, or approved equivalent in effect at the time of contract signing. Work should be performed in strict compliance with chapter 5, the BOCA field inspection manual entitled *Wood Frame* (or international equivalent), and with the contract drawings and documents.[3]

Miscellaneous Building Materials General (AIA Division 7)

All contract documents should complement the requirements in this section of the technical specifications. All other sections of the technical specification and the contract drawings should be referred to in order to determine the scope of work of Division 7, whether or not the scope is specifically detailed in this division. The scope of work in this division includes the furnishing of labor, equipment, and materials listed in the contract as appended by the subcontractor's proposal and as shown on the contract and shop drawings.

Erection of Wood Framing, Enclosures, and Windows or Doors (AIA #06100)

This section of the technical specifications specifies the wood frame construction. Dimensions, tolerances, and configurations of all wood framing should be in accordance with the BOCA UBC (or approved equivalent) in effect at the time of contract signing. Work should be performed in strict compliance with chapter 7 of the BOCA field inspection manual, entitled *Miscellaneous Building Materials* (or international equivalent) and with the contract drawings and documents.[4] In addition, the manufacturer's directions should be obtained from the supplier and complied with as an addendum to the technical specifications.

Installation of Structural and Miscellaneous Metals for Buildings

This section establishes methods and direction for controlling structural materials and workmanship used for buildings during vertical erection and for controlling the field-testing activities performed by the testing laboratories. This includes appropriate on-site testing in the areas of calibration control, bolting, welding, and NDE required by the A/E&C organization. The purpose of such testing is to verify and certify that site construction activities meet technical requirements. This responsibility is vested with the subcontractor. The information in this section applies to all activities associated with this work.

Responsibility for the implementation of the procedures in this section should fall to the subcontractor of steel installation responsible for structure, welding, and bolting. The subcontractor should be responsible for ensuring that materials delivered from the suppliers are as specified by the PO, in good condition, and properly stored.

Procedure

Preliminary Examination and Review of Specifications and Shop Drawings. An in-depth review of the specifications and construction drawings should be performed to ascertain constructibility and reveal any potential areas of concern. Any problem areas should be handled in accordance with the specifications. Particular areas of interest include the following, which are discussed in detail in Appendix H.

- Structural welding
- Structural steel
- Steel deck
- Miscellaneous metal
- Sheet metalwork for decking

The following measurement, inspection, and testing procedures shall be used, as explained in Appendix H.

- Measuring, sampling, and testing of materials
- Storing and handling of materials
- Line, grades, and plumbness
- American Institute Steel Connections (AISC) requirements for structural connections
- AWS (or international equivalent) requirements for welded connections
- Daily sampling and testing
- Protection of finished work
  —Structural: shop rust-proofed, primed, and painted
  —Steel deck: shop rust-proofed, primed, and painted
  —Miscellaneous metal: shop rust-proofed, primed, and painted
- Checking of the general installation

Other important construction attributes discussed in Appendix H include the following:

- Manufacturer's specifications
- In-process measurement
- As-built drawings (In many cases, as-built drawings are specified as submittal to the client. The as-built drawings should be in sufficient detail to permit maintenance activities to be properly performed.)

These final records are developed after completion of the project. This includes a complete set of reproducible sepia drawings to be submitted to the client as required. These drawings should include the following details.

- Location and dimensions of any changes within the building
- Revised grades and alignments of structures
- Revised elevations
- Changes in detail of design or additional information

Final Inspection and Reporting. A final inspection and walk-through should be performed prior to turnover of the building to the client.

Finish Construction Maintenance Instructions and Warranties.
Maintenance instructions should be prepared from commercial supplier data and furnished to the client for the items that require them. Commercial warranties provided by suppliers should be included.

Shop Drawings and Supplier Specifications
Shop drawings of the subject mechanical installations should be submitted to the client for approval by the methods and guidelines provided in the specifications. Ensure that the fire-system drawings conform to established work plans, are signed by a registered engineer, and are detailed as defined in the specifications. Ensure that the supplier specifications, data sheets, catalog cuts, and the like are submitted as required by the specifications.

Sheet Metalwork
Tasks for sheet metalwork include

- Observation of environmental conditions, number and skill level of sheet metalworkers, condition of substrate
- Verification of compliance of materials before, during, and after installation
- Inspection of sheet metalwork for proper size and thickness, fastening and joining, and proper installation
- Preparation of surfaces for receiving sheet metalwork
- Protection of dissimilar metals
- Forming, lapping, and sealing of joints
- Securing sheet metalwork to structure
- Watertightness
- Damage

Metal Frame Hatch (For Example, Clerestory)
Tasks for metal frame hatch include

- Inspecting for damage and defects
- Inspecting for conformance with requirements
- Protecting dissimilar materials

Calibration of M&TE Operations

Provide suitable facilities for controlling appropriate M&TE used on site by all project personnel. Calibration should follow a recognized guideline, and records should include the date of the next scheduled recalibration. If uncalibrated M&TE is inadvertently used to perform a verification, sufficient traceability should be employed to ensure satisfactory performance of the completed facility.

Mechanical and Welding Testing

Provide a program for certifying site welders in accordance with the appropriate code and addenda. Provide assurance that recertification is handled in a controlled manner.

Provide appropriate support in the mechanical testing activities for various destructive tests (for example, hydrostatic or pneumatic examination).

NDE Operations

NDE operations include

- VT. Provide examination by certified personnel in accordance with the recommended practice SNT-TC-1A (or international equivalent).
- MT. Provide examination by certified personnel and equipment in accordance with the recommended practice SNT-TC-1A (or international equivalent).
- PT. Provide examination by personnel and equipment in accordance with the recommended practice SNT-TC-1A (or international equivalent).
- UT. Provide examination by certified personnel and equipment in accordance with the recommended practice SNT-TC-1A (or international equivalent).

Shop Welding

Welding Guidelines. A procedural qualification record (PQR) and welding procedure specification (WPS) should be completed for every shop weld required by the appropriate sections of the ASME boiler and pressure vessel code (BPV) (or equivalent). The WPS data sheets should be added to the documentation as the need arises or prior to any welding. In preparing these documents, the manufacturer or subcontractor should report the specific values for the essential variables specified in the AWS or ASME codes (or equivalent). If there are any essential changes to a welding process since previously approved WPS and PQR, then a new guideline should be qualified.

The basic welding processes normally included are

- Shielded-metal arc welding
- Submerged arc welding
- Gas-metal arc welding
- Flux-cored arc welding
- Electroslag and electrogas welding

Welding Certification. The qualification tests used should be devised to determine the welder's ability to produce sound and flawless welds. The following guidelines apply for welder qualification.

- The welder's qualification should be specifically established.
- The welder should be qualified.
- A welder qualified for one process should be qualified for others as defined by the AWS or ASME BPV codes.
- A change in welder position should also require requalification.
- In the vertical position, a change in direction should also require requalification.

The welder's qualification to the AWS or ASME BPV codes should remain in effect unless (1) the welder is not engaged in a given process for more than 6 months, or (2) there is a specific reason to question the welder's ability. In either case requalification is required in accordance with AWS or ASME BPV codes.

Welding of Structures. Ensure that welding and nondestructive guidelines are in accordance with the paragraph above, that welders are qualified in accordance with AWS code, and that welding checking personnel meet the requirements of the SNT-TC-lA qualification practices, and are AWS welding inspector quality control (WIQC) certified (or international equivalent).

Ensure that the welding materials comply with Section II of the ASME BPV code, or the AWS code, as appropriate, and that welding materials are properly environmentally controlled prior to use.

Control of Finish Construction for Buildings

For methods and direction for controlling the quality of materials and workmanship during finishwork activities in light building construction, see Appendix H finishwork activities.

Installation of Hardwood Floors for Residential Buildings

This section establishes methods and direction for controlling the site hardwood floor installation activities. Responsibility is vested with the subcontractor as required. These methods apply to all project activities associated with this work.

Responsibility for the implementation of this guideline should fall to the subcontractor responsible for the supply, installation, and finish of—for example—red-oak flooring. The subcontractor should be responsible for ensuring that materials delivered from the suppliers are as specified by the POs, are in good condition, and are properly stored.

Procedure

Preliminary Examination and Review of Specifications. An in-depth review of the specifications and construction drawings should be performed to ascertain constructibility and reveal any potential areas of concern. Any problem areas should be handled in accordance with the specifications.

Measuring, Sampling, and Testing of Materials. Structural and finish structures, systems, and components should be inspected immediately upon receipt. Appropriate certified testing results should be obtained, reviewed, and approved as defined in the specifications.

Storing and Handling of Material. The storage and handling of materials should be performed on receipt, in strict compliance with the manufacturer's recommended practices. Storage should be such that there is no degrading of the received materials up to the point of installation. Additional guidelines are as follows:

- Excessive handling should be avoided, and environmental protection should be provided as required.
- Temperature and humidity control should be provided when deterioration of the material can occur.
- Materials should remain sealed and packaged, marked and labeled, identifying the manufacturer.

Line, Grades, and Plumbness. The alignment, grade, and plumbness of the installed materials should be performed in strict compliance with the manufacturer's recommended practices. Measuring devices should be appropriately calibrated and of the precision and accuracy specified in the technical specifications.

General Painting. Requirements should be checked on a random basis during installation.

Protection of Finishwork. Adequate protection should be provided to prevent deterioration of the finishwork.

Finish Carpentry. Areas include fabricated items, special mill items, and woodwork items.

Manufacturer's Specifications. When structures, systems, and components are being manufactured, conformance to requirements should be in the following order of precedence.

1. Specified codes and guidelines
2. Technical specifications and drawings

The manufacturer's specifications should adequately provide sufficient descriptive data, erection and installation construction details, and O&M instructions for turnover to the client.

Final Inspection and Reporting. A final inspection and walk-through should be performed prior to turnover of the building to the client.

Finish Cconstruction Maintenance Instructions and Warranties. Maintenance instructions should be prepared from supplier data and furnished to the client. The commercial warranties provided by the supplier should be included.

Hardwood Strip Checklist

- Since water and water vapor can severely damage the floor, correct any existing water problem.
- Ventilation under wooden floors is necessary to prevent damage.
- Ensure that a good subfloor has been installed with 1-inch-by-4-inch or 1-inch-by 6-inch, No. 1 or No. 2, common-seasoned, square-edged thoroughly dry lumber. These boards should be installed diagonally across the joists and nailed to every joist with two 10d

nails. Leave $\frac{1}{4}$ inch between the boards for expansion and contraction. In the case of plywood, use $\frac{1}{2}$-inch-thick sheets with grain on the outer plies at right angles to the joists. Nail the panels at 6-inch intervals along each joist with 7d (or larger) nails.

- Prepare the floor first. This should include covering a rough floor using an underlayment.
- Unwrap the flooring and leave it for at least 72 hours in the room in which it is to be installed.
- Tack the first two strips of flooring in place, and snap a chalk line on the subfloor for setup.
- Use a piece of scrap flooring as a buffer block when tapping the tongues and grooves together to protect the flooring from visible hammer tracks.
- Drive the flooring nails at a 45-degree angle through the tongue of the flooring.
- Stagger the flooring joints to make a neater-looking floor.
- To fill out a strip of flooring, run the gap board against the nailed board and scribe a line at the end of the nailed strip.
- If the strip has a tongue on the end that is to fit against the wall, cut it off; for openings, make a cardboard template for proper fitting.
- The final strip should be face nailed by wedging a bar between the wall and the strip to maintain tightness.
- If hardwood strip flooring is unfinished, sand and finish it using a penetrating sealer. Then buff and wax.
- Provide adequate protection of the finished surface with heavy-duty construction paper during remaining construction steps.

Finish Construction O&M Manuals and Warranties. O&M manuals should be prepared from supplier data and furnished to the client. Commercial warranties provided by the supplier should be included in the manuals.

Architectural Construction of Buildings

This section establishes methods and direction for controlling materials and workmanship used for constructing buildings during vertical erection, including architectural and finishwork. These guidelines apply to all project activities associated with this work.

Procedure

Preliminary Inspections and Review of Specifications and Shop Drawings. An in-depth review should be performed of the specifications and construction drawings to ascertain constructibility and reveal any potential areas of concern. Any problem areas should be handled in accordance with the specifications and contract. Particular areas of interest include the following:

- Miscellaneous metal. Areas include material thickness, type, grade, class, dimensions, and construction details.
- Finish carpentry. Areas include fabricated items, special mill items, and woodwork items.
- Exterior insulation and finish. Areas include certificates of compliance, instructions, samples, test data, and connections.
- Metal-frame clerestory. Areas include joint, member, anchorage, and glazing details.
- Caulking and sealants. Areas include samples and manufacturer's descriptive data.
- Steel doors and frames. Areas include location of each, elevation of each type, construction and assembly details, reinforcement locations, and details on sheets, anchors, and metal thickness. Areas also include catalog cuts, fire-door certifications, and appropriate UL labels.
- Aluminum doors and frames. Refer to the preceding paragraph about steel doors and frames.
- Wood doors. Areas include location of each, elevation of each type, construction and marking details, and hardware blocking locations. Areas also include fire-door certifications and samples.
- Accordion and operable partitions. Areas include certificates of compliance and manufacturer's descriptive data.
- Plaster. Areas include ceiling framing and lathing, special wall framing, openings, and seismic requirements.
- Gypsum wall board. Refer to the preceding paragraph about plaster.
- Acoustical treatment. Areas include exposed suspension system, method of anchoring and fastening, and reflected ceiling plan.
- Aluminum wall louvers. Areas include materials, sizes, thickness, fastenings, and profiles.

Storing and Handling of Material. The storage and handling of materials should be performed upon receipt in strict compliance with the manufacturer's recommended practices. Storage should be such that there is no degrading of the received materials up to the point of installations. Excessive handling should be avoided, and ground and weather protection should be provided when required.

Line, Grades, and Plumbness. The alignment, grade, and plumbness of installed materials should be performed in strict compliance with the specifications and the manufacturer's recommended practices. The measuring devices should be appropriately calibrated and should be of the precision and accuracy specified in the technical specifications.

Protection of Finishwork. Adequate protection should be provided to prevent deterioration of the finishwork.

As-Built Drawings. These final records should be developed after completion of the project. This includes a complete set of reproducible mylar to be submitted to the client. These drawings should include the following:

- Location and dimensions of any changes within the building
- Revised grades and alignments of structures
- Changes in detail of design or additional information

Other protection of finishwork includes

- Cement-base waterproofing: proper preparation of surfaces, proper application of materials, cleaning and protection, damage
- Exterior insulation and finish: proper attachment of suspension system, proper attachment of accessories, welding requirements, fitness and alignment of finished soffit, tightness of joints, cleanliness of soffit finish, damage.
- Caulking and sealants: condition of joint prior to application of compound, correct type of primer, back-up material, sealer and caulking compound, weather conditions, application of compound, including correct size and type gun, installation of back-up material, neatness of finished joint, and proper application of sealant, damage.

Finish Construction Maintenance Instructions and Warranties.
Maintenance instructions should be prepared from supplier data and

furnished to the client. Commercial warranties provided by the supplier should be included.

Control of Electrical Construction for Buildings
For methods and direction for controlling the quality of materials and workmanship during electrical installations in light building construction, see chapter 12 in the wiring section regarding electrical activities.

Security Installations
This section establishes methods and direction for controlling the materials and workmanship used in interior and exterior security installations, including distribution of power. For this area, the control of drawings, manufacturer's data, testing data and certification, inspections, and installations should be specifically defined in the contract or specifications.

This section also establishes methods and guidelines for controlling the field-testing activities performed by testing laboratories, including on-site NDE and electrical tests as required. The purpose of such testing is to verify and certify that site construction activities meet technical requirements. Operational testing of systems and components, however, is specifically excluded from the laboratory responsibility. This responsibility is vested with the subcontractor.

This section applies to all activities associated with installation of security devices. The selected security subcontractor is responsible for organization and management of the control of all security systems.

Procedure
General, Specifications, Shop Drawings. All work described in this section should comply with the following reference guidelines as applicable.

- Specified federal specifications
- Specified ANSI, ASTM, and IEEE standards (or international equivalents)
- International Conference of Building Official's Uniform Building Security Code
- NEMA guidelines (or international equivalent)
- NFPA publications (or international equivalent)
- UL
- Others as specified in the specifications

Shop drawings describing security installations should be submitted to the client for approval by the methods and guidelines provided in the specifications. The drawings submitted should include the following:

- Equipment and materials list
- Descriptive and technical data
- Catalog cuts
- Wiring diagrams and special inspections
- Equipment layout and anchorage
- Conduit and cable-tray runs

Interior Security-Wiring Installation. Examine the drawings and specifications to determine the nature and extent of the installation. Prior to placing the wiring, inspect the ground rods and ground-potential equalization bar for proper size, material, configuration, and installation. Prior to placing the walls, ceilings, and floors, inspect the cable sleeves, conduit, and other devices that are embedded in or penetrate the structure. Inspect the size, material, location, and alignment of these items.

Calibration of M&TE. Provide suitable facilities to control appropriate M&TE used on site by all project personnel. Equipment should be calibrated according to a recognized guideline and tagged with the date of the next required recalibration. If uncalibrated M&TE was inadvertently used for verification, sufficient traceability should be employed to ensure the definition of the work in question.

Security System Testing Operations. Provide appropriate support during testing activities for various tests such as ground resistance measurements, meggering, and the like.

O&M Manuals and Warranties. A complete set of O&M manuals should be prepared from manufacturer's information. Equipment and manufacturers' lists should also be included. In addition, warranties on the systems and components from the manufacturers should be included with the O&M manuals.

Final Acceptance Testing and Demonstration Evaluation. A system should be developed to identify activities and items requiring final testing and evaluation, methods to be used, instructions for performing tests with acceptance and rejection specifications, and forms to be used for recording results. Test results should be submitted to the A/E&C organization as required by the contract. Testing data sheets should be added to the plan as they are developed.

Final Inspection and Reporting. A final inspection and walk-through should be performed prior to turnover of the building to the client.

Mechanical Installations

This section establishes methods and direction for controlling the installation of materials, equipment, and workmanship for interior and exterior mechanical construction. This includes plumbing, HVAC, and special systems. These guidelines apply to all project activities associated with mechanical installations, from review of shop drawings through I&T to final acceptance and demonstration. The mechanical subcontractors should be responsible for the direct implementation of mechanical installations.

Procedure

General and Specifications. Ensure that the materials and equipment are at least equal to those of a manufacturer who is a regular supplier prior to the start of work. Check each major item for the proper information on the nameplate, and verify the dimensions.

Shop Drawings and Supplier Specifications

Shop drawings of the subject mechanical installations should be submitted to the client for approval using methods and guidelines in the specifications. Ensure that the fire systems conform to established work plans, are signed by a registered professional engineer, and meet the specifications. Ensure that the supplier specifications, data sheets, catalog cuts, and the like are submitted as required by the specifications.

Ventilation and Exhaust Systems

Preparatory Inspection. Examine the drawings and specifications to determine the location, size, construction details, and installation of the ventilators in accordance with approved shop drawings.

Initial Inspection. Inspect the ventilators prior to installation to ensure compliance with the shop drawings and construction details. Inspect installations for anchoring, bracing, and fitting to roof slope.

Ensure the vertical alignment of the ventilator and installation of screens. Inspect the connection to ducting (if required). Ensure that it is properly aligned and mechanically strong.

Follow-Up Inspection. Ensure that the rotor (fan), if installed, rotates freely, is well balanced, and does not vibrate excessively when in motion. Ensure that the vent controls are accessible, operate freely, close and open the vent completely, and remain in any position.

Air Supply and Distribution Systems

Preparatory Inspection. Examine the drawings, plans, and specifications to determine system requirements particularly related to the ductwork and air-moving devices.

Initial Inspection. Check the manufacturer's data on filters. Ensure that the installation is in accordance with the specifications and manufacturer's instructions.

Follow-Up Inspection. Witness all tests required by the specifications or by the manufacturer. Inspect the paint for preparation of surfaces, type of paint, color, and application. Ensure that the following testing plan is provided for the air-supply and air-distribution systems.

- Control devices: Certified performance tests are to be conducted on pressure sensing components of each control device.
- Field testing: Pneumatically test the system at 150 percent of design pressure for at least 2 hours. Leak test low-pressure duct work to a maximum of 5 percent, and leak test high-pressure duct work to a maximum of 0.8 percent (or as specified).
- Performance testing: Test the operation of the entire system at normal and possible abnormal conditions for a minimum of 5 days or as specified, and ensure that results are certified and recorded on forms as required by the Associated Air Balance Council (AABC) or American Refrigeration Institute (ARI) standard 210.

Sheetmetal Duct Work

Preparatory Inspection. Examine the shop drawings, plans, and specifications to determine the configuration, type, size, and extent of required ducts, plenums, and casings. Ascertain the requirements for air extractors, dampers, splitters, deflectors, diffusers, registers, louvers, hoods, grilles, access doors, supports, connections, and linings.

Initial Inspection. Inspect the ducts for material used in construction, dimensions, configuration, condition of joints, anchors, and hangers. Check the hoods for material used in construction, location, mounting, and ensure compliance with NFPA Guideline No. 96 (or international equivalent). Ensure that air deflectors are provided in accordance with specifications. Ensure that the test holes with covers are provided where indicated. Inspect the connection of dissimilar metals to ensure that the connections are made with flexible connections according to the specifications. Inspect the duct passage through floors, walls, ceilings, and roofs to ensure required sleeves and frames are installed and caulking and sealing are accomplished. Inspect the dampers for type, installation, and operational characteristics.

Follow-Up Inspection. Witness the tests for air leakage and performance of operational items. Take remedial action as required.

Gas Piping Systems

Preparatory Inspection. Examine the drawings and specifications.

Follow-Up Inspection. Ensure that the following test plan is executed. Prior to service, perform system tightness tests, and prior to applying gas under pressure, leak test the system to ANSI Z223.1 or ARI standards 240 and 270 (or international equivalent).

Plumbing, General Inspection. Inspect piping, penetration, hangers, hot-water heater, air lines, insulation, tanks, wash accessories, pumps, and oil skimmer. Pressure test the line to requirements when completed.

Forced Hot-Water Heating Systems, Oil, Gas, and Combination

Preparatory Inspection. Examine the drawings and specifications to determine the requirements of the subject system. Review equipment and materials to verify the nameplates, equipment guards, dimensions, and welding. Review the layout and anchorage of equipment and appurtenances.

Initial Inspection. Inspect the boiler, the fuel-burning equipment to ASME CSD-1 (or international equivalent), the combustion-control equipment to guidelines, the circulating pumps, any stacks to NFPA Guideline No. 211 (or international equivalent), and the fuel oil system to NFPA Guideline No. 31 (or international equivalent).

Follow-Up Inspection. Execute the following test plan.

- Pressure test the system.
- Pressure test the fuel oil system.
- Test the gas system to NFPA Guideline No. 54.

Air-Conditioning System

Preparatory Inspection. Examine the drawings, plans, and specifications to determine the system requirements.

Initial Inspection. Inspect the air-conditioning unit's nameplate data. Ensure that the unit meets specified requirements and that mounting and anchoring is in accordance with the shop drawings and manufacturer's recommendations.

Ensure that the duct work and filters are in accordance with the shop drawings and that the duct work connections are according to specifications. Inspect the chilled-water piping. Ensure that valves, fittings, and connections are of the type and size specified, and are installed in accordance with specifications. Ensure that tubing is of the type indicated and is installed and secured as indicated.

Ensure that caulking and sealants are installed as required. Inspect the pipe insulation and the control and indicating devices.

Follow-Up Inspection. Witness all tests required by the specifications, manufacturer, or other competent authority. Initiate remedial action when necessary.

O&M Manuals, Warranties, and As-Built Drawings. A set of O&M manuals and as-built drawings (when requested) should be prepared from the manufacturers' information.

Final Acceptance Testing and Demonstration Evaluation. A final walk-through and operation test should be performed as part of the system's turnover to the owner.

Kitchen and Casework Installation

This section establishes methods and direction for controlling the installation of materials and workmanship for kitchen and casework. This includes guidelines for installing products, ensuring the accuracy of identification, properly controlling drawings, preparing O&M manuals, inspecting the installation, and executing appropriate operating tests. This section applies to all activities associated with kitchen and casework installation according to ANSI A161 (or its international equivalent). The subcontractor should be responsible for the organization and management of the controlling functions for the installation of kitchen, equipment, and casework, as well as assuring the National Kitchen Cabinet Association (NKCA) certification and seal is affixed.

Procedure

Shop Drawings and Supplier Specifications. An in-depth review of the subject documents should be performed to ascertain constructibility and reveal any potential areas of concern. Shops drawings describing the subject installations should be submitted for approval by the methods and guidelines provided. The drawings should consist of the following:

- Equipment and materials list
- Descriptive and technical data
- Catalog cuts and O&M manuals
- Installation diagrams and special inspections
- Equipment layout and anchorage
- Mechanical and electrical connections

Appliances

Preparatory Inspection. Examine the drawings and specifications to determine National Sanitation Foundation (NSF), American Gas Association (AGAL), and UL guidelines to be complied with, dimensions to be checked, equipment nameplates, and field tests to be performed.

Initial Inspection. Ensure that any soldering or brazing meets the federal guidelines in the technical specifications. Inspect any exposed welds or otherwise-fused joints to ensure they are ground smooth, polished, and finished. Ensure that no overheating has occurred during these operations.

Ensure that the fastening devices are properly installed and of the same composition as the metal being joined. Ensure that the counters, sinks, utility distribution systems, hoods, refrigerators, burning equipment, and backflow preventers are properly installed.

Inspect the electrical connections for compliance to guidelines in the "Electrical Installations" section of this chapter. Check the plumbing connections for compliance to guidelines in the "Mechanical Installations" section of this chapter.

Follow-Up Inspection. Performance tests should be completed on selected items, such as refrigeration system to guideline mechanical specifications and electrical system to guideline electrical specifications. An operating test should be performed on refrigerators for a sufficient period to ensure both a complete control-system cycle and temperature stabilization.

General Kitchen Items
Preparatory Inspection. Ensure that the proper UL (or equal) labels are affixed.

Follow-Up Inspection. Ensure that top and sink, accessories, refrigerator, range and oven, cabinets, and hardware are properly installed, adjusted, and cleaned.

Kitchen and Vanity Cabinets
Preparatory Inspection. Examine certified test reports, drawings, catalog data, and samples to determine installation and layout details. Perform first-article inspections, which should be available for the A/E&C in the supplier's shop.

Follow-Up Inspection. Inspect the installation on the cabinets and countertops for level, plumb, trueness to line, and tightness against adjacent walls. Ensure that they are secure and that the joints are properly prepared.

Freezer
Preparatory Inspection. Examine the drawings and specifications to determine the details of construction, metal gauges, fittings and mounting, size and space of anchors, and interconnection to other work.

Initial Inspection. Inspect the installation of the wall and ceiling panels, hardware, and mechanical refrigeration in accordance with the manufacturer's recommendations. Ensure that care is exercised to assure plumbness, level, and trueness to line.

Follow-Up Inspection. Execute a test of operational readiness in accordance with the guidelines.

Interim Turnover of a Portion of a Light Construction Project
This section establishes the interim turnover method to the owner of a portion of a project. This material applies to all activities and disciplines associated with the project.

Procedure

A systematic program should be established for building and systems turnover to the client in a manner that verifies completeness and ensures satisfactory performance of the equipment. This program should include building turnover by area, using a series of checklists for the various areas (entitled, for example, Quality of Structural, Architectural, and Finish Construction). In addition, any required documentation, such as material testing reports (MTRs), certificates, reports, and warranties, should be sorted by building area.

During turnover of this portion of the light construction project, ensure the completeness of the following to obtain occupancy permit approval.

- Interface of the portion to be turned over to other external areas (for example, the garage)
- Fire protection (smoke alarms) in the specified zones
- Power to lighting and security-surveillance equipment
- Lighting operational and in accordance with the proper lighting drawing and revisions
- Proper temporary cutoff to ongoing construction areas
- Dimensional layout per contract and construction drawings
- HVAC system, including plumbing, per contract and construction drawings
- Stairways including connections complete with proper handrails
- Other finishing activities (for example, carpet, floor mats, wall board, vinyl carpet, cove caps, ceilings, signage, and so on) in accordance with the contract and construction drawings

Systems operation and testing should be performed to demonstrate to the owner that the system performs satisfactorily. A system testing plan should be developed to identify activities and items requiring final testing and evaluation as well as the methods to be used. The plan should include instructions for performing the tests and cover acceptance and rejection requirements, with the forms to be used for recording results. Test results should be submitted to the senior executive or designated representative. Testing sheets should be added to the plan as developed. For the interim area to be turned over, a checklist should be prepared that ensures completeness of electrical, plumbing, HVAC, smoke and heat detection, other fire-safing, external interfaces, utilities, and finishwork.

O&M Manuals, Warranties, and As-Built Drawings. A set of O&M manuals and as-built drawings should be prepared from the manufacturers' information. A facilities overview should be prepared defining the mechanical systems installed.

A comprehensive list of reference contract documents (primarily drawings) should be provided on the turnover checklist. Other applicable contract documents should be referenced on the checklist. This is for the purpose of having the latest, most accurate information during the final walk-through.

Notes

1. This numbering system refers to the MASTERFORMAT designated by the American Institute of Architects and Construction Specification Institute.

2. American National Standards Institute/American Society of Mechanical Engineering N626.3 "Qualifications and Duties of Specialized Professional Engineers," 1988, with Addenda b 1992.

3. International Conference of Building Officials. *Wood Frame.*

4. International Conference of Building Officials. *Miscellaneous Building Materials.*

18 Quality Systems on Hard-Money or Fixed-Price Contracts

Control of Bidding and Estimating

Guidelines for Contracting

Hard-Money Procurement System

A quality system is one of the most challenging programs to implement on hard-money contracts. The term *hard-money contracts* refers to a contracting mechanism also defined as *lump sum*. In this case, the A/E&C organization agrees to construct the facility for a fixed price. Successful use of lump-sum contracting requires completely detailed work-breakdown plans and specifications. The advantage of lump-sum contracts is that the owner can be assured profit considerations will motivate the contractor to complete the work in the least practicable time.

The rewards of an effective quality system will show up on the bottom line. They will be immediate and obvious. If followed religiously, the following rules can affect a project positively.

- Break down the project activities with a conventional work-breakdown structure (WBS). This should be detailed and should follow the natural flow of the job from beginning to end.
- Choose the significantly few work items that will make the largest impact on the job. To maintain a structured approach and obtain the most accurate list of items, use Pareto analysis.
- From the very beginning of the project, use an unbiased accounting system that will track the real COQ.
- In estimating the project, use an independently hired third-party estimator that provides a similar work-breakdown costing estimate.
- At the conclusion of the project, collect all direct and indirect costs and compare the results to the original independent estimate. They may be surprising!

Control of Bidding and Estimating

It is important to begin work on a hard-money project by establishing procedures to manage the estimating process and to control subcontractor and supplier bidding processes, thereby ensuring that qualified organizations are selected under clearly defined competitive guidelines. One must ensure that contracts are executed such that any contract changes receive the same level of control as did the original contract.

These procedures must apply to the entire project team and to company affiliates that are letting contracts in the development of the facility related to the construction process. In performing this function, the project manager should work with the engineering, procurement, and accounts payable departments. He or she should be responsible for executing these functions in accordance with the systems defined in these procedures and for ensuring proper review and approval.

Senior management must review and approve any supplier and contractor selections prior to award and maintain awareness of the status of the bidding and estimating processes. These responsibilities for review, approval, and reporting are equally important for a partnership as for a corporation.

Guidelines for Contracting

The project manager should determine the A/E&C process that will be used. In general, this will be based on

- Conceptual design
- Production of design output documents
- Procurement
- Grubbing and clearing
- Earthwork and excavation
- Foundation
- Structural erection
- Enclosure (roof and exterior walls)
- Mechanical work
- Electrical work
- Specialty items
- Partitions and drywall activities
- Finishwork
- Checklist and project closeout
- Analysis of project history

The project cost-control system must be used to monitor project quality costs from inception to final closeout and help ensure project completion within budget. Typically, quality cost variances are due to labor and productivity difficulties, excessive material usage, and loosely managed contracts. All data should be closely reviewed, monitored, and tracked. If a substantial amount of the work is subcontracted, the following elements must be closely tracked.

- Contract work
- Cost of each WBS element
- The schedule start and end dates for each element
- Quantities of material or equipment required
- Delivery schedules

The project cost system should provide the necessary information, through responsibility reports, exception listings, and other cost summaries, to minimize the opportunities for cost and productivity variances. The key to controlling costs is to provide responsible managers with accurate and timely information that highlights potential quality problem areas. These areas must be identified in a time frame that allows for CA before problems materialize. The project cost system should be simple, to the point, and commensurate with the complexity of the project. Regardless of the reporting format or complexity, the following information should be contained in any project cost system.

- Early warning of potential cost problems and isolation of anticipated performance variances
- Responsibility reporting to associate specific individuals with recorded results and to summarize results for successive levels of management
- Productivity control to permit cost controls to be applied in a manner consistent with the way the work is performed
- Supporting data for letting of contracts to ensure that the monetary amounts involved are reflected in the project budgets
- Control of reserves to ensure that various types of contingencies are properly established, given visibility, and closely monitored

Exception reporting can be used to highlight those areas requiring attention. The project cost-control system will rely on an accurate budget of costs and quantity amounts against which actual performance can be measured. A budget overrun projection should be brought to the immediate attention of the project manager for resolution. With this knowledge, the project manager can take preventive and corrective measures that will possibly keep the final cost within budget.

Cost forecasting is one of the essential functions of cost control. The cost forecast should be prepared using expenditures to date, commitment expenditures, and anticipated expenditures. The cost forecast is shown as a projected cost in the total cost report. The cost forecast is made in the same format as, but independently of, the budget estimate. This permits a direct comparison of the two. Since the cost forecast pinpoints overruns, forecasted values, quantities, and other costs will be tested for reasonableness and accuracy. In addition, the job and project cost codes associated with these values will be validated by the system. Job cost will encompass major cost categories. The key types of system reports include budget summaries, detailed performance exceptions, responsibility reports, change-order tracking, material usage, and labor and equipment productivity.

The estimating system should be used to quantify (including monetary value) the material and services required for the project. The cost-estimating function has several objectives to meet, including the following:

- A basis for supporting cost-control budgets
- A basis for funding requirements
- Resource summarizations to assist planning and scheduling
- A basis for the evaluation of contractor and subcontractor proposals

Project management should prepare every element of the construction sequence, including the

- Data base
- Historical data
- Labor quantities and rates
- Material quantities and rates
- Equipment quantities and rates
- Composite of rates
- Escalation rates
- Productivity rates and other factors
- Identification of estimating method used
- Preliminary or order-of-magnitude estimates
- Detailed estimates

- Changes in work scope
- Review and approval evaluation
- Evaluation of subcontractor proposals
- Construction activity monitoring
- Reestimation

The system should include the project baseline budget as derived from the cost-estimating process. The cost baseline can be used to monitor actual costs and productivity rates in order to accurately plan the future allocation and utilization of resources. In addition to providing estimates of the total cost of a project, the cost-estimating function can provide reestimates of the cost to complete the remaining portion of a project at any point in time. Also, the estimating function can be used to evaluate the cost effectiveness of alternative design decisions.

The system should also detail labor, equipment, and material resources required to perform a project initially calculated in the pre-project estimating process. This information, along with project milestones, allows for resource planning and rescheduling. The cost-estimating function also assists in the evaluation of various contractor proposals by estimating contractor work and reporting the estimate by line item. This estimate can then be compared with the proposal to determine whether the contractor understands the scope of work.

The key aspects of the estimating system are

- Summary cost estimates
- Detailed cost estimates
- Resource profiles
- Contractor proposal summaries

Hard-Money Procurement System

Approved Suppliers List (ASL). A list should be compiled of at least six suppliers qualified to perform a work element or series of elements as defined in the work-breakdown structure for the project. Development of the list may require visiting suppliers' shops and similar projects, or contacting clients of the potential subcontractor. In addition, during this process, encourage the potential suppliers and subcontractors to provide input into the conceptual design. Hard-money contracts can be very successful if this is enhanced.

Prequalification. A request should be sent to the potential subcontractors to prequalify them for a particular project. (In this prequalification step, the A/E&C firm should supply each potential subcontractor with specifications based on the conceptual design.) In addition, a preliminary estimate or bid should also be requested. Because of the time required to evaluate proposals, no more than three potential subcontractors should be contacted for any phase of the work.

Bid. A clearly delineated specification must be prepared, and a request for proposal (RFP) developed, along with a clear cost sheet. One will find in the hard-money process that typically six bids will be grouped one bid very low, three or four bids in the mid-range of the expected value, and the balance very high. Throw out the high and low bids and concentrate on the three in the mid-range. The three in the mid range probably will have commensurate quality. At this point concentrate on the lowest cost bidder. In today's A/E&C community, government contracting restricts your ability to procure in this manner. However, changes in both the commercial and governmental contracting world are occurring to allow this bid process.

Best and Final. The two low bidders should be asked for a best and final value—also known as best and final offer (BAFO)—based strictly on cost. Then a selection can be made.

Negotiation and Contract Award. A final contract should be negotiated based on the specifications and any exceptions identified. If problems occur in negotiations with the low bidder, then the next low bidder can be offered the work. Sometimes it may be advisable due to the size and scope of the A/E&C project to initially contract in a phase one, cost reimbursable manner. At the completion of phase one, a hard-money or fixed price is determined based on a much more definitive scope.

In summary, hard money can quickly show the financial benefits of an effective quality system. However, schedule and cost (as illustrated in Figure 4.5) will pressure quality.

19 Quality Systems on Cost-Plus Contracts

Control of Cost and Scheduling

The quality system employed for cost-plus contracts is considerably different from that for hard-money contracts. Although lump-sum contracts can be negotiated as any other type of contract, often some form of cost-plus management is used. Under a cost-plus contract, the A/E&C contractor's fee is computed on the basis of percentage of the cost of construction. When strong TQM partnering exists, the potential for financial abuse is less.

With cost-plus contracts, contractual incentive techniques can minimize litigation and preclude the owner's use of retainage (sometimes referred to as retained earnings) to improve both control of construction and project quality. Work under a cooperative, rather than an adversarial, environment leads to improved relationships with clients and subcontractors, as well as, competitive bidding.

Contractual incentives minimize the need for retainage in contracts and provide a competitive, but not adversarial, environment on cost-plus projects. Positive incentive techniques are effective based on a simple human TQM concept. Rewards and recognition have significantly more effect than punitive techniques such as retainage. Unfortunately, in today's contracting work of the A/E&C industry, punitive techniques are much more common.

Several incentive methods follow. These methods are general in nature; particular cases may not warrant their use. Another effective quality tool is teaming or partnering; it can be used effectively in cost-plus projects. Here is a list of some unusual teaming methods.

- Providing conceptual-alignment teaming meetings with the customer prior to beginning the design.
- On a continuing basis, relying heavily on communication and coordination meetings between personnel responsible for work-flow items.
- Encouraging extensive training of project personnel or other persons whose performance can affect quality.
- Encouraging the use of state-of-the-art materials or technology advances to improve cost, schedule, and quality.
- Providing surveillance at the supplier's shop, rather than inspecting the structure, system, component, or material when it arrives at the construction site.
- Providing more in-process checking or inspection, rather than relying on final inspection.

- Formally prequalifying both suppliers and subcontractors based solely on quality, even in the case of public projects. The public bidding process sometimes precludes this from occurring.
- Using quality audits or quality evaluations and assessments to improve project management.

Control of Cost and Scheduling

This section establishes methods and direction to control project costs and schedules throughout the life of a project. This system can be employed in both hard-money and cost-plus type contract projects. The rigor of this procedure is much more important in cost-plus projects. The following example is of a typical project-control system, though such systems may vary depending upon the complexity of a project. This section describes programs for procurement of documents, cost tracking, and schedule tracking.

The standards presented here apply to all personnel who have responsibility for generating, approving, and processing requisitions, purchase orders (POs), and change orders. This includes personnel responsible for tracking ongoing project schedules. Specifically, the project manager or procurement manager must be responsible for the preparation of requisitions and for ensuring that quality and technical requirements are included correctly in the documents. These requisitions should be inspectable, adequately controlled, and contain specific acceptance criteria. The project manager is also responsible for reviewing and approving all procurement documents and project schedules to ensure their completeness.

The following information must be contained in a procurement document.

- The scope of work to be performed by the supplier
- The technical requirements, keyed to specific drawings, specifications, codes, and regulations (including revisions thereto) that describe the items, materials, or services to be furnished
- A method for identifying or for providing later identification of test, agency inspection, and acceptance requirements, and any special instructions and requirements for such activities as identified in the contract specification
- Organization of activities
- Qualification of personnel

- Quality program applicability
- Design control
- Control of documents
- Control of purchased equipment and services
- Identification and control of materials, parts, and components
- Control of processes
- Inspection and test control
- Control of M&TE
- Handling, storage, and shipping
- Control of construction status
- Control of nonconforming items
- Control of CA
- Project records and audits

This information should be included on a procurement document to the extent required for proper completion of the work.

The supplier should be required to incorporate appropriate quality requirements in subtier procurement documents as necessary. At each tier of a procurement, the documents should allow for access to that supplier's shop and records for surveillance. Because there is a possibility that hold points will be required, the procurement documents must identify the specific characteristics to be checked and the method of communicating the location of these hold points.

The procurement documents at all tiers should identify the documentation that should accompany a material or component shipment, for example, supplier's procedures, certified material test reports (CMTRs), and certificates of compliance. Procurement documents should include requirements for reporting and approving disposition of nonconformances, as necessary. This information should be established during review of existing procurement documents.

In cases where the procurement documents are ready for approval, the person doing the review will sign and forward the document to the customer (if required), or other responsible party, who in turn will provide approval and forward the document to the project manager for further processing.

If the party responsible for approving a procurement document rejects it, the person who reviewed it sends it back to the originator with written comments for revision if the purchase is still needed. The originator will submit the revised document through the original channels. The project manager then verifies the package and records it along with its number on a separate procurement-document-review form. If the revision is satisfactory, the process proceeds. If not, the revision process repeats.

Project management should perform bid evaluations and review POs, contracts, and change orders prior to their issuance to ensure conformance to the procurement-document requirements.

The following subjects, as applicable, should be evaluated.

- Technical considerations
- Quality considerations
- Design-development effort
- Qualifications of supplier personnel
- Supplier's production capability
- Supplier's past performance
- Alternatives
- Exceptions

Prior to award of the PO or contract, project management should resolve all unacceptable conditions resulting from the bid evaluation. This review should be documented by the project manager's signature on the correspondence submitted with the original PO, contract, or change order issued to the supplier. Project management should ensure that the supplier selected has been evaluated in accordance with a management procedure that defines control of bidding and estimating.

A schedule should be maintained that breaks down work activities on a task-by-task basis with specific milestones and that follows a standard method. The method employed can be equivalent to SuperProject.[1] If a project manager uses a nonstandard scheduling method, it must be reviewed and approved by senior management.

Note

1. A software program developed by Computer Associates, 1240 McKay Drive, San Jose, CA 95131.

Appendix A   Standard Quality-Related Definitions for the A/E&C Community

This appendix contains definitions of quality terms that will help readers understand the text. Such definitions should be a standard part of every quality program. Documents such as International Standard 8402, published by the International Organization for Standardization (ISO); the text *Quality Management for the Constructed Project* published by ASQC Quality Press; and ANSI/ASQC A3, *Quality Systems Terminology,* are good references for quality terminology.[1,2,3]

Acceptance criteria—The specified limits of an item, component, process, or service defined in specifications, codes, standards, drawings, or other design documents.

Accuracy—The degree of conformity of measurement with a standard or true value.

Acknowledgment—The system established to document receipt of an initial issue or revision of a controlled document.

Adverse quality conditions—An all-inclusive term used in reference to any of the following: failures, malfunctions, deficiencies, defective items, and nonconformances. A condition that, if not corrected, could have a serious effect upon safety, contractibility, operability, or reliability.

AREA—Refers to standards, guidelines, and specifications published by the American Railway Engineering Association.

As-built drawing—A drawing that reflects actual installed conditions.

Attribute—A quality characteristic that may be qualitatively evaluated as a yes or no decision.

Audit—A systematically planned and documented activity to determine—by investigation, examination, and evaluation of objective evidence—the adequacy of and compliance with approved procedures, instructions, and drawings. An audit also reports on the effectiveness of implementation of the audited system to ensure that it is suitable to achieve predetermined objectives.

Batch (or lot)—An identifiable collection of items, or quantity of material, of single type, grade, class, size, or composition produced in the same plant under essentially the same conditions and at essentially the same time.

Calibration—Comparing two instruments, measuring devices, or standards, one of known accuracy traceable to nationally recognized standards. It is done to detect, correlate, report, or eliminate by adjustment any variation in accuracy of the instrument or measuring device of unknown accuracy.

Certificate of compliance—A written statement signed by a qualified party, attesting items, parts, components or services are in accordance with specified requirements and are accompanied by additional information to substantiate the statement.

Certificate of conformance—A document, signed or otherwise authenticated by an authorized individual, certifying that items, parts, components, or services meet specified requirements.

Certification—An act of determining, verifying, and attesting in writing to the qualifications of personnel, processes, procedures, or items in accordance with specified requirements.

Certified material test report (CMTR)—The written document signed by an authorized individual that identifies the tested chemical and physical properties of a material and certifies that the properties are within specified limits.

Characteristic—Any property or attribute of an item, process, or service that is distinct, describable, and measurable as conforming or not conforming to requirements. Quality characteristics are generally identified in specifications and drawings that describe the item, process, or service.

Checks—The tests, measurements, verifications, or controls on an activity by means of investigations, comparisons, or examinations to determine condition, accuracy, safety, or performance.

Client quality representative—The person employed by the customer to survey and verify the quality of a supplier's or subcontractor's work.

Cognizant office manager—The individual who has overall responsibility for the functional areas subject to readiness reviews.

Commercial grade—An item ordered from the manufacturer or supplier on the basis of specifications in the manufacturer's published product description (for example, catalog) within specified limitations.

Component—Any individually manufactured or fabricated unit or piece of a system or structure that is identifiable and installable.

Conceptual design—A design segment in which the objective is to provide adequately defined technical, cost, and schedule baselines to enable the project to proceed to detailed design activities and to establish the technical and management adequacy of the contractor to proceed with detailed design (project statement of work).

Concrete masonry unit (CMU)—A solid or hollow masonry unit made from water, portland cement, and suitable aggregates such as sand, gravel, crushed stone, bituminous or anthracite cinders, expanded clay or shale, pumice, volcanic scoria, or blast furnace slag, and molded into various shapes.

Construction—The erection, installation, fabrication, and assembly of items involving civil, mechanical, and electrical work at the permanent site of the facility.

Controlled copy—A copy of a procedure that is systematically updated and whose custodian is listed in the appropriate distribution list.

Controlled document—A document issued through an approved and documented system that may not be changed without going through a formal review and approval process.

Course—A specific training or indoctrination, instructional in nature, that has objectives and approved content, and is executed by a qualified instructor.

Defective material—Any material that does not meet specified requirements.

Deficiency—A characteristic that renders the quality of an item or activity unacceptable or indeterminate.

Design—The technical and management processes that lead to and include the issuance of documents such as specifications and drawings specifying technical requirements of structures, systems, and components.

Design change—A documented revision of the technical requirements that has been approved and issued as defined by design-output documents.

Design input—The criteria, parameters, bases, or other design requirements upon which detailed final design is based.

Design output—The formally approved and issued documents such as drawings and specifications defining technical requirements of structures, systems, components, and materials.

Design verification—An independent design review using alternate calculations or analyses, or the performance of qualification tests, to validate a design.

Deviation—A nonconformance or departure of a characteristic from specified requirements, considered synonymous with defective or unsatisfactory material.

Digital record imaging—A system whereby formal quality records are electronically scanned and entered as bits of data into a central quality records-management data base. The image of the initial record can then be retrieved with faithful restoration.

Document—Any written or illustrative information describing, defining, specifying, reporting, or certifying activities, requirements, procedures, or results.

Document control—The measures established to control the preparation, review, release, issuance, and disposition of documents, such as design calculations, purchase orders, specifications, instructions, procedures, and drawings, including changes thereto, that describe or document activities affecting quality.

Embedded reinforcement—The reinforcing steel embedded into the concrete of the building structure.

Engineered safety feature—The systems or design characteristics that are provided to mitigate the potential consequences of postulated design-based accidents.

Estimating system—The system used to quantify and put a monetary value on the resources required for a selected project.

External audit—The audit of those portions of another organization's quality assurance program not under the direct control or within the organizational structure of the auditing organization.

Fabrication—The actions required to manufacture components, parts, and appurtenances. These actions may include forming, machining, assembling, welding, brazing, heat treating, examining, testing, inspecting, and certifiying. Fabrication does not include design.

Failure—The inability of an item to perform within specified limits.

Final design—The complete and approved design, including approved design-output documents.

Footings—A generally rectangular prism of concrete larger in lateral dimensions than the column or wall it supports to distribute the load of a column or wall to the subgrade.

Hard-copy record—A paper record, often the original document, as opposed to a microfilm copy, data image stored on a computer, or other record such as disk, tape, or radiographic print.

Hold point—A planned point in the construction process at which work is halted to verify that the construction activities have been accomplished in accordance with applicable requirements.

Independent design review—A design review by a competent individual other than the originator or the originator's supervisor. Specific exceptions are permitted, when authorized.

Independent personnel—The individuals qualified to analyze, review, inspect, test, audit, or otherwise evaluate activities and work results for the following reasons.

- They have no direct responsibility for, or involvement in, performing the activity or work.
- They are not accountable for the activity or work result.
- They do not report directly to the immediate supervisors responsible for performing the activity or work being evaluated.

Individual training—The documented training provided by an individual's supervisor or project manager to enhance the individual's performance.

Indoctrination—A program of providing courses, initial on-the-job training, or mandatory readings performed immediately for a particular job function. This may be for new-employee orientation or an existing employee whose job function has changed.

Inspection/test point—The location or stage in the manufacturing or construction process where inspection or testing is performed by qualified personnel to determine the acceptability of products or services.

Instruction—The approved document that delineates the requirements with which a part, component, or service should conform, and specifies equipment, techniques, and the sequence of events required to establish the conformance.

Internal quality audit—An audit of those portions of an organization's quality assurance program under the control of its organizational structure.

Item—An all-inclusive word used in place of any of the following: appurtenance, assembly, component, equipment, material, module, part, structure, subassembly, subsystem, system, or unit.

Job-cost system—The system used to monitor project cost status from inception to final closing to help ensure project completion within budget.

Jurisdiction—The federal, provincial, territorial, or municipal agency or office having the lawful right and power to interpret a law and exercise authority.

Management review and assessment—An independent review and assessment of the overall status, adequacy, and effectiveness of a quality assurance program.

Mandatory hold points—Those hold points beyond which work may not proceed without client review.

Mandatory reading—A list of mandatory documents to be read that are appropriate for their function and that provide a means to ensure accomplishment of the task.

Manufacturer—The organization that constructs, produces, fabricates, and assembles any class of component, part, or appurtenance to meet design requirements.

Material—A substance or combination of substances forming components, parts, pieces, equipment, items (machinery, castings, liquids, formed steel shapes, aggregates, cement, and so on).

Materials—The permanent construction items used in the process or those nonpermanent items needing quality acceptance.

Material verification—A check to identify the number (such as the American Society of Mechanical Engineering/American Society for Testing Materials number), and the appropriate traceability to verify the material.

Measuring and test equipment (M&TE)—The calibrated devices or systems used to calibrate, measure, gauge, test, or inspect to control or acquire data to verify conformance to specified requirements.

Mill certificates—A manufacturer's certification, supported by test results, that the product supplied, generally metal, is of the quality, composition, and strength specified.

Mission-related reliability—The reliability of those structures, systems, and components, the failure of which has significant potential for preventing the project from attaining mission goals. This may also apply to a complex or hazardous task or operation that warrants an additional level of confidence in quality.

Monitor—To perform independent periodic checks of a process to verify that the essential characteristics of the process are maintained within specified limits as defined by the process procedure.

Nonconformance—A deficiency in characteristic, documentation, or procedure which renders the quality of an item or activity unacceptable or indeterminate.

Objective evidence—Any documented statement, fact, information, or record, either quantitative or qualitative related to the quality of an item or activity. This evidence is based on observations, measurements, or tests that can be verified.

On-the-job training (OJT)—An activity performed by an employee during his or her normal job function, assured by a supervisor, and intended to improve the employee's understanding and performance of the job. Also known as *on-the-job indoctrination*.

Open-item list—A listing of prerequisites that must be done in order to start or restart work that has not yet been completed.

Organizing quality—The functions and delineations of responsibility and authority of the field organization involved to fulfill its contract obligations.

Paving—The activity that includes placing concrete or bituminous material (asphalt concrete) to form a firm, level, horizontal surface.

Pile—The structural columns embedded into the ground, on end, for the purpose of supporting a load or compacting the soil under either tension or compression forces.

Plants—The operation for manufacturing and producing architectural concrete and precast concrete floor, roof, and manhole units (for purposes of this text).

Problem detection—The act of determining whether a nonconformance exists as measured against an established standard of acceptability. These problems are normally found through reviewing, inspecting, testing, or auditing activities.

Problem prevention—The act of forecasting that a nonconformance is highly probable and that remedial measures are required to prevent the nonconformance from occurring.

Problem report—The document record of a problem that is normally discovered during a readiness review and that could adversely affect the start or restart of work.

Procedure/practice—An approved document that specifies or describes how an activity is to be performed.

Procurement—The A/E&C system used to assist the project manager in acquiring materials and services of the requisite quality and within the time needed at the lowest reasonable cost, using competitive procurement methods to the maximum extent possible.

Procurement document—The requisitions, purchase orders, contracts, change orders, drawings, specifications, and instructions used to define purchases.

Qualification—The characteristics or abilities gained through training, indoctrination, or experience that enable an individual to perform a required function. This capability, when required, shall be indicated by comparison to an established or defined standard of performance.

Qualified procedure—The approved procedure that has been demonstrated to meet the specified requirements of its intended purpose.

Qualified reviewers—The persons who have qualifications at least equal to those needed to satisfactorily perform the work.

Quality—The totality of features and characteristics of a product or service that bear on its ability to satisfy a customer's perceived need.

Quality-affecting activities—The quality activities that directly affect the construction-related items, including designing, purchasing, fabricating, handling, shipping, storing, erecting, installing, inspecting, and testing.

Quality assurance (QA)—The planned and systematic actions necessary to provide adequate confidence that a product or service will satisfy given requirements.

Quality categorizing—The method of systematically determining levels of importance to quality of structures, systems, components, and materials.

Quality concern—A written comment by a responsible party or jurisdiction that raises a quality question about a program or the work activity. A concern is not necessarily a deviation; however, one may later be reflected and corrected in a timely manner.

Quality control (QC)—The operational techniques and activities used to ascertain that an established level of quality has been achieved and maintained.

Quality control organization—The functions and delineations of responsibility and authority that enable the field quality control staff to fulfill its contract obligations.

Quality inspector—The person who performs inspection activities to verify conformance to specific requirements.

Quality management—The portion of the overall management function that determines and implements the quality policy.

Quality policy—The expression by senior management that provides direction for a company's quality process.

Quality records—The records that furnish documentary evidence of the quality of items and activities affecting quality.

Quality system—The organizational structure, responsibilities, procedures, processes, and resources for affecting and ensuring quality systems.

Rail—The rolled-steel track and appurtenances manufactured by open-hearth furnace or basic-oxygen processes.

Readiness review—The independent, systematic, and documented review of an activity to determine and inform management of the readiness to proceed from one phase of the activity to the next.

Readiness-review presentation—During the beginning of a readiness review, a presentation (demonstration) is made by the organization being reviewed to the readiness review team, with appropriate audio-visuals.

Readiness-review work groups—After the presentation, the entire group is divided into smaller groups that work on individual issues. These work groups contain members from both the organization being reviewed and the review team.

Regulatory—Any one of the controlling organizations, federal, industry, state, or local, that imposes specific requirements on the design, procurement, or construction of a facility.

Review team—The group appointed by the client to perform activities associated with a readiness review. A review team is composed of a team leader and one or more team members.

Rework—The process by which an item is made to conform to original requirements by completion or correction.

Right of access—The legal authority of a purchaser or designated representative to enter the premises of a supplier for the purpose of a surveillance or audit.

Safety class items—The systems, structures, and components, including portions of process systems, whose failure could adversely affect the environment or the safety and health of the public. Further, those items necessary to ensure the capability to safely shut down operations of the completed facility, maintain the system in a safe condition, and maintain the integrity of the confinement barrier of hazardous material to prevent or mitigate the consequences of accidents and to monitor releases that could result in potential exposures to the public.

Scrap—The disposition of a nonconforming item when it is determined that the item is unfit for its intended use or that correcting the item is uneconomical. This is equivalent to the term *reject* in some military contracts.

Services—The performance of supplier activities such as design, fabrication, installation, nondestructive examination, or on-site repair.

Software validation—The process of evaluating software at the end of the development process to ensure compliance with requirements (for example, with the IEEE Standard 729). The process of testing a computer program and evaluating the results to ensure compliance with specified requirements (for example, ANSI/ANS-10.4). The test and evaluation of the integrated computer system (hardware and software) to ensure compliance with the functional, performance, and interface requirements (for example, ANSI/IEEE/ANS-7-4.3.2 and NQA-2).

Software verification—The process of determining whether the product of a given phase of the software development cycle fulfills requirements imposed by the previous phase.

Special process—A process whose results are highly dependent upon the direct control of the process or the skill of the operators, or both, and for which the specified quality cannot be readily determined by inspection or test of the product. The results of any such inspection or test vary depending on the control of the process and the skill of the operator.

Specification—An approved document that prescribes the design output requirements to which the product or service must conform.

Standard—An approved document that states the purpose and scope of an activity and specifies how to perform the activity.

Subtier procurement—The procurement of materials or services by a supplier from a subcontractor.

Supplier—Any organization that furnishes items or services in accordance with a procurement document. An all-inclusive term used in place of any of the following: vendor, seller, contractor, fabricator, consultant, and subcontractor.

Surveillance—The act of monitoring or observing to verify whether an item or activity conforms to specified requirements.

Systems planning—A series of steps used to organize a project. These steps can include the following: job costing, estimating, procurement, procurement tracking, material control, payroll, equipment management, scheduling, general accounting, personnel resources, and change-order tracking.

Technical review—A documented or traceable review performed by qualified personnel who are independent from those who performed the work and who have technical expertise at least equivalent to that needed to perform the original work. Technical reviews are in-depth, critical reviews, analyses, and evaluations of documents, material, or data that require technical verification or validation for applicability, correctness, adequacy, and completeness.

Testing—An element of verification that determines the capability of an item to meet predetermined requirements by subjecting the item to a set of physical, chemical, environmental, or otherwise measurable operating conditions.

Tightening sequence—The proper sequence for tightening bolts on the studs, thus ensuring proper lubricant.

Traceability—The ability to locate in a timely manner the history, application, or location of an item or like items and activities by means of documented identification.

Training—A program of providing courses, ongoing on-the-job training, or mandatory reading to ensure the maintaining of required skills for a job function. Training includes instruction, reading assignments, video presentations, and other instructional methods.

Training advisory board (TAB)—The discretionary body, appointed by the customer project manager, responsible for advising the training coordinator on technical matters in the formation of the training matrix and development of the training and indoctrination tasks.

Training coordinator (TC)—The individual, appointed by the project manager, responsible for training and indoctrination programs.

Training record—The approved and verifiable file on a person trained or indoctrinated that contains objective documentation on their currency in the training and indoctrination program.

Trend analysis—A systematic approach periodically analyzing adverse concerns that may be symptoms of an overall problem. As adverse concerns are identified, corrective action is taken for the purpose of preventing or at least minimizing future adverse trends.

Use as is—The disposition of a nonconforming item when it can be established that the discrepancy will in no way result in adverse conditions and that the item will continue to meet its intended functions, including performance, maintainability, fit, and safety.

Verification—The act of reviewing, inspecting, testing, checking, auditing, or otherwise determining and documenting whether items, processes, services, or documents conform to specified requirements.

Waiver—The documented action by the appropriate authority that foregoes, within the limits stated in the waiver document (such as a job bulletin), a contractual requirement or requirements. (This action occurs after the deviation has occurred.)

Warning devices—The mechanisms that include flashing lights, gate assemblies, and warning bells.

Weld—To build up or fasten together a joint made by bringing surfaces heated to plasticity (fusion) into close contact.

Notes

1. ISO Standard 8402. Geneva, Switzerland. Construction Technical Committee.

2. *Quality Management in the Constructed Project.* Milwaukee, Wis.: ASQC Quality Press, 1987.

3. ANSI/ASQC A3, *Quality Systems Terminology.* Milwaukee, Wis.: ASQC Quality Press, 1987.

Appendix B   Nonconformance and Corrective Action Procedures

First Type: Typical Regulated and Mandatory Control of Deviations

- Disposition Using the First-Level DCAR Form
- Disposition Using the Second-Level DCAR Form

Second Type: Control of Readiness Reviews and Assessments

Third Type: Control of Nonconforming Items

Fourth Type: Control of Nonconforming Contractor Items

First Type: Typical Regulated and Mandatory Control of Deviations

Purpose

This procedure describes the controls needed to ensure that deviations are promptly identified and corrected and that prevention measures are taken to preclude repetition. Many federal, state, and local rules require a controlled system of reporting and correcting deviations in specifications and programs. Deviations should be promptly corrected to ensure compliance with contract requirements, contractors, and suppliers.

Applicability

This procedure applies to all regulated activities performed to resolve a quality concern through action, verification, and closeout. This includes personnel interaction with subcontractors, and the subcontractors use to the extent agreed. The procedure is applicable to all areas of project performance from planning, design, development, fabrication, processing, and shipping to construction receipt, site installation, and turnover to the government agency.

This method involves reporting important defects and noncompliances that are covered by applicable government regulation.

Sources and References

Expected project sources may include

- Project management plan
- Occurrence reporting and processing of operations information
- QA requirements documents
- QA for facility applications

References may include

- Regulated surveillance program procedures of the government

Requirements

The objective of this procedure is to provide an effective and economical system for controlling quality deviations. The success of this procedure is dependent on both a clearly defined action system and effective communication throughout the project. The extent to which action is taken is dependent on the project element's level of importance as a whole and the significance of the deviation. Further, actions are periodically taken to monitor identified deviations and thereby to preclude repetition.

The procedure sets out a guideline for the timely resolution and close-out of any regulated concerns in the area of quality. These concerns may be found in such sources as comment sheets, consultant reports, and so on. Specifically, the procedure provides a method to identify and report significant deviations in fabrication, manufacture, construction, or operating of nuclear facilities.

Deviation and Corrective Action Report (DCAR). The procedure contains instructions for documenting deviations on DCAR forms by personnel subject to regulation and for subsequent evaluation and disposition by the respective line manager. A DCAR may be identified on other reports when they are generated. However, certain deviations and deficiencies, because of the amount of damage, repair evaluation, and required effort, or repetitiveness, should be documented on the second page of the DCAR form. DCAR criteria should be developed to identify specific requirements for generating them.

The CA system may use a review board to aid the government manager in tracking or identifying adverse indications. The board should meet periodically to review the need for CA. This review will ensure timely identification of adverse indications.

The board should be formed at the discretion of the government manager, as a function of the stage of the project and effectiveness of the DCAR system. In the event that hold points are required, the DCAR should reference a stop-work authority in accordance with a regulated stop-work implementation procedure.

Any employee can report a deviation using the DCAR form and can report of a deviation of suspected noncompliance. A copy of the procedure for reprinting a deviation should be posted conspicuously in the A/E&C organization's headquarters and job-site offices.

Responsibility

Responsibility for Identifying Deviations. All personnel are responsible for identifying possible deviations as they occur during the life of the project. This guideline is not intended to be restrictive, but to promote quality.

Responsibility for Issuing a DCAR. Personnel who draft DCARs are required to deliver them to the responsible manager. This manager will evaluate the validity of the deviation, issue the report, determine the severity of the deviation, and determine if prevention measures are necessary.

Responsibility for Disposition of a Deviation. The responsible manager may delegate to support personnel the responsibility for disposing of the deviation and providing action and justification.

CA Responsibility. The responsible manager must inform the government manager or designated representative of all CAs to be taken, including functional responsibilities and dates to be completed. The manager, must also ensure the timely resolution and closeout of each DCAR.

Responsibility for Reporting Adverse Indications. The responsible manager must hold periodic meetings and report on any adverse conditions identified through the CA system.

Deviation and CA Functional Responsibilities. Positions functionally within government that are part of the deviation and CA procedure should be defined on a flow diagram attached to the procedure.

Procedure

Identifying Deviations. The aim of any good quality system is to prevent quality-related problems. If problem conditions are identified, they should be promptly resolved. In cases where other report mechanisms are not available or appropriate, to prevent or minimize a recurrence, one should use the DCAR form. The back of the form should carry instructions for completing it.

Issuing a DCAR. The responsible manager must evaluate and issue the DCAR and identify to senior management any problems that have occurred. The DCAR should be retained and controlled and copies forwarded to the responsible manager for immediate attention. Care should be taken to produce objective evidence that the product or service does not meet requirements. The government manager or his or her delegated representative will document that objective evidence has been examined and evaluated for compliance to the project requirements. The evaluation may include a review of the work procedures followed, which may be verified by direct observation.

There may be two levels of DCAR forms. In the case of a nonsignificant deviation, a first-level DCAR form should be used. In the case of a significant deviation requiring immediate prevention measures that could adversely affect the safe operations of the facility, the second-level DCAR form should be used.

In processing DCARs, distribution should be controlled as specified on the form. In addition, a logging mechanism should be used to control status and ensure closeout of a DCAR.

Determining Whether CA Is to Be Taken. An evaluation should be made prior to distribution of the DCAR to determine whether definitive action is required to preclude recurrence of the problem. In the case of significant conditions adverse to quality or the case of a program breakdown, strong prevention measures are necessary to preclude repetition. In such cases, it is imperative that the second-level DCAR form requiring more severe measures be used.

Disposition Using the First-Level DCAR Form

Items identified as *deviating* should be segregated, tagged, or otherwise placed on hold if the disposition cannot be given immediately. One must ensure the removal of the item from the site if it is deemed unsuitable for construction purposes or is otherwise unsatisfactory. Numerous dispositions may be possible contingent upon the type and severity of the deviation. These dispositions may include (but are not necessarily limited to) the following actions.

- Supplier or manufacturer source surveillance may be conducted.
- Dispositions can use a hold point system either when required by procedure or when it is evident that damage to the quality of the construction process can occur beyond such points. This hold-point system should not be bypassed unless a limited work authorization is provided in a controlled manner.
- The disposition may require increased inspection, testing, and verification activities. This may or may not constitute a change in the plan or implementation procedures. The government representative should update the program plan to reflect changes in procedures.
- Requirements are changed as specified contractually.
- The process may consist of restoring a characteristic to a condition such that the capability of an item to function reliably and safely is

unimpaired, even though that item still may not conform to the originally specified requirements.

Ultimately, a disposition should resolve concerns or problems promptly, as they arise, to meet specific government requirements.

Justifying the Remedial Work and Evaluating the Disposition.
Comments on the DCAR should clearly show justification for problem resolution. This justification should indicate identifiable results. Resolution and closeout dates should be obtained as soon as possible. These dates should be realistic and rigidly enforced. The problem must be clearly resolved and closed in a timely manner. The following criteria should be used in evaluating the disposition of a DCAR form one.

- The resolution is clear.
- The resolution will be made in a timely manner.
- There will be objective evidence to measure.
- A decision is made whether further action will be necessary to prevent or minimize recurrence.

Resolution and action taken should be clearly identified and the previously listed criteria followed closely. Assurance must be provided that closeout of the problem has been verified.

Final verification may involve review of use of special instrumentation, simulating inputs, or a combination of both to prove that specified requirements have been met. This method is employed where specified external stimuli (hardware or software) or other external devices are required to produce or measure (record) predictable results (such as verification of response times). Government verification requires that the supplier offer objective evidence when these methodologies have been used.

Disposition Using the Second-Level DCAR Form

Any employee of a government, an A/E&C organization, or a subcontractor who discovers a deviation or noncompliance as defined by government federal regulations should report it on the second-level DCAR form. The employee should complete the form and submit it to a responsible officer or project manager, engineering manager, project engineer, site QA management, or the QA department. Copies of the form should be readily available. The manager who receives this completed form should immediately review the information and initiate the evaluation procedure. This form should then be forwarded to the senior manager responsible for evaluation and further action.

If the deviation involves a contract with a government contractor, the report should be forwarded to the contractor project manager for a check against other reports and contractual requirements. Following this check, the project manager should, in accordance with company procedure, request an evaluation and notification for regulatory disposition. This normally should be returned within a week. A copy of this notification should be furnished immediately to the responsible manager and the QA organization as should the disposition report when available.

The responsible manager should notify the government representative directly on matters involving a contractor if timely disposition has not been made or if the action appears to be nonresponsive. The QA organization should be free to notify the government representative directly on all other matters.

Determining, Evaluating, and Verifying CA. The following four-step process must follow during the course of determining the disposition with a second-level DCAR form: investigative action, root-cause analysis, recurrence analysis, and impact analysis. The following questions should be used in evaluating the disposition of this DCAR form: Is the resolution objectively clear and sufficient? Will the resolution be made in a timely manner? Will there be evidence to measure? Should further management action be taken to prevent or minimize recurrence?

The responsible manager should ensure a tracking system is controlled to ensure close-out of the problem. Tracking system records should be issued on a periodic basis and should show pending problems and those closed during the reporting period. Closed problems should be reported during one period and then deleted from subsequent issues. Distribution of these records should be to government management personnel, the originator identifying the problem (if requested) and the contractor (or other organization) responsible for taking action. It is essential that the verifier of the action check that the work is complete and if the disposition is indeed what has been done to resolve that problem.

Tracking, Identifying Significance, and Taking Action on Adverse Conditions. When project activity is sufficiently complex to justify tracking, a logging system should be used to ensure proper identification of adverse conditions.

Accumulated deviations and other data should be analyzed to identify adverse trends or generic system problems. Individual reports may not identify potentially significant or generic problems. However, grouped or combined data may reveal conditions or causes that will require further CA to preclude recurrence. In any case, whether a detailed analysis is necessary or not, the responsible manager should review and analyze adverse indications with a task force on a periodic basis. Numbers or percentages of deviations within a category should serve as a guide in determining the need for further investigation of possible adverse trends. The responsible manager should promptly issue reports of these meetings and document the results of the analysis and any investigations, including any recommended actions to correct adverse indications with the DCAR forms and methods noted.

A description of an unsatisfactory response or any further adverse indications from the first-level DCAR form should be identified along with any recommended actions such as further disciplinary action as the need arises. In such cases, DCAR level-two forms are used. A satisfactory response and verification of closeout is considered resolution on an adverse indication report.

Records
Individually completed records and copies of any related correspondence completed as a result of the disposition and closeout are considered QA records. After approval, each resolution and revision should be processed in accordance with the records-management program. The records should include the following:

- One's procedure modeled after this one and any subsequent revisions
- All document closeout sheets
- Level-one and level-two DCAR forms
- Adverse indication results reports

Second Type: Control of Readiness Reviews and Assessments

Purpose

The purpose of the second type is to provide guidelines for promptly controlling the preparation, execution, and closure of readiness reviews and assessments, to aid in ensuring the control of major project milestones.

Applicability

This procedure applies to all A/E&C activities associated with controlling readiness reviews, including determining the need for the review, organizing it, assigning personnel to it, preparing checklists, presenting them, developing work groups, documenting findings, and closing out the effort. The procedure is applicable to all areas of a project. It applies to general management and to technical and QA aspects of a project.

Sources and References

Plans and systems related to readiness reviews may include the following:

- Project management plan
- Guidelines for application of readiness reviews
- A uniform reporting system
- Cost and schedule control systems

Responsibility

The Readiness Review Assessment Team. This group is responsible for identifying and documenting any findings or observations during the readiness review of the project. These findings or observations should be ones of both potential improvements as well as potential problems.

The Readiness Review Board. This group is responsible for ensuring that the review process meets the objectives of this procedure, including the decisions involving the timing of the review and the personnel who will make up the review team. The review board does the following:

- Reviews the severity of the findings and observations of the readiness review and recommends a notice to proceed (NTP) validation.
- Holds periodic meetings and reports on the schedule of activities of readiness reviews throughout the life of the project, including operational readiness reviews (ORRs).

Line Management. This level of management has the following responsibilities in the readiness review process.

- Prepares for the readiness review presentation (or demonstration) and sets up the work groups to ensure that the project is presented accurately and factually. When observations and findings are made by the review team, line management takes immediate action and prepares individual replies to the readiness reviews (assessments).
- Ensures the timely resolution of identified observations and findings; also ensures closeout whether or not an NTP (validation) has been issued.

Procedure

General Requirements. This program provides an effective and economical system for controlling readiness reviews and assessments. It depends on a clearly defined review system of preparing, executing, closing observations, and releasing the milestones. The extent of the readiness review is a function of the significance of the milestone under review.

The readiness review ensures that any observations and identified potential improvements, as well as problems, are properly closed prior to release of the major milestone. A conditional NTP can be issued; however, approved justification has to be provided prior to this notice being given. The review also defines a guideline to control the entire process, which may include presented documentation by the line management to the readiness review team during the general presentation and work groups.

The review process defines instructions for preparing the various required documents, including announcements, review checklists, team question or observation sheets, and NTPs.

When to Perform Readiness Reviews—Readiness Review Board. The project manager should appoint a readiness review board whose prime objective should be to control the review process. The board, headed by a review director, should consist of at least one member each from project management, engineering, and QA. The board should meet periodically to review project schedules and progress in order to determine when the impending review is to be performed and who shall be on the readiness review team. The board's purpose is to help the project manager make correct decisions on proceeding. Schedules should be provided to the readiness review board by line management that should ensure the following:

- The interrelationships of project activities of all contractors.
- The use of the critical path method (CPM). This method should be in both such standard scheduling as PERT and Gantt formats.
- The level of detail should be acceptable to the board and include the following topics.

  —Architectural and engineering services
  —Overall design
  —Configuration management
  —Cost and schedule controls
  —Environmental compliance
  —Construction services
  —Overall project controls
  —QA and safety
  —Systems tests, and evaluations
  —Budget, authorization, and costs

With each impending readiness review (assessment), an implementation plan should be provided by the board that defines the approach, process, and organizational responsibilities.

Selecting the Review Team—Readiness Review Board. The board should select a team chief who is responsible for the day-to-day activities and preparation of the team's review report. The team chief should be someone with demonstrated qualifications in all of the major areas listed under "When to Perform Readiness Reviews." The other team members should have demonstrated qualifications in the major areas in which they will be assigned. A sufficient number of members should be chosen to ensure that there will be adequate depth of capability on the team. The team can be augmented as required with functional specialists. The team should be trained in the methods of performing readiness reviews to ensure proper execution of the review.

Making Team Assignments—Readiness Review Board. The review board should evaluate each team member and ensure that his or her demonstrated qualification amply covers the assigned scope of review. In addition, during the course of the review, a team member should notify the team chief if the assistance of a functional specialist is required.

Preparing Checklists—Readiness Review Team. The readiness review team chief should ensure that each team member prepares a checklist to be used by the entire team in his or her respective area. This checklist should be reviewed and approved by the team chief and the readiness review board. After the checklists have been approved, they should be duplicated and distributed to all team members and the line management of the organization to be reviewed. Instructions on the use of a checklist should be provided on its reverse side.

Executing the General Presentation or Demonstration—Line Management. The line management of the organization to be reviewed should coordinate with the team chief to provide the necessary announcements, meeting rooms, and other agenda details to ensure smooth presentation or demonstration. Attendance of all parties, including specialists, should be mandatory. Line management should clearly state the complete mission of the project and, in particular, how their organization should ensure its accomplishment. In addition, line management should, in a step-by-step, objective manner, display its plan for meeting the project mission and provide evidence to demonstrate that this plan will allow the organization being reviewed to proceed to the next major project milestone. The review team should be free to ask questions at any time during the presentation or demonstration.

Implementing the Work Groups—Line Management. At the conclusion of the presentation or demonstration, participants should be divided into work groups or technical modules whose purpose is to further define how the organization being reviewed can meet or exceed its project mission and objectives in each work group area. The leader of each work group should be the responsible line manager from the organization being reviewed. Team members should generally participate in the group that corresponds to their specialty or technical discipline unless the need arises in an associated work group. The work groups should not adjourn until agreed by the readiness review (assessment) team members.

Preparing Observations—Readiness Review Team. The team chief should hold a caucus with the team at the end of each day during the review. The purpose of the caucus should be to summarize the accomplishments of the day, questions for the next day, closed checklist items, and any other observations or findings. All observations and findings should go on a technical question form. Observations documented on this form should not necessarily be only potential problems or deviations, but should also be ideas for project improvement.

Preparing Replies to Observations—Line Management. At the conclusion of the readiness review, the team chief should issue a report recommending whether the project under review should or should not proceed to the next milestone. This report should contain observations and findings used to make the recommendation. The line management should clearly answer the review questions and provide the required positive action to satisfy the review team chief. In the case of a problem, care should be taken not simply to correct the specific problem cited, but to propose a solution to the more general problems illustrated by the specific case.

Verifying and Providing Notice—Readiness Review Board. The review board and team chief should approve the action plan committed to by line management of the organization being reviewed. Final verification may require the use of special instrumentation, simulating inputs, or a combination of both to prove that specified requirements have been met. Verification requires objective evidence that these methodologies have been used. Only the review board with the concurrence of the team chief can issue an NTP. If the notice is conditional, care should be taken to ensure that the notice clearly details closeout and the possibility of a further hold point if actions are not completed.

Records

The following individually completed records and copies of any related correspondence completed as a result of this guideline are considered QA records. After approval by the review board, each resolution and revision should be processed in accordance with the records-management program, as follows:

- One's procedure modeled after this one and subsequent revisions
- The completed checklists
- The technical question sheets with answers
- The readiness review team report
- NTPs

The documents on the following list, completed as a result of this procedure, are not quality records and are to be controlled for a minimum of 90 days as a working file, at which time they should be sent to the project records-management center for disposition.

- Noncompleted checklists
- Readiness review flow diagrams
- Readiness review checklists

Third Type: Control of Nonconforming Items

Purpose and Scope
A controlled system should be in place for reporting and correcting both deviations in specifications and deficiencies in structures, systems, and components. Dispositions should be promptly determined and corrections made to ensure conformance to contract direction to subcontractors and suppliers. Further, actions should be taken periodically to monitor identified deviations and deficiencies to preclude their repetition. The magnitude of such preventive measures should be a function of the item's criticality.

Procedure
All project personnel should be responsible for preventing problems on projects under his or her control. During the course of A/E&C activities, certain quality problems may arise, identified on a contractor quality control (CQC) daily report or any similar means. Such problem conditions should be promptly identified and resolved.

In cases where it is apparent that further action needs to be taken to prevent or minimize problem recurrence, a problem action request (PAR) should be used. It is the responsibility of the CQC systems manager to control a daily CQC report and identify any problems that have occurred, for reporting to project management. This CQC daily report should be filed on each A/E&C activity day, with copies forwarded to the corporate office and senior management at the end of each work week.

Fourth Type: Control of Nonconforming Contractor Items
Purpose and Scope
The purpose and scope of this fourth type is basically the same as the third type. In this case, contractual controls should be in place to ensure contractors take timely and effective actions to remediate the condition and to preclude any recurrence.

Procedure
Contractors should be responsible for preventing problems on projects under their control. During the course of construction, certain quality problems may arise, identified on a CQC daily report, or any similar means. This report, as well as others necessary to preclude repetition of any problems, should be the same as noted under "Third Type" in this appendix. All project personnel, including subcontractors, are responsible for clearly identifying and reporting quality problems to the project manager, who will in turn prepare and issue the reports of any problems in a form such as a PAR.

The problem should be identified concisely, and any preliminary investigations or recommendations should be explained. The problem should be one that requires preventive measures because of the potential amount or severity of damage, repair, and effort required or because of its repetitiveness. Realistic, but firmly enforced, response and action dates should be set by the project manager.

The resolution recommended on the PAR by the contractor should be approved or modified by both the assigned architect or engineer and senior management. After action has been taken, the CQC system's manager must verify the CA taken at the job site. On a periodic basis, the project manager, contractor, assigned architects or engineers, and procurement management should meet to review all PARs and CQC daily reports generated since the last such meeting to uncover any systematic or repetitive conditions. If one is identified, then it should be reported to senior management, as noted on the PARs. These reports normally include the following components.

- Status of the project as related to the overall schedule
- A historical record of quality concerns
- An analysis of any adverse trends
- Plans for improving the quality program during the next reporting period

The meeting should be chaired by project management. The agenda should respond to concerns raised in the PARs. The goals of the meeting should be to analyze and assess all the data from these reports. Management should then authorize implementation of any CAs recommended in these reports. This meeting can be held in conjunction with a construction-review board meeting, at the project manager's discretion.

The CQC systems manager is responsible for maintaining all CA records throughout the life of the project by providing a suitable logging system of PARs.

CQC Daily Report Instructions

(The CQC Daily Report is to be completed as detailed in chapter 15 except as denoted here.)

Heading. Page numbers should appear on all pages. Attachments should have page numbers in sequence. The project day should be entered on Page 1 of the report. The project day should be calculated from the NTP date and should coincide with the actual contract calendar. The date of the report should appear in the heading and should coincide with the actual project calendar.

Parts I, II, and III: Preparatory, In-Process, and Follow-Up Activities. All descriptions of work performed should be adequately reported. The activity section under here should be listed. Each activity should be checked as either satisfactory or unsatisfactory. A "not applicable" (NA) should be entered if the description does not reflect a required satisfactory condition. All field activities by subcontractors should be identified on this report.

Appendix C Management Audit of a Main Architectural/Engineering Office

Sample Document

- Attachment One: Summary of Quality Audit Activities
- Observation One

The purpose of a management audit is to review the quality activities currently associated with general A/E office work. This includes the areas of problem reporting, training, document control, design and procurement, records management, and procedural control. This should cover a review of any previous audits. Further, the purpose of this review is to ensure that

- Efforts to support planned, ongoing, and completed activities are adequate and in compliance with customer quality commitments
- Consistency exists between A/E documents and the requirements of the quality system
- Unique quality requirements have been identified and properly addressed in program documents and implementation procedures
- Responsibilities of the main A/E office personnel are effectively accomplished

The following sample document provides a record of the audit, for future reference and as evidence to potential clients.

Sample Document

The audit was performed at the headquarters office during the period _____ by _____ as audit team leader (ATL) and _____ auditors. The audit encompassed the in-depth A/E quality activities performed for selected work-related projects, and several departmental general activities of A/E and (technology information). Additional checklist items were generated during the course of the audit to evaluate current work-related activities not covered directly by A/E quality procedures. Personnel contacted during the audit (including those who attended the postaudit conference as indicated by an asterisk) are as follows:

_____   _____

_____   _____

_____   _____

_____   _____

All selected responsible individuals and auditors

_____

Projects covered during this audit include:

_____

The scope of the audit was limited to the projects listed previously, certain general main A/E office functions, and associated activities. This report covers a sample of a substantial majority of the work performed. Other projects were spot checked for conformity to requirements. The activities of design quality control (QC) should be evaluated for consistency particularly in the area of small-task engineering services being administered by assigned project-management organizations.

With the exception of _____ control of the _____ (see Observation One), A/E activities and other portions of its functions are determined to be adequate. The governing project quality program documents comply with the quality system description and customer requirements.

Observations and Recommendations

Attachment One of this report contains a summary of the activities audited and numbered observations of those items either not in compliance with defined requirements or those determined to be in need of improvement. Supporting information concerning the audit is on file at the quality auditing organization office where it is available for review.

Audit performed by:

_____

Approved by: quality auditing organization

Attachment One: Summary of Quality Audit Activities

As confirmed by the review of the work activities being performed in the A/E office, work-related services were performed for at least ____ projects during the year. The audit entailed the review of quality activities performed on behalf of the following projects (which represent the substantial majority of the work completed this year):

Work-related projects:

_____

_____

General Departmental Activities

The activities of the projects consisted exclusively of design services. On this basis, the audit focused on items other than purchasing and construction. The items covered included project A/E program development and administration and use of implementation procedures, training, problem reporting, document control, design and procurement control, quality surveillance, records management, and procedural controls.

Quality-system development and administration for each project was reviewed for conformance to quality procedures. The scope of each was adequate with regard to the tasks performed, and each plan addressed the requirements. Each adequately identified customer concerns and unique customer quality requirements, and each sufficiently referenced the project, departmental, or client procedures necessary to satisfactorily direct project activities. In that each was issued in the form of a project procedure, project procedural controls were reviewed by confirming required approvals of these documents, sufficient and controlled distribution, and the maintenance of the latest edition of these instructions. Nevertheless, it is recommended that a draft _____ A/E procedure be issued soon to further enhance the quality program.

The activities of the design and procurement group controlled by the A/E quality procedures met program requirements. This included control of design-related documents, change control, purchasing and specification control, A/E service scopes of work (including changes thereto), supplier preaward surveys, and control of supplier quality programs. In addition, procured-service supplier-quality audits were reviewed for compliance to policy on postaward activities of A/E service suppliers. The review encompassed quality-review frequency, plans, reports, distribution, and responses. The review also included the general audit file system, scopes of work, and files. Results were satisfactory.

The A/E activities associated with work and projects not being controlled by procedures were meeting program requirements. This included management plans, unique project implementation procedures, design reviews, and independent investigations. There were procedures on a project-by-project basis that were controlling the _____ activity which were satisfactory to program requirements. However, the following procedures should be completed and issued:

_____

_____

_____

The A/E activities associated with the records management system as related to the records guidelines conformed to program requirements. This included a records custodian; timely transfer, accuracy, and retrievability of records; and finally, the periodic review of the master-records code-classification list. Results were satisfactory.

Records pertaining to personnel qualifications of auditors met compliance requirements. The required training records were maintained and used in the computerized training-records system. Job-performance and auditor-qualification records of each auditor were evaluated and documented annually on the auditor-qualification form. A new employee was oriented and indoctrinated by attending supervisory conferences and completing reading assignments.

An A/E training matrix provided necessary required courses, including quality training, and complied with program requirements. In regard to written examinations, no new certifications were issued that required examination; however, supplemental examinations were administered to personnel as necessary. Results were satisfactory.

The A/E&C reporting system was governed by problem action reports. Implementation of problem action report preparation and review complied with program requirements. This included the report of a problem evaluation and screening process and the determination and distribution of initial problem reports. This review determined that all material had been assigned a task number, and those not requiring a number had been documented and justified. All were filed in chronological order to provide a historical record of the evaluation process. Results were satisfactory.

The A/E design program complied with quality assurance (QA) program requirements. Reviews of conceptual design plans and reports of project A, project B, project C and internal reviews of other projects were performed. Project A's conceptual design plans were in conformance with current procedures. Area offices were reviewed, schedules were maintained, logs were kept up to date, corrective action (CA) was maintained, and closure was handled in a timely manner on these projects. No outstanding observations were noted.

Except for Observation One (following) the design function complied with QA program requirements. The historical file and master list appeared to be up to date. However, manual requests, manual revisions, and numerous other documents were not being maintained in a timely manner (see Observation One).

Observation One

The quality system description requires in part that "measures shall be defined to control the issuance of documents, such as instructions, procedures, and drawings including changes thereto . . ." Contrary to these requirements, the following observations were reported of the design records located in Building A.

- Manuals returned were not being processed (removed from a controlled distribution) in a timely manner.

- Requests for manuals were not being honored in a timely manner, that is, interoffice correspondence was awaiting processing.
- Original drawings (mylar, sepia, or other forms) were stored on top of file cabinets and not logged in or filed in the area.
- Pages in the latest revisions were not completed.

Recommendations

Process the requests for controlled manuals as soon as possible. For drawings waiting to be filed and logged, complete the process quickly to prevent a potential loss due to fire. Send requests to verify that manuals are up to date.

Action

During this audit period, some program elements did not have any appreciable activity and therefore were not audited. These included the following attributes:

_____

_____

_____

Appendix D An Example of a Regulated Research and Development Quality Technology A/E&C Project

Background, Technical Approach, and Anticipated Benefits

- Overall Background
- Technical Approach
- Anticipated Results

This appendix covers a sample quality A/E&C research and devlopment (R&D) project for the regulated industry. It is an example of a project likely to be submitted to governmental bodies.

In-Service Inspection of Reactors

Future work within the nuclear industry will concentrate on the O&M of existing facilities, particularly as they age. An important aspect of this future work will be the use of novel methods to inspect the highly radioactive portions of a power plant. The need for unique in-service inspection (ISI) of existing power plants alone could provide significant justification for an important R&D effort.[1]

The example in this chapter, which is related to chapter 12, addresses the development of new, remote techniques for examining steam generators, critical components of a nuclear power plant. These techniques must be predictable based on measured data in important areas which serve to permit modified operating techniques well in advance of timed major replacements. Further, the application of modern, emerging technologies—such as AI or virtual reality—will improve on existing techniques. These remote ISI methods are intended to have high reliability, and in the case of operating decisions, should have response times shorter than ones currently available.

This project should help to meet the energy needs of the twenty-first century in improving nuclear power plant economics, availability, and safety. It will address Public Law 95-91 (dated August 4, 1977), whose purpose is to achieve effective management of energy functions in meeting and solving national energy problems.

As a final evaluation measure, the breeder concept should be analyzed for the use of such advanced remotely controlled ISI systems (such as EBR-II) being developed relative to planned shutoff using only the immutable principles of physics (passive shutdown). This reactor design is expected to use sodium-cooled media to greatly reduce engineered safety systems.

Background, Technical Approach, and Anticipated Benefits
Overall Background

Steam generators in pressurized water reactors (PWRs) typically are heat exchangers that contain hot, radioactive coolant from the reactor. This coolant enters the generators through inlets that distribute the heat from the coolant to a second loop which transfers the heat energy to power the turbine generator. These steam generators typically consist of two integral sections: an evaporator section and a steam drum section. The evaporator section consists of a U-tube heat exchanger, and the steam-drum section houses moisture-separating equipment. Steam generators are designed and manufactured to Sections II, III, and IX of the ASME BPV Code.

High-pressure, high-temperature reactor coolant flows into the steam-generator channel head, through the tubes, and back to the channel head. A partition plate divides the channel head and the inlet and outlet channels. An access opening for inspection and maintenance is provided in each of the two sections. To prevent leakage across tube joints, the tubes are welded to a tube sheet. The tubes are supported at intervals by horizontal tube-support plates.

Secondary side access for inspection or maintenance is typically provided by including several access openings in the shell near the top of the tube sheet. Wet layout is normally practiced to maintain water chemistry during shutdown periods by recirculating water through the steam generator.

Technical Approach

In accordance with the requirements defined in Section XI of the ASME BPV Code, this ISI system can provide complete and remote preservice and ISI with the techniques described herein. These services require engineering assistance to formulate specific ISI for each designated plant or design, including hardware, automated analysis, and reporting of suitable data. These data can be obtained during ISI cycles in an automatic manner. Significant changes in the cycles will then be evaluated based on the data to ensure primary system integrity. Beyond technological hardware and techniques, the practical training of field-crew technicians should be an integral part of an ISI system.

A unique steam-generator inspection scanner might be able to remotely inspect the welds of the steam generator stay cylinder. The scanner could be installed vertically along the axis of the steam generator. While the concept can be similar to a reactor vessel scanner, different geometry and space limitations require a different design for the steam-generator scanner. A hydraulically driven vertical carriage could be attached to a pole. A base that can be rotated 360 degrees with 2 degrees of freedom could be mounted to the vertical carriage on the pole.

A power manipulator arm could be mounted on the base and the search unit mounted on the end of the arm. The ultimate combination of three degrees of freedom would enable the search unit or probe to be properly positioned inside the steam generator.

Traditionally, operator-controlled manipulators used in this manner to carry out such tasks in radioactive environments have not been precise or accurate. Such an ISI system could control these devices remotely if supervised by an AI-based control system. A virtual-reality-controlled device could be used to control the subject inspections.

The purpose of the sensor probes would be to perform multifrequency eddy-current testing of the tubing. This method of testing by using multifrequency-multiparameter concepts overcomes most of the limitations of single-frequency techniques. These limitations include the following:

- Conditions are often abnormal, and anomalies exist that are not effectively solved by single-frequency methods.
- Some extraneous discontinuities (such as tube support plate, tube sheet, internal noise, fins, probe wobble, and dents) distort or hide signals from defects located under them; this can cause the misinterpretation that tubes are plugged when they are not.
- Detection of discontinuities (such as wall thinning, sludge height, and dent sizing) requires several successive probe pullings.

Thus, multifrequency techniques would markedly decrease inspection time compared to present methods. One probe scan could provide the data from several frequencies, giving the ISI system the capability of comparing a discontinuity signature from different views, which would more positively identify a defect through complex signal interpretation. ISI has the further capability to mix frequencies in order to blank one or several disturbing signals simultaneously, revealing only the underlying defect.

The purpose of this ISI system would be to integrate all its aspects into a single AI/virtual-reality-controlled data analysis. The system would also automatically generate a report. This control command would, through AI manipulations, scan inspection areas, analyze data received through the scan, assimilate the data, and report it to personnel.

Basic commands to the computer center would be simple and straightforward. The feasibility of voice input technological advances would be addressed.

All information and data gathered would be subjected to analysis based on the science of fracture mechanics.[2] Information would be substantiated with existing data on current problems with steam generator assemblies, including the following:[3, 4, 5]

- Loose parts in secondary side of steam generators
- Tube problems such as denting, sludge, tube-to-tube wear, internal noise, ovalization, conductive deposits, finned tubing, or damage underneath plates
- Water chemistry
- Intergranular stress-corrosion cracking (IGSCC)

Anticipated Results

The potential benefits of a verifiable and completely automated ISI remote system is tremendously significant for existing pressurized water reactors as well as for reactors under development such as the liquid-metal fast-breeder reactors. Successful completion of such an R&D undertaking will make a significant contribution toward nuclear power from the standpoints of safety and cost.

From salvaging questionable tubes to replacing an entire nuclear steam generator, this system will provide new knowledge and experience on materials, water chemistry, and corrosion during operation. It should provide a comprehensive solution to these unique technical issues. The use of this system would probably use the following examination method.

- Prior to the outage, a pattern of tubes to be tested is determined; locations are selected to reach all the tubes in the pattern; technicians suitably protected enter the primary head and install the internal devices.
- The tubes are examined for obvious abnormalities at the appropriate frequency; in addition, selected tubes within the pattern may be scanned to determine the presence of sludge on the hot side tube supports and secondary side of the tube sheet. These data would make up the baseline.

- Responses to eddy current tests and scans are fed through computer analysis; due outputs are provided to monitor computer assimilation.
- Special sensing probes, designed to be used in bends and coils, are fabricated for the specific tubing to be tested.
- Calibration is handled carefully, again with a computer providing standard measures and traceability.
- The probe insertion and withdrawal mechanism ensures a constant speed when test data are being collected and recorded.

A variety of probes is available from numerous suppliers. Use of currently available components would allow the design to be standardized. During this design effort, inspection methods would be developed and equipment would be basically designed. At a later stage, the final design, manufacture of the inspection manipulators, and supply of complete computer facilities and the probe modules would take place.

The control unit would be programmed for all inspection tasks and would perform automatically. It would also monitor the path functions by comparing actual and target points through a closed-loop method. The inspection techniques would improve the probability of successful flaw detection, with due consideration of more difficult orientations. The system can be used for the scanning area to be subdivided into inspection zones, which would be scanned from various orientations using the multifrequency and multiparameter techniques. An aim of this use would be to develop an ISI system that embraces extended use of probe modules, the latest electronic and evaluation units, and appropriate software programs. If successful, this system will improve the degree of automation and the interpretation of results compared to existing methods for examining pressurized water reactors.

One of the ultimate technological aims of this ISI system developmental project is to provide insight into the recurring problems associated with steam generators, thereby enabling researchers to develop more permanent solutions to such problems as stress and corrosion cracking.

Notes

1. Details on in-service inspection of nuclear facilities are contained in the American Society of Mechanical Engineering Boiler and Pressure Vessel Code, section XI.

2. Sanford, R. J. *Fracture Mechanics*, American Society for Testing Materials 15th Symposium, STP 833, July 1982.

3. Steigerwald, R. F. *Intergranular Corrosion of Stainless Alloys*, American Society for Testing Materials, STP 656, 1985.

4. Ugiansky, G. M. and J. H. Payer, *Stress Corrosion, The Slow Strain Rate Technique*, American Society for Testing Materials, STP 665, 1985.

5. Steele, L. E. *Radiation Embriddlement and Surveillance of Nuclear Reactors: An International Study*, American Society for Testing Materials, STP 819, 1986.

Appendix E Selective Standard Procedure: Project Organization for Medium and Light Construction

Organizing for Project Quality

- Project Engineer
- Earthwork and Paving Subcontractors
- Electrical Subcontractors
- Mechanical Subcontractors
- Building Subcontractors
- Laboratory Subcontractors

This appendix contains a sample procedure for organizing and controlling personnel on a medium to light construction project. Although requirements and craft disciplines will vary from one project to the next, the basic organization presented here can be followed. This procedure is also applicable to light and residential projects. In the latter case, considerable tailoring and simplifying may be required; nevertheless, the basic procedure still applies.

Organizing for Project Quality

This guideline describes the organization, positions, responsibilities, and qualifications of the business in medium-sized projects.[1] It applies to all employees involved with internal and external aspects of quality.

Responsibility

The designer or builder should be responsible for informing the designated customer representative of all changes in the responsibilities, qualifications, directives, and organization in the QA function. A project engineer should be responsible for reviewing and incorporating design changes.

Procedure

The organization chart should depict the project's areas and levels of responsibility. To execute the provisions of this quality system, overall project quality organizational and functional responsibilities should provide guidance and control in areas affecting the quality of the project. This guidance and control involves the following:

- Detailed requirements for construction quality in contracts, inspection, procedures, and identification of items requiring special documentation, handling, and installation.
- Implementation of the quality-program contract requirements.
- Incorporation into the prepared quality documents of factors reflecting contract quality requirements.
- Execution of the day-to-day management of the project's A/E&C quality on preengineered projects by enforcing the contract's quality provisions and requiring subcontractors and suppliers to adhere to the intent of the quality program.

- Performance of quality tasks on important work-breakdown tasks. Each task has its own emphasis as delineated in the technical specifications. Complexity, type, and location factors must be considered when deciding the amount of monitoring, surveillance, and inspection to apply.

Functional Responsibilities

The responsibilities of various positions that affect quality should be identified and explained in the position descriptions and responsibilities on a quality chart. The descriptions should be keyed to the following positions for an A/E&C project.

- PE
- Earthwork and paving subcontractors
- Electrical subcontractors
- Mechanical subcontractors
- Building subcontractors
- Laboratory subcontractors

Organization Chart. An exhibit should contain a chart of the organization related to quality.

Quality Functional Responsibilities. This exhibit describes functional responsibilities. Each position is referenced to a particular subparagraph above.

Project Engineer

Under the technical direction of the project director or manager, the project engineer should

- Remain aware of all activities under the contractor's scope of work, contract documents, and structures, systems, and components to be inspected or tested that ensure and affect quality.
- Establish and implement a quality program for controlling the work required by contract documents.
- Ensure approval of any design changes through appropriate project control systems.
- Ensure the training, supervision, and evaluation of assigned personnel.

- Monitor and review project and management reports in relation to their effect on the quality program.
- Execute duties outlined in the special procedures that follow.
- Report on quality activities and assess the effectiveness of recommendations and actions taken.
- Ensure the development of adequate project-control procedures.
- Provide resolution of potential and actual problems during A/E&C activities.
- Actively participate in project-management meetings.
- Interact with the customer representative.
- Determine the adequacy of the quality program and field effort.

Authority. The project engineer should be assigned authority and organizational freedom to identify quality-related adverse conditions and to initiate actions that correct discrepancies, thus ensuring quality workmanship and products and precluding problem recurrence. (Such discrepant conditions and materials are those that do not comply with approved specifications and guidelines and for which authorization for use has not been granted.)

Specific Functions. The project engineer performs the following activities and any others that may be assigned by the project manager.

- Provides overall management coordination of I&T efforts
- Ensures that the subcontractors' material control, electrical, mechanical, and buildings comply with contract documents
- Ensures early and timely correction of faulty work
- Oversees all life-safety testing specified by contract documents
- Ensures the inspection of all work, materials, and equipment delivered to the site, including those furnished by others
- Ensures that any repetitive or significant problems are immediately corrected, and provides solutions that preclude their repetition
- Coordinates project quality activities to ensure timely execution of the work

Earthwork and Paving Subcontractors

Under the direction of the customer, the earthwork and paving subcontractors should

- Keep informed of all aspects of the work, drawings, specifications, and material to be inspected or tested
- Establish and implement the program for inspecting, testing, and controlling all work required by specifications
- Review and approve, as warranted, material substitutions
- Ensure that A/E&C quality reports are issued on a timely basis
- Train, supervise, and evaluate assigned field personnel
- Execute duties outlined in the contracted quality procedures
- Maintain communication with the PE, including making regular reports on project quality activities and providing information and recommendations
- Participate in project staff meetings to assist project management and A/E&C support and control groups
- Maintain communication and cooperate with counterparts in federal, state, county, and local governments

Authority. Subcontractors should be assigned authority and organizational freedom within the earthwork and paving efforts to identify quality-related discrepancies and to initiate actions that correct these discrepancies, thus ensuring quality workmanship and products.

Specific Functions. Specific duties of the earthwork and paving subcontractors include the following activities and others that may be assigned by competent authority.

- Direct I&T of earthwork and paving operations
- Coordinate testing parameters and requirements
- Ensure that all earthwork and paving are constructed to the design plans and profiles, that all embankments and fills are compacted to the specified densities, and that all drainage channels and structures are properly located, constructed, and backfilled
- Provide the proposed soil-testing program to ensure the moisture content of embankments, backfill, and the like
- Control operations to obtain the specified material placed at the proper density, and ensure that the field-testing schedules provide timely and accurate data to A/E&C personnel so that work can proceed on schedule

- Inspect all rock, soil, asphalt, and concrete pavement construction
- Schedule all rock, soil, asphalt, and concrete tests
- Review and certify the results of the rock, soil, asphalt, and concrete tests

Electrical Subcontractors

Under the direction of the project manager, electrical subcontractors should

- Keep fully informed of all aspects of the work, drawings, specifications, and material to be inspected or tested
- Establish and implement the program for inspecting, testing, and controlling all of the electrical work required by specifications and directives
- Train, supervise, and evaluate assigned personnel
- Execute duties outlined in the quality procedures or as assigned by the project manager
- Report regularly on electrical quality activities with information and recommendations
- Assist the project manager in revising control procedures when necessary
- Certify all correctly installed and properly operating electrical and instrumentation and controls (I&C) installations
- Ensure that installed life-safety protection systems are operating properly during interconnections
- Review life-safety system operating instructions provided by the supplier, and submit written approval if these instructions are satisfactory
- Cooperate with other subcontractors to ensure proper installation and operation of electrical devices
- Ensure and certify that required tests of electrical-related devices are performed
- Work out A/E&C configurations and interfaces with other subcontractors and customer representatives to minimize electrical interference problems while maintaining optimum operational capability
- Exercise control of electrical material substitutions, that is, determine if material and equipment to be substituted conform to design

drawings and specifications, and approve or disapprove their use as appropriate
- Participate in project staff meetings to assist project management, field engineering, construction, and other support and control groups when required
- Maintain communication and cooperate with counterparts
- Exercise overall supervisory control of quality activities of all electrical and I&C installations, including alternating current (AC) power, electrical lighting systems, life-safety protection systems, interior communication systems, lighting protection systems, and so on

Mechanical Subcontractors

Under the direction of the project manager, the mechanical subcontractor should

- Keep fully informed of all aspects of the mechanical work, drawings, specifications, and material to be inspected or tested
- Establish and implement the program for inspecting, testing, and controlling all of the mechanical work required by specifications and directives
- Review and approve, as warranted, material substitutions
- Ensure that A/E&C daily reports are issued on a timely basis
- Monitor and review quality-related mechanical reports generated by assigned personnel
- Execute duties outlined in quality procedures or assigned by the project manager
- Report regularly on mechanical quality activities
- Inform the project manager of problems and assist in their resolution
- Participate in project staff meetings to assist management, A/E&C personnel, and support and control groups when required
- Maintain communication and cooperate with counterparts in the customer's organization

Specific Functions. Specific duties of the mechanical subcontractor include the following activities and others that may be assigned by competent authority.

- Exercise overall supervisory control of I&T of all mechanical systems, including welding, plumbing, HVAC, gas systems, and the fire-sprinklers portion of life-safety equipment.
- Ensure that welders are properly qualified for their duties by testing or other means in accordance with contractual and code requirements.
- Review and evaluate welding processes when appropriate and certify those found to be adequate.
- Inspect plumbing and HVAC systems and facilities and ensure that the systems meet contract requirements.
- Inspect all boiler and tank installations.
- Witness pneumatic and hydrostatic leak tests of piping systems.
- Ensure that sanitary-piping tests are performed satisfactorily.
- Ensure that piping, fixtures, equipment, hangers, and insulation comply with design criteria.
- Cooperate with other disciplines to ensure that pipe embedding, backfill, and compaction operations are properly completed.

Building Subcontractors

Under the direction of the owner of the project, the building subcontractor should

- Keep fully informed of all aspects of the building work, drawings, specifications, and material to be inspected or tested
- Establish and implement the program for inspecting, testing, and controlling all of the building work required by specifications and directives
- Review and approve, as warranted, material substitution
- Ensure that A/E&C QC reports are issued on a timely basis
- Train, supervise, and evaluate assigned subcontractor personnel
- Prepare QC and other reports directed by the owner
- Monitor and review quality and other reports
- Execute duties outlined in the quality procedures or assigned by the owner
- Make regular reports on building quality activities, and provide information and recommendations

- Inform the owner of potential and actual problems and assist in their resolution
- Participate in project staff meetings to assist project management, A/E&C activities, and support and control groups
- Maintain communication and cooperate with counterparts in the customer organization

Specific Functions. Specific duties of the building subcontractor include the following activities and others that may be assigned by competent authority.

- Exercise overall supervisory control of I&T of all aspects of building construction
- Ensure that line, grade, and base preparation comply with drawings and specifications
- Ensure that forms are properly placed and of correct dimensions
- Ensure that rebar and embedments are of adequate quality and quantity and are properly placed with necessary ties and weldments
- Ensure that waterproofing, waterstops, and expansion media are properly installed
- Ensure that structural masonry work is installed as specified by contract design drawings
- Ensure that architectural and finishwork activities are performed as specified by contract drawings
- Ensure that concrete is properly placed

Laboratory Subcontractors

Under the direction of the owner of the completed facility, the laboratory subcontractor should

- Keep fully informed of all aspects of the laboratory testing work, drawings, specifications, and material to be tested
- Establish and implement a quality program for inspecting, testing, and controlling all of the laboratory work required by the contract and drawings directives

- Ensure that A/E&C QC reports are issued on a timely basis
- Monitor and review QC and other reports generated by assigned personnel
- Execute duties outlined in the QC procedures
- Inform A/E&C personnel of potential and actual problems, and assist in their resolution
- Participate in project staff meetings to assist project management, A/E&C personnel, and support and control groups when required
- Maintain communication and cooperate with his or her counterparts in the customer organization

Specific Functions. Specific duties of the laboratory subcontractor include the following activities and others that may be assigned by competent authority.

- Ensure that all scales and other M&TE devices are properly calibrated at specific intervals
- Ensure that temperature-control devices, thermometers, pressure-control devices, pressure-measuring devices, and pressure applicators are calibrated at specified intervals and whenever their accuracy is suspect
- Assemble a reference collection of applicable testing and materials data
- Ensure that all tests are carried out according to the applicable specifications or authorized procedure
- Maintain accurate and complete records of all tests
- Generate and distribute all required reports
- Coordinate adjustments and calibration of M&TE devices
- Ensure that required test samples are collected and processed
- Cooperate with personnel to resolve discrepancies and to preclude their repetition
- Develop practical mix ratios for all concrete and asphalt requirements
- Develop and ensure that appropriate NDE testing—including visual examination (VE), magnetic-particle testing (MT), and liquid penetrant testing (PT)—is performed satisfactorily as required

- Conduct tests as required to ensure that dispensing devices, mixing devices, temperature-control devices, moisture-control devices, and other designated equipment is functioning properly

Note

1. For further details, see the sample contract in American Institute of Architects Document A111.

Appendix F   Selective Standard Procedure: Quality of Earthwork and Other Geotechnical Activities for Medium and Light Construction

Quality of Earthwork and Other Geotechnical Activities

- Subsurface Exploration
- Clearing, Grubbing, and Stripping
- In-Situ Density Testing
- Excavation, Filling, and Backfilling for Buildings
- Excavation, Trenching, and Backfilling for Utility and Drainage Systems
- Excavation, Embankment, and Preparation of Subgrade for Roadways and Parking Areas

This appendix contains a sample procedure for ensuring the quality of earthwork and other geotechnical activities on medium and light construction projects. Although requirements will vary from one project to the next, the basic organization presented here can be followed. This procedure is also applicable to a light or residential project. In the latter case, only portions of the procedure may be applicable.

Quality of Earthwork and Other Geotechnical Activities

This guideline establishes methods and direction for controlling the earthwork quality and other geotechnical quality activities. This includes earthwork; subsurface exploration; earth and rock excavation for roads, trenches, ditches, structures, and foundations; backfill for structures and trenches; compacted fills; borrow; select materials; and fine grading. This applies to all earthwork and other geotechnical activities of project personnel including studies, testing, and inspection. The testing agency should be responsible for the organization and management of the quality of earthwork and other geotechnical operations.

Subsurface Exploration

Subsurface exploration is the responsibility of the customer's geotechnical consultant.

Preparatory Inspection. Review the area maps, seismic test reports and other local area data, if available, to determine where cores/borings are to be taken. Inspect the equipment to determine its suitability.

Initial Inspection. Ensure that borings are made at the specified locations and to the specified depth. Ensure that samples are collected and processed. Evaluate and document the results of the explorations.

Final Inspection. Ensure that areas where borings and tests were made are returned to their proper ecological state. Ensure that boring logs are maintained and that a presentation of the investigative results is made to the customer and the customer's consultant.

Follow-Up Inspection and Recommendations. Examine the plans and drawings to identify the designs based on geotechnical data. Review the geotechnical design, such as the foundations, slopes, retaining elements, and the like. Make the appropriate recommendations to the customer's consultant, providing justification for the recommendations.

Clearing, Grubbing, and Stripping

Inspection. Inspect the clearing, grubbing, and stripping operations as necessary.

In-Situ Density Testing

Preparatory Inspection. Examine the drawings, technical specifications, and project schedules to learn when, where, and how testing is performed.

Initial Inspection. Inspect the area to be sampled and tested.

Sampling and Testing. Upon determining the suitability of the sampling method at a location, obtain samples free from loose particles with a suitable implement. Determine the in-place density and conformance to requirements.

Follow-Up Inspection and Recommendations. Evaluate the test results, including any special instructions such as logging of holes and classification and identification of the soil deposits. Comment and provide recommendations on the results.

Excavation, Filling, and Backfilling for Buildings

Line and Grade. Monitor the preparation of the subgrade that is to receive fill in excavated areas. Excavation to the final grade should be made to the required elevation. Layout should be checked for conformance to drawings and specifications.

Initial Inspection. Inspect the area to be tested and the excavation site. Ensure that the location and dimensions are correct; that the proper drainage is provided; that the excavation is not below the specified depth, except to remove unsatisfactory material; that satisfactory material is placed and compacted properly, as described in subsequent paragraphs (backfilling); and that the required piling, shoring, and bracing is accomplished. Inspect the trenches and foundation beams, and ensure proper depth, location, dimensions, and configuration.

Ensure that surplus is disposed of as directed. Inspect the utility and drain trenches and ensure that the trenches are of proper depth, location, and configuration. Ensure that each earth bed is of proper material and properly sloped. Inspect the final grade to support concrete. Ensure that the surfaces are prepared to provide satisfactory bonding. Inspect the fills and subgrades, and ensure that satisfactory materials are used. Ensure that sloped surfaces are properly stepped, benched, or broken to retain the fill.

Ensure that subgrades of less-than-specified density are compacted. Ensure that unsatisfactory material is replaced with satisfactory material. Ensure that compacting is accomplished as necessary. Inspect the capillary water barriers. Ensure that fine aggregate is of the proper depth. Inspect soil-treatment activities. Ensure that specified soil treatment agents are used in accordance with the manufacturers' inspections.

Sampling and Testing. Sample and test the following:

- Backfilling and in-place density of subgrade and fill outside the building lines
- Moisture density relationships

Follow-Up Inspection and Recommendations. Inspect and make recommendations on the following:

- Foundation excavation
- Trench excavation and subgrade bedding in the building
- Capillary water barrier
- Straightedge of finished surfaces
- Disposal of excess or unstable material
- Maintenance of baseline and benchmark

Inspect backfilling activities. Ensure that backfilling does not start before completion and approval of underground-utilities work. Ensure that backfill is of satisfactory material and compacted properly. Ensure that heavy equipment remains outside the specified minimum distance from the structures. Ensure that topsoil is spread and compacted in accordance with specifications.

Excavation, Trenching, and Backfilling for Utility and Drainage Systems

Line and Grade. Monitor the preparation for receiving fill in the excavated and trenched areas. Excavation should be performed to the lines and grades indicated. Layout should be checked for conformance to drawings and specifications.

Support and Protection. Monitor the dewatering and support of excavations. This includes locating and protecting existing utilities.

Initial Inspection. Inspect the backfilling operation to be tested. Inspect the trenches for the gas-distribution lines. Ensure that their depth is not less than the specified cover over the top of the pipes; that the pipe bed is of specified material; and that satisfactory excavated material is properly stockpiled and that unsatisfactory excavated material is properly disposed of. Inspect the trenches for the water lines. Ensure that water lines are beyond the minimum required distance from sewer lines and that the trench depth is not less than the specified cover over the top of the pipe. Ensure that the pipe bed is graded to avoid highs and lows.

Inspect the trenches for the electrical systems. Ensure that the depth is as specified. (The trench walls need not be vertical.) Ensure that overexcavation and backfill with satisfactory material are accomplished where rock is encountered.

Inspect trenches for sanitary sewers. Ensure that sewer lines are beyond the minimum required distance from water lines. Ensure that the trench is of proper depth and dimensions; and that the bottom of the trench is rounded to fit the pipe.

Inspect the excavations for appurtenances. Ensure that dimensions and locations are as specified.

Sampling and Testing. Sample and test the in-place density and moisture content.

Follow-Up Inspection and Recommendations. Inspect and make recommendations on the following:

- Removal and replacement of unsatisfactory or unstable material
- Installation of marking tapes as indicated
- Test results and their conformance to requirements

Inspect the backfilling operation. Ensure that backfilling does not start before utilities are checked and tested. Ensure that backfill is of satisfactory material, and applied and compacted in courses as indicated.

Excavation, Embankment, and Preparation of Subgrade for Roadways and Parking Areas

Line and Grade. Monitor the shaping of the subgrade as to line and grade. Ensure that excavation to final grade is made to required surfaces. Inspect layout for conformance to drawings and specifications.

Initial Inspection. Inspect the surface of excavations, embankments, and preparation of subgrade prior to sampling and testing. Inspect the area of the excavation. Ensure that the location, dimensions, and configuration are correct; that drainage structures are as specified; that unsatisfactory materials are removed from excavation and disposed of as directed; and that the use of satisfactory excavated and borrow material are in accordance with directives. Inspect the surface preparations for embankments. Ensure that foreign material and debris are removed; that the surface is properly prepared and that the moisture content is within specified limits; and that the embankment material is placed on and compacted in horizontal layers.

Inspect the subgrade. Ensure that surfaces are prepared according to specification. Remove unsatisfactory material and replace it with properly compacted and satisfactory material. Ensure that shoulders are configured as indicated.

Sampling and Testing. Sample and test for in-place density of subgrades. Test the moisture content in the stockpile, excavation, and borrow areas.

Follow-Up Inspection and Recommendations. Inspect and make recommendations on the following:

- Straightedge requirements for finished grades
- Disposal of excess and unsatisfactory material

Ensure that all surfaces are smooth, compacted, and in accordance with lines, grades, and cross sections or elevations indicated. Ensure that surfaces are properly maintained during subsequent construction activities.

Appendix G Selective Standard Procedure: Quality of Bituminous and Portland-Cement Concrete Pavements

Quality of Subbase and Base Courses, Bituminous and Portland-Cement Concrete Pavements, Pavement Markings, and Curbing

- Subbase and Baase Courses (Plant Material)
- Bituminous Prime Coat
- Bituminous Tack Coat
- Bituminous Surface Treatment (Single or Double)
- Bituminous Binder and Wearing Courses for Streets, Roads, and Open Areas
- Manhole Frames and Covers, Boxes, and Other Structures in Pavement
- Portland-Cement Concrete for Parking and Other Areas
- Pavement Marking
- Concrete Sidewalk and Curbing

This appendix contains a sample procedure for ensuring the quality of subbase and base courses, bituminous and portland-cement concrete pavements, pavements markings, and curbing on a medium-construction project. Again, as with other appendices, although requirements will vary from one project to the next, the basic organization presented here can be followed. This procedure is also applicable to light or residential projects. In the latter case, only portions of the procedure may be applicable.

Quality of Subbase and Base Courses, Bituminous and Portland-Cement Concrete Pavements, Pavement Markings, and Curbing

This guideline establishes methods and direction for controlling the quality of materials and workmanship for subbase and base courses, bituminous and portland-cement concrete pavements (for roads, streets, sidewalks, and parking areas), pavement markings, and curbing. This guideline applies to all project activities associated with this work.

Subbase and Base Courses (Plant Material)

Line and Grade. Monitor subbase and base courses and check layout for conformance to drawings and specifications.

Grade Sampling and Testing. Sample and test the density of one random sample from the mat and of one sample from the joint of each sublot.

Material Sampling and Testing. Asphalt content should be in accordance with ASTM D2172. Aggregate gradation should be in accordance with ASTM C136 and C117.

Initial Inspection. Inspect the subbase and base-course surfaces for adequate compaction and tolerances as specified. Unsatisfactory areas should be corrected.

Final Inspection and Recommendations. Inspect and make recommendations on tolerance and protection of subbase and base courses.

Bituminous Prime Coat

Line and Grade. Monitor the line and grade of the applied prime coat and check for conformance to drawings and specification.

Material Sampling and Testing. Sample and test to the requirements noted in the paragraph about subbase and base courses. Review laboratory test reports of bituminous material. Ensure that all specified requirements are complied with.

Initial Inspection. Inspect the bitumen distributor. Ensure that the tires are of sufficient size so that excess surface pressure is not applied to the base course; ensure that the distributor is capable of maintaining bitumen at the specified temperature and is spreading it at the specified pressure; that the calibration of measuring devices is accurate; that the ambient temperature and humidity are within specified limits for spreading bitumen; that the correct amount of bitumen is applied at the correct temperature and pressure; and that the required amount of sand is spread to blot up and cure any excess bitumen.

Final Inspection and Recommendations. Inspect and make recommendations on monitoring of all prime coat applications.

Bituminous Tack Coat

Line and Grade. See instructions for Bituminous Prime Coat.

Material Sampling and Testing. See instructions for Bituminous Prime Coat.

Initial Inspection. Inspect bitumen distributor. Ensure that the tires are of the type and size to prevent damage to the surface of the base course; that heating, agitating, and pressurizing equipment are adequate for their purpose; that arrangements are made for adequate pressure at the beginning and end of each surface to be treated; that the calibration of all measuring devices is accurate; that ambient temperature and humidity are within prescribed limits for applying bitumen; that bitumen is applied at the correct pressure and temperature and in the correct amounts; and that all specified surfaces are treated.

Bituminous Surface Treatment (Single or Double)

Line and Grade. Monitor the line and grade of the final course and check for conformance to drawings and specifications. Ensure that the finished surfaces do not vary more than specified from the plan gradeline or from the established and approved elevation. Finished surfaces should not deviate more than $\frac{1}{4}$ inch in any direction from the testing edge of a 10-foot straightedge.

Material Sampling and Testing. Sample and test to the requirements noted in the previous paragraph for plant material. Review the laboratory test reports on bituminous material. Ensure that all specified requirements are complied with.

Preparatory Inspection. Inspect the spreaders, distributors, and rollers. Ensure the calibration of measuring devices. Ensure that the distributors are capable of delivering the material at the temperature, pressure, and amounts required. If single-pass equipment is to be used, ensure its capability to make acceptable joints. Ensure that tires are of the type and size to prevent damage to the base course.

Initial Inspection. For the application of the first course, ensure that the ambient temperature and humidity are within the specified range. Ensure that the correct amounts of material are applied in proper sequence. Ensure that the course is properly compacted and that joints are smooth and of proper density. If a second treatment is required, inspect the application of the second course. Ensure that the course is applied within 48 hours of the first course, weather permitting. Ensure that the requirements delineated for the first course have been complied with. Ensure that the joints of the second course strips are offset by at least 1 foot from the joints of the first course.

Final Inspection and Recommendations. Ensure that the final course is dragged and rolled as specified and that the surface texture and smoothness are within the specified requirements.

Bituminous Binder and Wearing Courses for Streets, Roads, and Open Areas

Line and Grade. Ensure that control lines are properly placed and check the line and grade for conformance to drawings and specifications.

Grade Sampling and Testing. Check that the finished surfaces do not vary more than specified from the plan gradeline or from the established and approved elevation. Finished surfaces should not deviate more than $\frac{1}{4}$ inch in any direction from the testing edge of a 10-foot straightedge.

Material Sampling and Testing. Sample and test to the requirements noted in the previous paragraph noted for plant material. Review the laboratory test reports on bituminous material. Ensure that all specified requirements are complied with.

Initial Inspection. For bituminous mix design, examine the job-mix formula and ensure that it is as specified. Review the reports from the asphalt concrete plant. Ensure that the measuring equipment is calibrated properly. Ensure that the mixing equipment is in acceptable operating condition. For leveling or shim courses, inspect the base course and ensure that the degree of surface smoothness is acceptable and that no foreign materials are present. Inspect the placing of the leveling or shim courses. Ensure that the first strip is placed on the crown or high side of the area to be paved. Ensure that the adjustment and speed of the spreader are such that there is no surface pulling or tearing. Ensure that the temperature of the delivered material is correct and that the length of strips is adjusted as necessary to maintain temperature for compacting. Ensure that each strip is compacted before the succeeding strip is placed. Ensure that the thickness is as specified. Inspect the course joints. Ensure that the joints are straight and properly prepared for adjacent bituminous pavement.

Manhole Frames and Covers, Boxes, and Other Structures in Pavement

Preparatory Inspection. Examine the drawings, specifications, and survey reports. Determine the location, dimensions, and requirements. Verify the actual results.

Initial Inspection. Inspect the spreaders, compactors, blowers, brooms, saws, drills, and hand tools to be used. Ensure that all equipment is of approved type and in acceptable operating condition. Inspect the transport equipment; ensure that the truck beds are clean, tight, smooth, and properly coated to prevent adhesion of the bituminous concrete.

Inspect Pavement Edges. Ensure that they are neatly trimmed to accommodate shoulders. Inspect the binder course. Ensure that the thickness of pavement is as specified. Check the smoothness with a 10-foot straightedge to be sure that surface variation is within specified limits. Ensure that CA is taken, if warranted.

Sampling and Testing. For patch and core tests of binder and wearing courses, test the binder and wearing courses in accordance with the requirements of the specifications.

After completion of final rolling of a lot, check the compacted surface with a 10-foot straightedge.

Final Inspection and Recommendations. Inspect and report the tolerance of the finish layer. Ensure that the minimum time interval has elapsed before traffic is allowed on the pavement.

Portland-Cement Concrete for Parking and Other Areas

Line and Grade. Ensure that control lines are properly placed, and check the line and grade for conformance to drawings and specifications.

Initial Inspection. Inspect the equipment to be used, including pavers, vibrators, saws, finishing equipment, jointing, cleaning, and sealing equipment, and equipment for the application of curing compound. Ensure that all equipment is of the approved type and in acceptable operation condition.

Concrete Mix Design. Review the job-mix concrete formula. Ensure that the necessary tests have been made and that approval has been granted. Review the geotechnical reports on the base course. Ensure that the specifications are complied with for construction of the base course.

Inspection and Calibration of Concrete Batch Plants and Concrete Batch, or Agitator, Trucks. Inspect and calibrate the batch plant in accordance with American Concrete Institute (ACI) guidelines. Examine the concrete delivery schedule. Ensure that the schedule enables continuous placement of concrete at the specified rate. Inspect the trucks; ensure that they are clean, capable of mixing or agitating the concrete and of discharging the load as required, and of sufficient number to ensure that the delivery schedule can be kept. Ensure that all vehicles are in acceptable operating condition and capable of speeds that ensure the depositing of concrete between the forms within the time and at the temperature specified in ASTM C685 and ACI 305R after all ingredients have been placed into the mixing drum.

Inspection of Forms or Guide Wires (for Slip Forms) for Line and Grade. Inspect the forms; ensure that they are steel, except in special cases where wood forms are authorized by competent authority. Ensure that the forms are set on firm material cut true to grade and that they are well staked and braced and in firm contact with the underlying layer. Ensure that the forms are properly located, cleaned, and oiled for each setting. Inspect the string line. Ensure that it is accurately and securely installed and properly tightened.

Grade Sampling and Testing. Check that the finished surfaces do not vary more than specified from the plan gradeline or from the established and approved elevation. Finished surfaces should not deviate more than $\frac{1}{4}$ inch in any direction from the testing edge of a 10-foot straightedge.

Inspection of Keyways, Dowels, Tie Bars, and Pavement Reinforcement. Inspect the installation of reinforcement steel. Ensure that the amount and type of steel are as indicated on the drawings. If the pavement thickness is 12 inches or more, ensure the strike-off method of rebar installation is used. If the pavement thickness is less than 12 inches, rebar may be positioned on suitable chairs prior to the pouring of concrete.

Inspect the Longitudinal Construction Joints. Ensure that the keyway forms are of the dimensions and configuration specified and that they are securely fastened at middepth of the pavement. Ensure that the dowels and tie bars are located as indicated; check the location with a template. Ensure that the dowels and tie bars are fastened to prevent movement when concrete is placed.

Inspect the Transverse Joints. Ensure that they are installed where indicated. Ensure that transverse construction is installed any time placement of pavement is interrupted for 30 minutes or more. Insofar as possible, ensure that transverse construction joints are installed at least 10 feet from planned transverse joints. Ensure that dowels and tie bars are placed as indicated and are fastened to prevent movement when concrete is placed; use an approved template to check the placement of dowels. Ensure that one-half of each dowel placed in planned transverse joints or construction joints located as planned joints is painted and oiled. Inspect the embedded items. Examine the drawings, specifications, and survey reports. Confirm locations, dimensions, and requirements. Verify actual locations.

Inspection of Placing and Finishing Operations. Inspect the concrete placement activities. Ensure that the pavement is of specified thickness; that vibrators are used as prescribed; that there is no shifting of dowels, tie bars, rebar, or forms; that the required field test specimens are taken and processed; that finishing and surface texturing are accomplished while the concrete is in the plastic state; that the surface of the concrete is not manipulated to the point where excess water and mortar rise to the surface; and that the edges of the pavement are configured as specified.

Daily Sampling of Concrete. Test the moisture content of each size of course aggregate at least once. Perform sieve analysis at the batch plant at prescribed intervals. Make tests for air content on randomly selected batches of concrete, and make slump tests on randomly selected batches of each class.

Sampling, Curing, and Testing of Beams. Collect four concrete specimens for strength tests from each 100 cubic yards or fraction thereof for each strength of concrete placed during each shift.

Straightedging of Plastic Concrete. Inspect the finishing operations started immediately after placement of the concrete. The sequence of operations includes finishing, floating, straightedging, texturing, and the joint edging. Straightedges should be 10 feet in length. Operate straightedges from the sides of the pavement and from bridges, and test them for trueness.

Curing and Protection. Witness removal of the forms. Ensure that the required time has elapsed prior to forms removal. Ensure that the edges of the concrete are not damaged during forms removal.

Inspect the Curing Activities. Ensure that the curing method used is prescribed for the particular concrete installation under consideration. Ensure that all phases of the curing method used are carried out in accordance with specifications or directions of competent authority. Verify that necessary precautions are taken to ensure the proper curing of concrete at sawed joints while preventing curing compound from entering the joint.

Saw Joints. Inspect the sawed joints. Ensure that they are properly located and of proper depth. Ensure that saw faces are not undercut and that there is no chipping, spalling, or tearing except at exposed aggregate concrete. Ensure that there is no cracking of concrete near sawed joints. Ensure that saw cuts are thoroughly flushed with water immediately after the joint is sawed. Ensure that any membrane-cured surface that was damaged during sawing is sprayed again.

Joint Sealing. Inspect the joints for cleanliness prior to application of the joint sealer. Ensure that all foreign material, concrete protrusions, and debris are removed from the joint. Ensure that sandblasting activities and washing and blowing out of joints with compressed air are carried out in the prescribed manner and sequence. When saw cuts are sealed, ensure that the lower portion of the groove is sealed or plugged to prevent the entrance of sealants.

Inspect the sealant application activities. Ensure that ambient and pavement humidity and temperature are within specified limits. Ensure that the nozzle used is shaped for insertion into the joint to prevent air pockets. Ensure that sealants are applied according to the manufacturers' recommendations, if any.

Remedial Action. Remove and replace defective pavement as required.

Concrete Cores. When questionable pavement has been visually identified, analyze core samples to determine strength prior to taking remedial action.

Final Inspection and Recommendations. Inspect joints after the application of sealant. Ensure that bonding to joint walls is complete and sealant is cured. Inspect expansion joints; ensure that they are formed by means of preformed filler material held in position by metal supports. Ensure that a removable metal cap is provided to facilitate sealing of the joint. Ensure that joints are installed where indicated and around structures that project into, through, or against pavement.

Pavement Marking

Inspection of Surface and Layout. Examine the drawings and specifications to determine the location, type, and extent of pavement marking. Examine the manufacturer's application instructions.

Inspection and Calibration of Equipment. Inspect the paint and reflective-media application equipment. Ensure that the equipment is of the type required and that it is in acceptable operating condition.

Sweeping and Cleaning. Inspect the application activities. Ensure that marking locations and configurations are as specified. Ensure that the application of paint and reflective media is in accordance with the manufacturer's instructions.

Inspection of Operation. Inspect the paint for damage by construction activity, weather, and the like. Ensure that CA is taken when required.

Final Inspection and Recommendations. Inspect the surface condition and make recommendations.

Concrete Sidewalk and Curbing

Line and Grade. Examine the drawings and specifications to determine the location, type, line, and grade of curbs.

Grade Sampling and Testing. Check that finished surfaces do not vary more than specified from the established and approved plan.

Inspection of Forms, Line, and Grade. Inspect the forms; ensure that they are properly located for line and grade and that they are of correct dimension and configuration. Ensure that the forms are clean and oiled.

Concrete Mix Design. Review the job-mix concrete formula. Ensure that the necessary tests have been made and that approval has been granted.

Initial Inspection. Inspect curb-placing activities. If cast-in-place (CIP) concrete is used, ensure that expansion joints are properly placed. Ensure that the concrete is properly consolidated and that the top of the concrete is struck off even with forms. Ensure that the minimum curing time has elapsed before the forms are removed and that curbs are not damaged by removal of the forms.

In the case of extruded curbs, ensure that they are of correct dimensions, that they are properly placed, and that their concrete does not slump.

In the case of precast curbs, ensure that units are properly located, plumbed, and set with proper grade line. Inspect their joints, and ensure that they are properly placed and of approved material.

Curing and Protection. Witness removal of the forms. Ensure that required time has elapsed prior to forms removal. Ensure that the edges of the concrete are not damaged during forms removal.

Inspect the Curing Activities. Ensure that the curing method used is prescribed for this concrete installation. Ensure that all phases of the curing method are carried out in accordance with specifications or directions of other competent authority. Verify that necessary precautions are taken to ensure the proper curing of concrete at sawed joints while preventing the curing compound from entering the joints.

Final Inspection and Recommendations. Inspect the surface condition and make recommendations.

Appendix H   Selective Standard Procedure: Quality of Structural, Architectural, and Finish Construction

Quality of Structural, Architectural, and Finish Construction for Buildings

- Daily Sampling and Testing

This appendix contains a sample procedure for ensuring the quality of structural, architectural, and finish construction on a medium construction project. Although requirements vary from one project to the next, the basic organization presented here can be followed. This procedure is also applicable to light or residential projects. In the latter case, only portions of the procedure may be applicable.

Quality of Structural, Architectural, and Finish Construction for Buildings

This section establishes methods and direction for controlling materials and workmanship used for A/E&C buildings during vertical erection, including architectural and finishwork. This information applies to all project activities associated with the work. The testing agency and the A/E&C organization should be responsible for the quality programs in this area for structural, welding, metals and metalwork, metal doors and frames, and sanitary systems.

Procedure

Preliminary Inspection and Review of Specifications. An in-depth review should be performed of the specifications, design, and construction drawings to ascertain constructibility and any potential areas of concern. Any problem areas should be handled in accordance with the specifications.

Shop Drawings and Supplier Specifications. An in-depth review should be performed of the subject documents to ascertain constructibility and any potential areas of concern. Particular areas of interest include the following:

- Precast architectural concrete. Indication of identification marks, location of units, elevations, fabrication details, welding details, reinforcement, connections, dimensions, interface of members, and any special handling.
- Structural welding. Areas include prequalified procedures, welder and other personnel qualification certificates, and identified weld records.
- Structural steel. Give attention to shop and erection details, member and connection details, use of American Welding Society (AWS) weld symbols, and minimum number of indicated bolts.

- Steel deck. Watch type configuration, structural properties, location, detailing, holes to be cut, and reinforcement to be provided.
- Miscellaneous metal. Keep in mind material thickness, type, grade, class, dimensions, and A/E&C details.
- Finish carpentry. Areas include fabricated items, special mill items, and woodwork items.
- Elastomeric-membrane waterproofing. Areas to watch for include size and position of sheets, splicing, flashing, terminating, and expansion-joint detailing.
- Bituminous-membrane waterproofing. Conform to the certificate of compliance and manufacturer's instructions.
- Exterior insulation and finish. Follow the direction of the certificate of compliance, instructions, samples, and test data.
- Sprayed-on fireproofing. Verify against samples and certified test reports.
- Fire stopping. Areas to watch include descriptive data, typical installation details, fire-test data, and certification.
- Metal roofing and siding. Areas of concern include catalog cuts, design and erection details, coating and finishing details, materials, sizes, layouts, and fastener data. Also watch design calculations, section modules, and the moment of inertia of the sheet steel, as necessary.
- Metal wall panels. Listed in the paragraph about metal roofing and siding.
- Single-ply roofing (for example EPDM). Check the outline of roof and roof size, sheets, splices, flashing details, and expansion joints; penetration locations and types, perimeter and penetration details; and special details. Also samples, manufacturers' data, and certifications.
- Sheetmetal work. Areas include weights, gages, thickness, type of material, further detailing, and installation procedures. Also samples of material.
- Roof accessories. Check against samples and manufacturer's product data.
- Metal frame clerestory. Pay careful attention to joint, member, anchorage, and glazing details.
- Caulking and sealants. Verify against samples and manufacturer's descriptive data.

- Steel doors and frames. Areas of concern include location and elevation of each type, construction and assembling details, reinforcement locations, and details on sheets, anchors, and metal thickness. Also stripping, catalog cuts, fire-door certifications, and appropriate Underwriters Laboratories (UL) labels.
- Aluminum doors and frames. Listed in the paragraph about steel doors and frames.
- Wood doors. Areas to watch include location and elevation of each type, construction and marking details, and hardware blocking locations. Also fire-door certifications and samples.
- Miscellaneous doors. Listed in the paragraph about wood doors.
- Special doors. Listed in the paragraph about steel doors and frames.
- Accordion and operable partitions. Conform to the certificates of compliance and manufacturer's descriptive data.
- Automatic doors. Listed in the paragraph about wood doors.
- Aluminum door and windows equipment. Areas of concern include details of connections, complete layout, and dimensions.
- Plaster and gypsum wall board. Pay special attention to ceiling framing and framing, special wall framing, openings, and seismic requirements.
- Gypsum wallboard. Listed in the paragraph about plaster.
- Acoustical treatment. Areas to watch include exposed suspension system, method of anchoring and fastening, and reflected ceiling plan.
- Epoxy flooring. Give attention to the type and location of joints.
- Aluminum wall louvers. Areas of concern include materials, sizes, thickness, fastenings, and profiles.
- Postal specialties. Keep in mind plans, elevations, large-scale details, location, and template drawings.
- Shelving. Give attention to materials, thickness, and fastening details.
- Wardrobes. Areas to watch include plans, elevations, sections, thickness, fastening, hardware, and finishing specifications.

Inspection, Sampling, and Testing of Materials. Architectural, structural, and finish structures, systems, and components should be inspected immediately upon receipt. Appropriate certified testing results should be obtained, reviewed, and approved as defined in the specifications.

Storing and Handling of Material. The storage and handling of materials should be performed as they are received in strict compliance with the manufacturer's recommended practices. Storage should be such that there is no degrading of the received materials through installations. Additional guidelines are as follows:

- Excessive handling should be avoided, and ground and weather protection should be provided when required.
- Welding material should be stored in a controlled manner in accordance with AWS requirements.
- NDE materials should be stored in a controlled manner in accordance with ASNT recommended practices.
- Temperature and humidity control should be provided when deterioration of the material might occur.
- Materials should remain sealed and packaged, marked, and labeled, identifying the manufacturer. These materials include sprayed-on fireproofing, fire-stop material, insulated metal wall panels, caulking and sealants, and accordion partitions.
- Glass items should be protected on the corners to prevent impact damage.

Inspection of Installation. A well-planned and executed inspection provides the customer and subcontractors with the confidence that items or services meet specific requirements. During construction, project personnel should develop a good working relationship with subcontractors and the customer. The inspection program should interact with the customer's or other's quality program to meet requirements specified in the contract and codes, such as inspection, status indicators, calibration status indicators, and quality records.

Establishment and Implementation of the Inspection Program. This A/E&C program should be established and implemented to

- Produce objective evidence that structures, systems, components, or services meet contract requirements
- Detect and dispose of concerns or problems, as they arise, to the specific customer requirements

- Appropriately satisfy customer requirements as specified contractually. The A/E&C organization should plan and document the program, describing the inspection, testing, and verification activities as specified in the contract, and should request the customer's acceptance of the program plan. During the life of the contract, the plan should be updated to reflect changes in procedures.

In-process inspection refers to all inspection performed between receiving and final inspections. This activity is directed toward the control and verification function and as such can contribute significantly to overall quality. In-process inspection activities are planned and performed to ensure quality of the finished work. The A/E&C items should be inspected, tested, and identified as noted on the quality plan. Hold points should be designated until the required inspections and tests are satisfactorily completed, including identification of nonconforming conditions.

Final inspection is the activity upon which final acceptance is based. However, there may be occasions when completion or final construction of any item may not allow its final inspection to establish conformance, and therefore final inspection may be necessary during construction. Inspection at an intermediate stage is necessary if succeeding construction activities would prevent inspections at a later date or if a nonconformance would jeopardize succeeding operations.

Recognition of Hold Points. During the course of A/E&C activities, a positive program should be established to ensure that an item is released in a manner that minimizes quality concerns. This program should use a hold point system either when required by the customer or when it is evident that damage to the quality of the A/E&C process can occur beyond such points. This hold point system should not be bypassed unless a limited work authorization is provided in a controlled manner.

Inspection and Testing Results. To execute A/E&C activities whose characteristics are within specification, the A/E&C organization should demonstrate that material acceptance decisions used objective evidence from suitable inspection and testing (I&T) methods. This documented evidence should be relevant to the quality of the item and should testify that the constructed item can perform as intended and in compliance with customer and contractual requirements.

I&T results should be prepared, reviewed, safely stored, and maintained by the contractor. Storage and maintenance length should be a function of the item's operating life. In addition, the contractor should be cautioned that, in some cases, significant customer and contractual record requirements may be imposed and that due allowance for this provision be given.

Inspection and Test Status. Inspected and noninspected items should be distinguished using suitable status indicators, such as stamps, tags, routing cards, or other control devices.

Inspection and test status identification of structures, systems, components, and services should be maintained and controlled from initial receipt, through release, to fabrication, erection, and operation of the constructed item. The status of I&T should be physically indicated on the constructed item if possible, or traceable to the item as prescribed by the customer and contract requirements. The status should normally indicate the

- Extent to which the item can be used
- Acceptance by the customer authority when applicable
- Calibration of testing equipment when applicable
- Extent to which I&T was performed
- Limited work authorization

Suitable controls should be established for prevention or timely correction of loss, theft, destruction, or deterioration of the means used to identify the status.

Items should be inspected on receipt for completeness, proper type, and transit damage detection. Any concerns, including nonconforming conditions, should be promptly reported in writing to the customer.

The customer should be provided with reasonable access to A/E&C activities for the purpose of monitoring item inspection. Careful consideration should be given to the design of quality document forms used for the recording of inspection and test activities. Whenever possible, the forms should be serialized and include adequate provision for the item or batch identification or description, drawing or specification identification, quality, construction-site location, description of quality concerns, disposition and closure of quality concerns, and signatures (with dates) of the appropriate subcontractor, supplier, or customer. Reinspection and retesting should be to the same degree as the original I&T.

Line, Grades, and Plumbness. The alignment, grade, and plumbness of the installed materials should be performed in strict compliance with the manufacturer's recommended practices. Measuring devices should be appropriately calibrated, and of the precision and accuracy specified in the technical specifications. Additional requirements are as follows:

- For precast architectural concrete and exterior insulation, tightness of joints should be monitored.
- For structural connections, use American Institute Steel Connections requirements.[1]
- For welded connections, AWS requirements should be used.[2]

Daily Sampling and Testing

Structural Welding. The frequency of field testing should meet the following specifications.

- Visual (VT).[3] Every weld.
- Ultrasonic testing (UT), liquid penetrant testing (PT), and magnetic-particle testing (MT). Refer to CSI specification section 1400.
- Structural and miscellaneous metal. Random checking of high-strength (HS) bolt torques as noted in the *CRSI Handbook.*[4]
- Steel deck. One percent of headed stud connectors on any deck struck with hammer and bent at least 15 degrees.

Elastomeric-Membrane Waterproofing. One-time-only samples of butyl rubber, plastic elastomeric sheeting, and composite, self-adhering membrane should be tested according to the test methods listed in the specifications.

Exterior Insulation and Finish. One-time-only tests should be performed on the insulation and finish system as explained in ASTM E695.[5]

Sprayed-On Fireproofing. One-time-only samples should be taken for surface-burning characteristics, fire endurance, and performance; testing should be performed as noted in the technical specifications.

Metal Roofing and Siding. One sample should be taken of covering, roof, and wall, and tested as noted in the specifications.

Single-Ply Roofing. Installations should be tested one time only for each roof substance.

Painting, General. Requirements should be checked on a random basis during installation according to standard painting specifications (SPS) 1, 2, and 3.

Vinyl-Coated and Fabric Wall Covering. Refer to the paragraph about general painting and to manufacturer's recommendations.

Wardrobes. Static load should be tested once only to the capacities indicated in the specifications.

Temporary Supports, Templates, Screens, and Guides. Temporary supports, templates, screens, and guides should be used according to the specifications. Structural calculations and design layout should be performed to ensure the final installed product conforms to drawing and specification requirements. In addition, assurances should be provided to prevent these items from damaging the final installed product. Temporary welds, run-off plates, and backing strips used during structural erection need not be removed except in the case of interference. Sample calculations should be available for review. When guide patterns or mock-ups are required, their conformance to specifications should be ensured, and first-piece witness should be made available to the customers.

Manufacturer's Specifications. When structures, systems, and components are being manufactured, conformance to requirements should be in the following order of precedence.

- Technical specifications and drawings
- Specified codes and guidelines
- Manufacturer's specifications

If requirements conflict, the document with higher precedence should rule. The manufacturer's specifications should adequately provide descriptive data, erection and installation details, and sufficient O&M instructions for turnover to the customer.

Protection of Finishwork. Adequate protection should be given to prevent inadvertent deterioration of the finishwork. This protection includes

- Structural: field priming
- Steel deck: field painting
- Miscellaneous metal: field painting

- Elastomeric-membrane waterproofing: vertical with protective board, horizontal with mortar
- Bituminous-membrane waterproofing: slab edges should be protected by bending membrane edge
- Sprayed-on fireproofing: should act as protective barrier for structures
- Metal roofing and siding: protect from surface staining
- Roof accessories: installer should advise
- Metal-frame skylight: protect glass until accepted
- Steel doors and frames: adequate measures to prevent water penetration
- Aluminum doors and frames: protect from contact with dissimilar metals
- Aluminum windows: protect frame from contact with dissimilar metals and protect glass with contact paper
- Glass and glazing: protect surfaces with paper until accepted
- Gypsum wallboard: water-resistant treatment as recommended by manufacturer
- Ceramic tile: building paper and noncorrosive soap
- Wood, resilient, and epoxy flooring: building paper

As-Built Drawings. In many cases, as-built drawings should be specified for submittal to the customer. These drawings should be in sufficient detail to permit proper O&M activities after installation. These final records should be developed after completion of the project and should include a complete set of reproducible sepia drawings. These drawings should include the following:

- Location and dimensions of any changes within the building
- Revised grades and alignments of roads, structures, and utilities
- Revised elevations
- Changes in detail of design or additional information
- Topography and grades of all lumber
- Workmanship, joining, fitting, nailing, and hanging
- Sizes and installation of any special structures, systems, and components
- Grading and marking

- Delivery, storage, and damage and defects
- Elastomeric-membrane waterproofing. Preparation, installation, and application of waterproofing, primer, and insulation board, including types of membrane. The following should be checked.
  —Ambient temperature as specified
  —Requirements for reinforcing strips
  —Flashing waterstops, lapping, wrinkles, and buckles
  —Location of flammable material (away from open flames)
  —Adhesion, additional mopping coats, and protective layers for insulation board
  —Damage, defects, and protection
  —Temperature and poundage of pitch

- Bituminous-membrane waterproofing. Preparation, installation, and application of waterproofing membrane. The following should be checked.
  —Ambient temperature as specified
  —Requirements for reinforcing strips
  —Flashing, waterstops, lapping, wrinkles, and buckles
  —Location of flammable material (away from open flames)
  —Damage, defects, and protection
  —Cement-based waterproofing
  —Proper preparation of surfaces
  —Proper application of materials
  —Cleaning and protection

- Exterior insulation and finish. Proper attachment of suspension system and accessories, fitness and alignment of finished soffit, tightness of joints, cleanliness of soffit finish, and damage.
- Sprayed-on fireproofing. Proper application, cleaning, protection, and damage.
- Firestopping. Installation of material, proper locations, filling of voids and pipe penetrations, repairing of damage and defects.
- Metal roofing and siding. Storage, installation, and sealing of joints.
- Single-ply roofing. Observation of environmental conditions, number and skill level of roofing workers, start and end time of various

tasks, readiness of substrate for application of roofing. Verification of compliance of materials before, during, and after installation. Inspection of cants, flashings, penetrations, and work requiring coordination with roofing. Inspection of membrane placement, splicing, and anchoring. Inspection of placement of walkways.

- Sheet metalwork. Observation of environmental conditions, number and skill level of sheet metalworkers, and condition of substrate. Verification of compliance of materials before, during, and after installation. Inspection of sheet metalwork for proper size, thickness, fastening joining, and installation. Preparation of surfaces to receive sheet metalwork. Protection of dissimilar metals. Forming, lapping, and sealing of joints. Securing sheet metalwork to structure. Watertightness. Damage.
- Roof accessories. Damage and defects. Conformance to requirements. Protection from dissimilar materials.
- Metal-frame skylights (for example, clerestory). Damage and defects. Conformance to requirements. Protection from dissimilar materials.
- Caulking and sealants. Condition of joint prior to application of compound. Correct type of primer, back-up material, sealer, and caulking compound. Weather conditions. Application of compound with correct size and type gun, installation of back-up material, neatness of finished joint, and proper application of sealant. Damage.
- Steel doors and frames. Installation of doors and frames. Fitting of hardware and accessories. Setting of acoustic seals and saddles. Smooth and free operation. Damage or defects. Installation of weatherstripping. Thickness and gauge requirements. Mounting. Swing of door. Fasteners.
- Aluminum doors and frames. Framing covered with protective material. Framing and doors delivered to site in undamaged condition and stored as specified. Framing installed with tight joints and proper anchoring. Finish within color range. Aluminum in contact with dissimilar materials protected as specified. Framing properly cleaned.
- Wood doors. Installation of doors and frames. Fitting of hardware and accessories. Setting of acoustic seals and saddles. Smooth and free operation. Damage or defects. Thickness and gauge requirements. Mounting. Swing of door. Fasteners.

- Miscellaneous doors. Erection and installation of doors and frames. Fitting of hardware and accessories. Setting of acoustic seals and saddles. Smooth and free operation. Proper operation of motor operators. Field test by approved testing laboratory. Damage or defects.
- Special doors. Units stored and protected in accordance with requirements. Specified type and quantity of frame anchors provided. Type and quantity of door silencers provided as specified. Damaged surfaces repaired per specifications. Doors and frames installed and clearances maintained as specified. Doors and frames undamaged, and doors operate freely. Doors and frames installed with swing as indicated on drawings
- Automatic doors. Installation of door operators. Fitting of accessories. Smooth and free operation. Proper operation of motor operators. Damage or defects.
- Aluminum door equipment. Fitting of operators. Swing of doors. Proper operation of operators. Damage or defects.
- Aluminum windows. Erection and installation of windows. Fitting of hardware and accessories. Installation of weatherstripping. Smooth and free operation. Protection from dissimilar materials. Damage or defects.
- Builders hardware, general purpose. Mounting. Swing of door. Fasteners. Key and master key operation. Damage or defects.
- Glass and glazing. Fabrication and installation. Proper thickness. Damage or defects. Correct types. Protection. Cleaning.
- Veneer plaster. Installation and location of studs, furring, and baseboard. Joint reinforcement. Proper plaster thickness. Damage and finish.
- Gypsum wallboard. Correct type, size, and finish of gypsum wallboard. Preparation, application, and installation of fasteners, accessories, compounds, and taped joints. Type, size, and location of fasteners and adhesives. Type, size, and location of hangers, tie wires, and clips, including ceiling and floor runner channels, furring channels, and main runner channels. Delivery and storage.
- Waterproofing. Steel and wood. All edges have continuous bearing. Joint and fastener concealment. Least number of horizontal and vertical joints. Damage and defects.

- Ceramic tile. Correct sizes, colors, patterns, and finishes. Preparation, installation, setting, and placement of tile and accessories. Location of anchorage of studs and furring, including lath lap and support, tied with zinc-coated wire. Metal studs covered with polyethylene film if required. Walls installed prior to floor installation.
- Acoustical ceilings. Proper attachment of suspension system. Proper attachment of moldings and splines. Flatness and alignment of finished ceilings. Tightness of joints. Cleanliness of ceiling finish. Damage.
- Wood flooring. Proper temperature and ventilation for installation. Condition of subfloor. Layout of flooring. Installation. Cleaning and protection. Damage.
- Resilient flooring. Proper temperature and ventilation for installation. Condition of subfloor. Layout of tile. Installation. Cleaning and protection. Damage.
- Elastomeric flooring. All materials approved, including samples and accessories. Correct colors, patterns, and finishes. Preparation, installation, setting, and placement. Certificates furnished. Walls installed prior to floor installation. Location of expansion and control joints. Damage and defects.
- Vinyl-coated wall covering. Correct type of material, primer, sealer, and adhesive, including weight and bearing surface. Correct flame-spread rating certificates. Walls clean, dry, and otherwise ready for installation of vinyl-coated wall covering. Damage and defects.
- Fabric wall covering. Correct type of material, primer, sealer, and adhesive, including weight and bearing surface. Correct flame-spread rating certificates. Walls clean, dry, and otherwise ready for installation of fabric wall covering. Damage and defects.
- Toilet partitions. Erection and plumbness. Door swings. Fitting of hardware and accessories. Damage or defects.
- Aluminum wall louvers. Samples, finish, and metal substrate. Storage and handling. Protection of dissimilar materials. Securing to adjoining work. Installation.
- Fire-extinguisher and fire-hose cabinets. Correct and proper installation of units. Protection of units after erection and until final cleaning.

- Postal specialties. Submittal received and approved. Proper location. Damage and defects. Units and locks operate properly.
- Shelving. Correct location. Fastener type and size. Damage and defects.
- Toilet accessories. Proper location. Damage.
- Wardrobes. Installation of door and frames. Fitting of hardware and accessories. Smooth and free operation. Damage or defects.

Final Inspection and Recommendations. A final inspection and walk-through should be performed prior to turnover of the building to the customer.

O&M Manuals and Warranties. O&M manuals should be prepared and furnished to the customer from supplier data. Manuals should include the commercial warranties provided by the supplier.

Notes

1. American Institute Steel Connections has several standards pertinent to structural steel, including the *CRSI Handbook*, which is particularly useful in the area of bolted connections.

2. The American Welding Society has a primary code pertinent to structural welded connections, AWS D1.1.

3. These nondestructive examination methods are standard ones noted by the American Society of Nondestructive Examination in SNT-TC-1A for visual testing, ultrasonic testing, magnetic particle testing, and liquid penetrant testing.

4. American Institute of Steel Construction. *CRSI Handbook*.

5. The American Society for Testing Materials has several volumes of testing standards which are used throughout the A/E&C community.

Appendix I Sample Contracts Controlling Quality for Light and Residential Constructed Projects

Job number: XX-XX	Model contract	Date of issue: Month 19XX
cc: officer project director	Company name Point of issue: project location site city, state	Contract number: XX-XX-XXX

| Sales tax-exempt___
-taxable___ | Note: The contract number must appear
on all correspondence, packages, etc. | |

| S
u
p
p
l
i
e
r | Issue to:
exterior enclosure
address
city, state, zip code | Delivery date: below | Freight on board
point: NA |
| | | Payment terms:
Bill upon task
completion. Pay
within X days. | Ship via:
NA |

Consignee/destination: project job site address city, state, zip code	Invoice address: A/E&C organization central office address city, state, zip code

Quantity	Description	Cost code	Unit price	Amount
Task 1	Fascia and soffit on XX wing of building	XX-X		XXX.XX
Task 2	Fascia and soffit on back section of building	XX-X		XXX.XX
Task 3	Fascia and soffit front	XX-X		XXX.XX
Task 4	Trim windows	XX-X		XXX.XX
Task 5	Front, west, and back side	XX-X		XXX.XX
Task 6	Completion of trim and side and drive through activities	XX-X		XXX.XX
		Total		$XX,XXX.XX

1. Execute copy and return.
2. Excess material subject to
   rejection and return.
3. All changes must be agreed
   to us in writing.
4. Separately state labor and
   material charges.
5. Other conditions are
   attached herewith.
6. 10 percent retained until
   satisfactory completion.
	Subcontractor signature
	Federal I.D. number XXX-XX-XXXX
	
	By: _____
	
	A/E&C organization name
	
	By: _____
	    company officer
	Constr: _____

Figure I.1.   This sample contract is a general purchase order for material and its installation.

Job number: XX-XX	Model contract	Date of issue: XX Month 19XX
cc: operating officer project director	A/E&C organization affiliate Point of issue: project name, city, state	Contract number: XX-XX-XXX

Sales tax-exempt___ -taxable___	Note: The contract number must appear on all correspondence, packages, etc.

S u p p l i e r	Issue to: coating contractor address city, state, zip code attn: owner	Delivery date: below	Freight on board point: NA
		Payment terms: Bill upon task completion. Pay within X days.	Ship via: NA

Consignee/destination: project name address city, state, zip code	Invoice address: A/E&C organization central office address city, state, zip code

Quantity	Description	Cost code	Unit price	Amount
Task 1	Prime the interior walls of the building that are smooth plaster, including the ceiling in room X. Also, lightly sand the walls and ceiling ready for the final coat of paint. The contractor is responsible for cleanup of his own work after completion. Note all original contract provisions remain in effect and binding.	XX-X		XXXXX.XX
		Total		$XX,XXX.XX

1. Execute copy and return. 2. Excess material subject to rejection and return. 3. All changes must be agreed to us in writing. 4. Separately state labor and material charges. 5. Other conditions are attached herewith. 6. 10 percent retained until satisfactory completion.	Subcontractor signature Federal I.D. number XXX-XX-XXXX _____ By: _____ A/E&C organization name By: _____ company officer Constr: _____

Figure I.2. These two contracts pertain to the application of a moisture coating to a foundation and coating to a wood structure.

Job number: XX-XX	Model contract	Date of issue: XX Month 19XX
cc: operating officer project director	A/E&C organization affiliate Point of issue: project name, city, state	Contract number: XX-XX-XXX

Sales tax-exempt___ -taxable___	Note: The contract number must appear on all correspondence, packages, etc.

S u p p l i e r	Issue to: exterior enclosure address city, state, zip code	Delivery date: below	Freight on board point: NA
		Payment terms: Bill upon task completion. Pay within X days.	Ship via: NA

Consignee/destination: project job site address city, state, zip code	Invoice address: A/E&C organization central office address city, state, zip code

Quantity	Description	Cost code	Unit price	Amount
Task 1	Kilstain all knots as needed to prevent leeching through paint, prime all pine including putty, and fill all nail holes. Prime all external doors that are weathered and provide good exterior sealer on all other exterior doors. The work deadline is XX Month 19XX. The subcontractor warrants all related work and manufacturer defects through the same period as the one specified in the P&S agreement.	XX-X		XXXX.XX
		Total		$XXX,XXX.XX

1. Execute copy and return. 2. Excess material subject to rejection and return. 3. All changes must be agreed to us in writing. 4. Separately state labor and material charges. 5. Other conditions are attached herewith. 6. 10 percent retained until satisfactory completion.	Subcontractor signature Federal I.D. number XXX-XX-XXXX By: _____ A/E&C organization name By: _____ company officer Constr: _____

Figure I.2. *continued*

Job number: XX-XX	Model contract	Date of issue: XX Month 19XX
	A/E&C organization affilate Point of issue: project name, city, state	
cc: operating officer project director		Contract number: XX-XX-XXX

| Sales tax-exempt___ -taxable___ | Note: The contract number must appear on all correspondence, packages, etc. |

| S u p p l i e r | Issue to: mason contractor address city, state, zip code | Delivery date: below | Freight on board point: NA |
| | | Payment terms: 1/2 after material on site, 1/4 after rough, balance upon completion. Due on X day as specified. | Ship via: NA |

| Consignee/destination: project job site address city, state, zip code | Invoice address: A/E&C organization central office address city, state, zip code |

Quantity	Description	Cost code	Unit price	Amount
Task 1	Procure masonry materials and deliver to site.	XX-X		XX,XXX.XX
Task 2	Place two mason structures in the rough.	XX-X		XXX.XX
Task 3	Preform brickwork for mason structures.	XX-X		XXX.XX
Task 4	Complete finishwork activities.	XX-X		XXX.XX
		Total		$XXX,XXX.XX

| 1. Execute copy and return. 2. Excess material subject to rejection and return. 3. All changes must be agreed to us in writing. 4. Separately state labor and material charges. 5. Other conditions are attached herewith. 6. 10 percent retained until satisfactory completion. | Subcontractor signature Federal I.D. number XXX-XX-XXXX _____ By: _____ A/E&C organization name By: _____ company officer Constr: _____ |

Figure I.3. This contract pertains to masonry work on chimney structures in the rough.

Job number: XX-XX	Model contract	Date of issue: XX Month 19XX
cc: operating officer project director	My company affiliate Point of issue: project name city, state	Contract number: XX-XX-XXX

Sales tax-exempt___ -taxable___	Note: The contract number must appear on all correspondence, packages, etc.

S u p p l i e r	Issue to: stone mason contractor address city, state, zip code	Delivery date: below	Freight on board point: NA
		Payment terms: X days after receipt of work performed.	Ship via: XX

Consignee/destination: project job site address city, state, zip code	Invoice address: My company central office address city, state, zip code

Quantity	Description	Cost code	Unit price	Amount
Task 2	Install at least XXX feet of granite curbing, backfill behind curb, and spread topsoil.	XX-X XX-X XX-X XX-X XX-X XX-X	XXXX.XX	XXXX.XX
	New total not to exceed	Total		$XX,XXX.XX

1. Execute copy and return. 2. Excess material subject to rejection and return. 3. All changes must be agreed to us in writing. 4. Separately state labor and material charges. 5. Other conditions are attached herewith. 6. 10 percent retained until satisfactory completion.	Subcontractor signature Federal I.D. number XXX-XX-XXXX By: _____ My company name By: _____ company officer Constr: _____

Figure I.4. This contract pertains to a stone mason supplying and installing granite stone curbing.

Job number: XX-XX	Model contract	Date of issue: XX Month 19XX
	My company affiliate	
cc: operating officer project director	Point of issue: project name city, state	Contract number: XX-XX-XXX
Sales tax-exempt___ -taxable___	Note: The contract number must appear on all correspondence, packages, etc.	

S u p p l i e r	Issue to: Security Design Co. address city, state, zip code	Delivery date: below	Freight on board point: NA
		Payment terms: 25% at prewire, 25% after prewire, 25% day of installation. Balance upon completion.	Ship via: XX

Consignee/destination: project name address city, state, zip code	Invoice address: My company central office address city, state, zip code

Quantity	Description	Cost code	Unit price	Amount
Task 1	Prewire fire and security systems including contacts and sound wire (switching in study and volume control at other locations).	XX-X	XXX.XX	XXX.XX
Task 2	Review wiring after sheetrock after prewire.	XX-X	XXX.XX	XXX.XX
Task 3	Install fire and security equipment (control panel, key siren, switches, and smoke detectors).	XX-X	XXX.XX	XXX.XX
Task 4	Perform final walk through and satisfactory operational test. (Note: A change order may be issued on the number of smoke detectors to meet requirements.)	XX-X	XXX.XX	XXX.XX
		Total		$XX,XXX.XX

1. Execute copy and return. 2. Excess material subject to rejection and return. 3. All changes must be agreed to us in writing. 4. Separately state labor and material charges. 5. Other conditions are attached herewith. 6. 10 percent retained until satisfactory completion.	Subcontractor signature Federal I.D. number XXX-XX-XXXX ___ By: ___ My company name By: ___ company officer Constr: ___

Figure I.5.   This contract pertains to the supply and installation of a fire-alarm and security-alarm system.

Job number: XX-XX	Model contract	Date of issue: XX Month 19XX
	My company affiliate	
cc: operating officer project manager	Point of issue: project name city, state	Contract number: XX-XX-XXX
Sales tax-exempt___ -taxable___	Note: The contract number must appear on all correspondence, packages, etc.	

S u p p l i e r	Issue to: elevator fabricator address city, state, zip code	Delivery date: below	Freight on board point: XX
		Payment terms: X days after receipt of bill of work/task completion defined in attachment 1	Ship via: XX

Consignee/destination: project name address city, state, zip code	Invoice address: My company name address city, state, zip code

Quantity	Description	Cost code	Unit price	Amount
Task 1	Produce and issue an approved set of shop drawings.	XX-X	X	X.XX
Task 2	Fabricate elevator structures in the rough.	XX-X	XXXX	XXXX.XX
Task 3	Install elevator. (Attachments herewith are an integral part of this contract.)	XX-X	XXXX	XXXXX.XX
If Task 2 is not released in writing		Total		X.XX
If Task 2 is released in writing		Total		$XXX,XXX.XX

1. Execute copy and return. 2. Excess material subject to rejection and return. 3. All changes must be agreed to us in writing. 4. Separately state labor and material charges. 5. Other conditions are attached herewith. 6. 10 percent retained until satisfactory completion.	Subcontractor signature Federal I.D. number <u>XXX-XX-XXXX</u> By: _____ My company name By: _____ operating officer Constr: _____

Figure I.6. This contract pertains to the supply and installation of a residential elevator.

Job number: XX-XX	Model contract	Date of issue: XX Month 19XX
cc: operating officer project director	My company affiliate Point of issue: project name city, state	Contract number: XX-XX-XXX

Sales tax-exempt___ -taxable___	Note: The contract number must appear on all correspondence, packages, etc.

S u p p l i e r	Issue to: earthwork contractor address city, state, zip code	Delivery date: below	Freight on board point: NA
		Payment terms: Bill upon task completion. Pay within X days.	Ship via: NA Telephone (XXX) XXX-XXXX

Consignee/destination: project name job site address city, state, zip code	Invoice address: A/E&C organization central office address city, state, zip code

Quantity	Description	Cost code	Unit price	Amount
Task 5	General site work	XX-X		XXXX.XX
	All labor and materials are to be in accordance with drawings/specifications as with attachments 1, 2, and 3			
	909 Excavator (XX hours)		XXXXXX	
	D 4 dozer (XX hours)		XXXXX	
	10 wheeler (XX hours)		XXXXX	
	6 wheeler (XX hours)		XXXXX	
	2 ½ yard loader (X hour)		XXXXX	
	Backhoe loader (X hour)			
	*Based upon above rates	Total		$XXX*

1. Execute copy and return. 2. Excess material subject to rejection and return. 3. All changes must be agreed to us in writing. 4. Separately state labor and material charges. 5. Other conditions are attached herewith. 6. 10 percent retained until satisfactory completion.	Subcontractor signature Federal I.D. number XXX-XX-XXXX _____ By: _____ A/E&C organization name By: _____ company officer Constr: _____

Figure I.7. This contract pertains to earthwork on miscellaneous sitework, without supplying earth material.

Job number: XX-XX	Model contract	Date of issue: XX Month 19XX
cc: operatoring officer project director	A/E&C organization affiliate Point of issue: project name, city, state	Contract number: XX-XX-XXX

Sales tax-exempt__ -taxable__	Note: The contract number must appear on all correspondence, packages, etc.	

S u p p l i e r	Issue to: misc. labor contractor address city, state, zip code	Delivery date: below	Freight on board point: NA
		Payment terms: Bill upon task completion. Pay within X days.	Ship via: NA

Consignee/destination: project name job site address city, state, zip code	Invoice address: A/E&C organization central office address city, state, zip code

Quantity	Description	Cost code	Unit price	Amount
Task 1	Install heat enclosure in basement, level the earth per direction of superintendent, and provide miscellaneous labor during this time period of Month XX through Month XX. Note: All attachments, terms, and conditions remain in effect.	XX-X	XXX	X.XX
New contract total not to exceed on XX-XX-XX				$XXX,XXX.XX

1. Execute copy and return. 2. Excess material subject to rejection and return. 3. All changes must be agreed to us in writing. 4. Separately state labor and material charges. 5. Other conditions are attached herewith. 6. 10 percent retained until satisfactory completion.	Subcontractor signature Federal I.D. number XXX-XX-XXXX _____ By: _____ A/E&C organization name By: _____ company officer Constr: _____

Figure I.8. This contract pertains to the supply of miscellaneous labor at a project site.

Job number: XX-XX	Model contract	Date of issue: XX Month 19XX
cc: company officer project director	A/E&C organization affiliate Point of issue: project name, city, state	Contract number: XX-XX-XXX

Sales tax-exempt___
       -taxable___
      Note: The contract number must appear on all correspondence, packages, etc.

S u p p l i e r	Issue to: plumbing contractor address city, state, zip code	Delivery date: below	Freight on board point: XX
		Payment terms: XX days upon delivery of material to the site.	Ship via: XX

Consignee/destination: project name address city, state, zip code	Invoice address: A/E&C organization central office address city, state, zip code

Quantity	Description	Cost code	Unit price	Amount
Task 1	Install underground sewer in main building and parking.	XX-X	XXXX	XXXXX
Task 2	Core hole in designated walls.	XX-X	XXXX	XXXXX
		Total		$XX,XXX.XX

1. Execute copy and return.
2. Excess material subject to rejection and return.
3. All changes must be agreed to us in writing.
4. Separately state labor and material charges.
5. Other conditions are attached herewith.
6. 10 percent retained until satisfactory completion.

Subcontractor signature
Federal I.D. number XXX-XX-XXXX

By: _____

A/E&C organization name

By: _____
      company officer

Constr: _____

Figure I.9. This contract pertains to the supply and installation of embedded water lines and sewer work in the rough.

Job number: XX-XX	Model contract	Date of issue: Month 19XX
cc: operating officer project director	A/E&C organization affiliate Point of issue: project name, city, state	Contract number: XX-XX-XXX

Sales tax-exempt___ -taxable___	Note: The contract number must appear on all correspondence, packages, etc.

S u p p l i e r	Issue to: window supplier address city, state, zip code	Delivery date: below	Freight on board point: NA
		Payment terms: XX days upon delivery of material to the site.	Ship via: XX

Consignee/destination: project name address city, state, zip code	Invoice address: A/E&C organization central office address city, state, zip code

Quantity	Description	Cost code	Unit price	Amount
D-2	D1636 SDH, 4/1 IDL, two units temp glass, R.O. XXXX	XX-X	XXXX	XXXXX
D'-2	X XX"		XXXX	XXXXX
W-2	D3636 SDH, 4/1 IDL glass XX" x XX"	XX-X	XXXX	
				XXXXX
	Tax			XXXX
		Total		$XX,XXX.XX

1. Execute copy and return. 2. Excess material subject to rejection and return. 3. All changes must be agreed to us in writing. 4. Separately state labor and material charges. 5. Other conditions are attached herewith. 6. 10 percent retained until satisfactory completion.	Subcontractor signature Federal I.D. number XXX-XX-XXXX ___ By: _____ A/E&C organization name By: _____ company officer Constr: _____

Figure I.10.   This contract applies to the supply of specialty and custom window glazing.

Job number: XX-XX	Model contract	Date of issue: XX Month 19XX
cc: operating officer project director	A/E&C organization affiliate Point of issue: project name, city, state	Contract number: XX-XX-XXX

| Sales tax-exempt___
-taxable___ | Note: The contract number must appear
on all correspondence, packages, etc. | |

S u p p l i e r	Issue to: foundation contractor address city, state, zip code	Delivery date: below	Freight on board point: XX
		Payment terms: XX days after receipt of bill of work performed.	Ship via: XX

Consignee/destination: project name job site address city, state, zip code	Invoice address: A/E&C organization central office address city, state, zip code

Quantity	Description	Cost code	Unit price	Amount
Task 10	Satisfactorily place the concrete slabs in buildings A and B in accordance with latest design documents. All other previous specifications remain in affect.	XX-X	XXXX	XXXXX
			Total	$XX,XXX.XX

1. Execute copy and return. 2. Excess material subject to rejection and return. 3. All changes must be agreed to us in writing. 4. Separately state labor and material charges. 5. Other conditions are attached herewith. 6. 10 percent retained until satisfactory completion.	Subcontractor signature Federal I.D. number XXX-XX-XXXX By: _____ A/E&C organization name By: _____ Constr: _____

Figure I.11. This contract applies to the installation of foundation slabs in a constructed building.

Bibliography

ASQC. *Quality Systems Terminology. ANSI/ASQC A3-1987.* Milwaukee, Wis.: ASQC Quality Press, 1987.

————. *Quality Management and Quality Assurance Standards— Guidelines for Selection and Use. ANSI/ASQC Q90-1987.* Milwaukee, Wis.: ASQC Quality Press, 1987.

————. *Quality Systems—Model for Quality Assurance in Design/- Development, Production, Installation, and Servicing. ANSI/ASQC Q91- 1987.* Milwaukee, Wis.: ASQC Quality Press, 1987.

————. *Quality Systems—Model for Quality Assurance in Production and Installation. ANSI/ASQC Q92-1987.* Milwaukee, Wis.: ASQC Quality Press, 1987.

————. *Quality Systems—Model for Quality Assurance in Final Inspection and Test. ANSI/ASQC Q93-1987.* Milwaukee, Wis.: ASQC Quality Press, 1987.

————. *Quality Management and Quality System Elements—Guidelines. ANSI/ASQC Q94-1987.* Milwaukee, Wis.: ASQC Quality Press, 1987.

ASQC Construction Technical Committee. *Quality Management in the Constructed Project.* Milwaukee, Wis.: ASQC Quality Press, 1987.

Center for Chemical Process Safety. *Chemical Process Quantitative Risk Analysis.* New York: American Society of Chemical Engineers, 1989.

Hart, Roger D. "The Quality of Construction." *Transactions of the 41st ASQC Annual Quality Congress.* Milwaukee, Wis.: ASQC, 1987.

————. "Construction Quality Institute." *Transactions of the 43rd ASQC Annual Quality Congress.* Milwaukee, Wis.: ASQC, 1989.

————. "Quality Measurement Engineering and Construction." *Transactions of the 46th Annual ASQC Quality Congress.* Milwaukee, Wis.: ASQC, 1992.

————. "Leadership in Quality Systems of Design and Construction." *Transactions of the 47th Annual ASQC Quality Congress.* Milwaukee, Wis.: ASQC, 1992.

International Organization for Standardization. *Quality Management and Quality Assurance Standards—Guidelines for Selection and Use. ISO 9000-1987.* Geneva: International Organization for Standardization, 1987.

————. *Quality Systems—Model for Quality Assurance in Design/ Development, Production, Installation, and Servicing. ISO 9001-1987.* Geneva: International Organization for Standardization, 1987.

————. *Quality Systems—Model for Quality Assurance in Production and Installation. ISO-9002-1987.* Geneva: International Organization for Standardization, 1987.

————. *Quality Systems—Model for Quality Assurance in Final Inspection and Test. ISO 9003-1987.* Geneva: International Organization for Standardization, 1987.

————. *Quality Management and Quality System Elements—Guidelines. ISO 9004-1987.* Geneva: International Organization for Standardization, 1987.

————. *Quality—Vocabulary. ISO 8402-1986.* Geneva: International Organization for Standardization, 1986.

Ireson, W. Grant. *Reliability Handbook.* New York: McGraw-Hill, 1966.

TF-10 Quality Management Task Force. *Measuring the Cost of Quality in Design and Construction.* Austin, Tex.: Construction Quality Institute, 1987.

U.S. Department of Commerce. *Malcolm Baldrige National Quality Award Criteria.* Washington, D.C.: U.S. Government Printing Office, 1993.

Index

515